FUNDAMENTALS
OF
QUANTUM OPTICS

THE MATHEMATICAL PHYSICS MONOGRAPH SERIES

A. S. Wightman, EDITOR
Princeton University

Ralph Abraham, *Princeton University*
FOUNDATIONS OF MECHANICS

Freeman J. Dyson, *The Institute for Advanced Study*
SYMMETRY GROUPS IN NUCLEAR AND PARTICLE PHYSICS

Robert Hermann, *Argonne National Laboratory*
LIE GROUPS FOR PHYSICISTS

Rudolph C. Hwa, *State University of New York at Stony Brook*
Vigdor L. Teplitz, *Massachusetts Institute of Technology*
HOMOLOGY AND FEYNMAN INTEGRALS

John R. Klauder and E. C. G. Sudarshan, *Syracuse University*
FUNDAMENTALS OF QUANTUM OPTICS

André Lichnerowicz, *Collège de France*
RELATIVISTIC HYDRODYNAMICS AND MAGNETOHYDRODYNAMICS

George W. Mackey, *Harvard University*
THE MATHEMATICAL FOUNDATIONS OF QUANTUM MECHANICS

Roger G. Newton, *Indiana University*
THE COMPLEX *j*-PLANE

R. F. Streater, *Imperial College of Science and Technology*
A. S. Wightman, *Princeton University*
PCT, SPIN AND STATISTICS, AND ALL THAT

FUNDAMENTALS OF QUANTUM OPTICS

JOHN R. KLAUDER

Syracuse University
(formerly of Bell Telephone Laboratories)

and

E. C. G. SUDARSHAN

Syracuse University

W. A. BENJAMIN, INC.

New York Amsterdam 1968

FUNDAMENTALS OF QUANTUM OPTICS

Library of Congress Catalog Card Number 68-13129
Manufactured in the United States of America

The manuscript was put into production on May 31, 1967;
this volume was published on February 20, 1968

W. A. BENJAMIN, INC.
New York, New York 10016

12345M321098

PREFACE

Several events of the past decade have fundamentally changed the nature and outlook of the venerable subject of optics. On the experimental side these events include the invention of radically different sources, such as the laser, and the introduction of photon counting correlations and the associated intensity interferometry to which they give rise. Both of these have profoundly affected the theory of partial coherence and have elevated it to a full-fledged theory of stochastic processes of a very general character. On the theoretical side has been the development of a quantum theory of partial coherence and the delineation of similarities as well as differences in the classical and quantum theories. Although fundamentally quite different, the concept and formulation of the classical and quantum theories can be put in a form so nearly identical as to make our study of both of these theories doubly beneficial.

The present text derives much of its spirit and philosophy from a series of lectures and associated lecture notes presented by E. C. G. Sudarshan in the fall of 1963 at the University of Bern, Switzerland. Since that pioneering period of the quantum formulation of coherence theory, many developments of a formal and technical nature have been made. We have attempted to include these more modern formulations in as complete and logically consistent a fashion as seems reasonable at the present time.

Our presentation is addressed to the graduate student and research worker who wishes to understand the fundamentals of the modern theory of quantum optics. Prerequisites include an appreciation of classical optics and quantum theory such as is available from the texts of Jenkins and White, and of Schiff, respectively. While the topics of some of our chapters are not new, we have frequently sought to instill a new insight or emphasis, or to give an alternative proof to the one commonly encountered. On the other hand, we believe that much of our discussions in Chapters 7, 8, 9, and 10 are not generally available at the present time in textbook form. Indeed, some of our analysis is original and has not been previously published elsewhere.

There are, of course, several sources that are basic to the subject and from which the reader may gain additional insight into similar or related topics. Notable among these are the following:

1. M. Born and E. Wolf, *Principles of Optics*, Pergamon, Oxford, 3rd ed. (1965).
2. R. J. Glauber, *Quantum Optics and Electronics* (C. DeWitt, A. Blandin, and C. Cohen-Tannoudji, eds.), Gordon and Breach, New York (1964).
3. L. Mandel and E. Wolf, "Coherence properties of optical fields," *Rev. Modern Phys.* **37,** 231 (1965).

Indeed, the last article has a veritable wealth of references to the recent literature which we do not attempt to duplicate here. Occasionally in our chapter bibliographies we include texts or articles not explicitly cited in which further relevant discussion may be found.

Several general remarks on notation are in order. We occasionally let a single summation or integration symbol do the work of many, and also we often do not explicitly put in summation or integration limits when they are sufficiently clear from the context. Since our discussion is largely theoretical we have chosen the convenient Heaviside electromagnetic units and further have chosen units such that the velocity of light $c = 1$. On the other hand, since we cover both classical and quantum coherence theories, we display the dependence of our equations on Planck's constant h (or on $\hbar \equiv h/2\pi$). Both the angular frequency ω and ordinary frequency ν are used, sometimes in the same equations; these are invariably related by $\omega = 2\pi\nu$.

Thanks are due to a number of scientists for their comments on and criticism of preliminary versions of this text. We should especially like to acknowledge the advice put forth by E. I. Blount, R. J. Glauber, J. P. Gordon, M. Lax, L. Mandel, J. McKenna, C. L. Mehta, H. Pendleton, R. Rosenberg, E. Wolf, and A. S. Wightman. Thanks are due also to F. Ghielmetti and T. Jordan for their compilation of the notes on the original lectures, and to A. Mercier who has provided opportunities for both authors to spend an enjoyable sabbatical period at the Institute for Theoretical Physics at Bern. Finally, we wish to express our gratitude to Mrs. N. Cullen, Miss D. Domanski, and Miss S. Talada, and especially to Mrs. B. Chippendale, Mrs. P. DeMatteo, and Mrs. M. Svilar, for their general assistance and preparation of the typescript, and who, as in all such undertakings, have made our task feasible.

The text for this book was completed during a period when one of the authors (J.R.K.) was a member of the Bell Telephone Laboratories, Inc., the support of which is gratefully acknowledged.

JOHN R. KLAUDER
E. C. G. SUDARSHAN

Syracuse, New York
October 1967

CONTENTS

CHAPTER 1

PARTIALLY COHERENT LIGHT

1-1 INTRODUCTION

Although the geometric or ray picture of optics adequately describes many phenomena, we know that the wave properties of light are frequently important. For example, these properties are fundamental for an understanding of diffraction or interference experiments, such as the classical double-slit experiment of Young shown in Fig. 1-1. This familiar and intuitive interference experiment provides a convenient starting point for us to motivate the picture of partially coherent light that we shall adopt.

On the basis of the standard classical wave theory, a single wave impinging on the two slits S_1 and S_2 undergoes subsequent self-interference which may, depending on the relative intensities involved, lead to complete destructive interference at various points of observation Q. The possibility of such destructive interference is intimately connected with the existence of a definite phase relationship between the constituent signals, and under these circumstances we may say that these two beams are coherent. But this picture of complete destructive interference is not fully in accord with experimental findings if, for usual thermal sources S, the angle subtended by the source at the screen is not too small, as, for example, in Fig. 1-1. When such a source is moved inward toward the screen (thus increasing the subtended angle) it commonly occurs that the interference pattern gradually washes out, namely, that the maximum and minimum intensities become relatively less pronounced. As a quantitative measure of this aspect we may introduce, following Michelson, the *visibility* $\mathcal{V}$ given by

$$\mathcal{V} = \frac{I_{\max} - I_{\min}}{I_{\max} + I_{\min}} \tag{1-1}$$

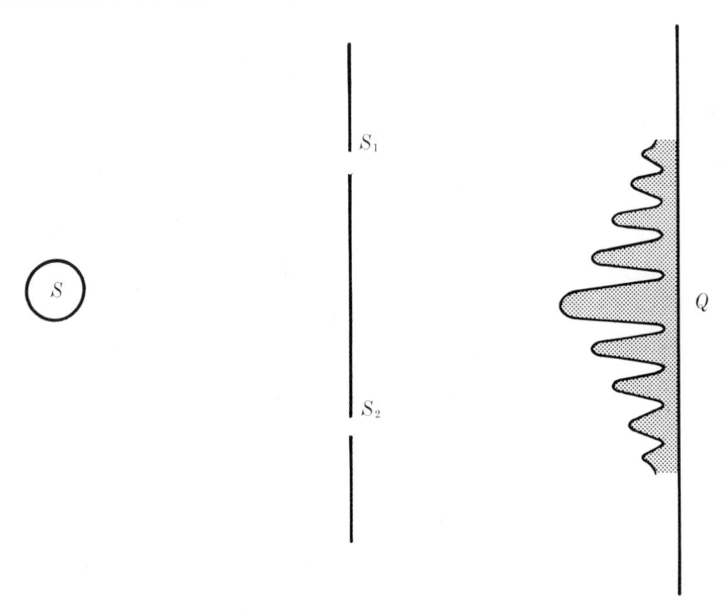

Fig. 1-1 Schematic representation of two-slit interference experiment. Light from an extended thermal source S passes through slits S_1 and S_2, and gives rise to an interference pattern qualitatively as shown. The intensity at a point Q is formed by the superposition of waves from both slits and is determined by the geometry of the experiment and the nature of the light source.

Thus as the source moves closer to the screen, it may be imagined that the visibility $\mathcal{V}$ decreases. Finally as the source comes up very close to the screen, the interference pattern may tend to wash out completely and $\mathcal{V}$ may vanish. The behavior in the latter circumstance is comparable to that obtained when the source and slits are replaced by two independent thermal sources at the original locations of the slits. In other words, a thermal source such as a lamp, when sampled at two reasonably separated points on its surface, displays the same kind of independence that we intuitively ascribe to two completely different thermal sources. This is, of course, quite reasonable since even on one source the individual atomic radiators contributing to the total optical signal have essentially independent histories of absorption and emission of energy at reasonably separated points. When the source is very close to the screen, or when the source and slits are replaced by two independent thermal sources, it is reasonable that the interference pattern is lost due to a complete lack of any definite phase relationship between the two sources. During the time involved for a photographic "observation" to take place—surely not less than characteristic atomic transition times of the order of 10^{-9} sec—many optical vibration cycles take place (since optical frequencies $\nu \simeq 10^{15}$ cps), and there is ample time for two independent phase histories to wash out any pattern. In such a case we may say that the two light signals are incoherent.

Intermediate to these cases of complete and vanishing destructive interference is the case of partial interference which commonly occurs, when, as in Fig. 1-1, the source S is neither too close nor too far from the slits. Here we can speak of partial coherence. Its intuitive description is of necessity somewhat more general than that adequate for the two extreme cases, but they too may be included as limiting cases. Thus, the model of partial coherence which we try to make plausible here corresponds to the most general classical model we need and is, in essence, the one we study and develop in the first four chapters of this text. Its appropriate quantum generalizations are the principal subject matter dealt with in the remainder of the text.

On reference to Fig. 1-1, it is plausible to observe that the light received at various points, say at the slits S_1 and S_2 or, as a consequence, also at the observation point Q, is composed of a very complicated superposition of the freely propagating output of all the atomic radiators on S. Although a detailed, precise, and instantaneous description of this light would entail a correspondingly detailed knowledge of the behavior of each atomic radiator, certain simple questions can be studied which involve only a limited knowledge of the atoms. For example, the average intensity at a point S_1 may conceivably depend in some sense on just the average intensities of the individual atomic radiators each of which may, in many applications, be assumed to have equal average intensity. The overriding advantages afforded by asking average-type questions leave us little choice but to adopt a *statistical approach* toward and a *statistical description* of optical fields as they are produced by the vast majority of practical, macroscopic sources. Mathematically speaking, we choose as our model of partially coherent light a *stochastic process*, namely, that the light wave is a *stochastic variable*, each of whose possible field realizations, if they propagate in empty space, obeys the classical wave equation. The averages in question leading to meaningful, observable quantities are given by averages over the ensemble of possible field realizations. In turn, the specific ensemble of possible fields is ultimately governed by the source producing the radiation. As we shall elucidate, the statistical approach is applicable to laser light as well as to thermal light, or to various and sundry types of sources, if for each case the appropriate statistical ensemble is chosen.

It has been traditional in earlier treatments of partial coherence to employ the theory of stationary random processes; namely, to calculate the averages in question by means of time averages and, then, to invoke the ergodic hypothesis to equate fully these results with those that would follow from an ensemble of light fields. We adopt the ensemble approach from the outset since, on the one hand, it is not wedded to stationary, ergodic processes whose various averages are of necessity independent of the origin of time; and since, on the other hand, it provides the most convenient analog to the statistical picture commonly adopted in quantum theory.

Besides the statistical picture of light suggested by the two-slit experiment with extended thermal sources, there is also another common aspect of light which suggests a statistical description. As is well known, light consists of transverse waves each possessing two distinct states of possible polarization. Polarized light can be specified by its components of linear polarization or, alternatively, by its components of circular polarization. More generally, any polarized wave may be described by its elliptic polarization. In the other extreme, light of thermal origin contains all polarizations with equal probability, i.e., it is unpolarized. Such light, on reflection from certain metals or on transmission through certain crystals, acquires a certain degree of polarization and thus becomes "partially polarized." The analysis of partial coherence and of partial polarization are in many respects very similar. For simplicity our initial discussion is restricted to the scalar theory of partial coherence as would be appropriate to light waves all of the same polarization. In the remainder of this chapter, which is devoted to a brief review of the classical theory of partial coherence, we shall, therefore, examine only the scalar theory. Interested readers can find further details and additional topics in the classical theory of partial coherence from the texts of Born and Wolf [1-1], Chapter X, O'Neill [1-3], and Beran and Parrent [1-2].[1]

1-2 ANALYTIC SIGNAL DESCRIPTION

The electromagnetic field or, more specifically, its scalar analog as we are considering here are real functions of space and time, which we may denote by $V^{(r)}(\mathbf{r}, t)$. Let us for the moment focus on the temporal behavior at an arbitrary position $\mathbf{r}$, which we leave implicit, and consider the corresponding real time function $V^{(r)}(t)$. For a number of purposes the quantity of ultimate physical interest may not be the real wave field $V^{(r)}(t)$ itself. For example, a number of physical phenomena are sensitive to the "envelope" or to the "average intensity" of the field $V^{(r)}(t)$, the

[1] Numbers in square brackets refer to the bibliography located at the end of the book.

latter of which we may adopt as the average of $\frac{1}{2}\{V^{(r)}(t)\}^2$ over time intervals (e.g., 10^{-9} sec) long compared to typical optical periods (10^{-15} sec) but short compared to envelope changes. Phenomena sensitive to such average intensities include all usual forms of photographic emulsions, photocounters, photoemission processes of various sorts, etc. (There is a familiar analog of such envelope sensitivity in the square-law detection followed by a low-pass filter that is the essence of the reception mechanism for AM radio signals.) We may borrow a convenient mathematical description, first introduced into similar calculations by Gabor [1-4], to eliminate the high-frequency components without the need of actually averaging the term $\frac{1}{2}\{V^{(r)}(t)\}^2$ over small time intervals. To illustrate this procedure consider the following idealized example. Suppose, for a sufficiently short time interval, we can set $V^{(r)}(t) = 2A \cos 2\pi\bar{\nu}t$, then the short time, average intensity A^2 is immediately given by the definition $V^*(t)V(t)$, where $V(t) \equiv A \exp(-i2\pi\bar{\nu}t)$ is a positive frequency, complex signal associated with the original one in such a way that $V^{(r)}(t) = 2\,\mathrm{Re}\{V(t)\}$. Here, Re denotes the real part of the expression which follows. Thus direct use of $V(t)$ and $V^*(t)$ permits instantaneous computation of the requisite quantities of physical importance.

In the case of more general time signals we may proceed as follows. The reality of the scalar field $V^{(r)}(t)$ implies that the Fourier transform

$$\tilde{V}^{(r)}(\nu) = \int_{-\infty}^{\infty} e^{2\pi i\nu t} V^{(r)}(t)\, dt \tag{1-2}$$

fulfills the relation

$$\tilde{V}^{(r)}(-\nu) = \tilde{V}^{(r)*}(\nu) \tag{1-3}$$

Thus the complete function $\tilde{V}^{(r)}(\nu)$ can be determined from its values for $\nu \geq 0$ through Eq. (1-3). Let us, therefore, associate with the real signal $V^{(r)}(t)$ the *analytic signal* $V(t)$ defined by

$$\begin{aligned} V(t) &\equiv \int_0^{\infty} e^{-2\pi i\nu t} \tilde{V}^{(r)}(\nu)\, d\nu \\ &\equiv \int_{-\infty}^{\infty} e^{-2\pi i\nu t} \tilde{V}(\nu)\, d\nu \end{aligned} \tag{1-4}$$

where $\tilde{V}(\nu) = \tilde{V}^{(r)}(\nu)$, $\nu > 0$, and $\tilde{V}(\nu) \equiv 0$, $\nu < 0$. By definition, $V(t)$ is composed only of positive frequencies ν. We can always recover the real signal from the relation $V^{(r)}(t) = 2\,\mathrm{Re}\, V(t)$. It is clear by construction that

$$V(t + i\tau) \equiv \int_0^{\infty} e^{-2\pi\nu(it-\tau)} \tilde{V}^{(r)}(\nu)\, d\nu \tag{1-5}$$

defines a function of the complex variable $z = t + i\tau$ analytic in the lower-half plane, $\tau < 0$, and that $V(t)$ is the boundary value of such an analytic function as $\tau \to 0^-$. In addition, the real and imaginary parts of $V(t)$ are Hilbert transforms of one another, which means specifically that the relations

$$V^{(i)}(t) = \frac{1}{\pi} \mathcal{P} \int_{-\infty}^{\infty} \frac{V^{(r)}(t')}{t' - t} \, dt' \tag{1-6a}$$

$$V^{(r)}(t) = -\frac{1}{\pi} \mathcal{P} \int_{-\infty}^{\infty} \frac{V^{(i)}(t')}{t' - t} \, dt' \tag{1-6b}$$

hold, where $V(t) = \frac{1}{2}[V^{(r)}(t) + iV^{(i)}(t)]$ and where $\mathcal{P}$ signifies that the principal value of the integral is to be taken at the singular point $t' = t$. These two relations are elementary restatements of the identity $\tilde{V}(\nu) \equiv \epsilon(\nu)\tilde{V}(\nu)$, where $\epsilon(\nu) = \pm 1$, $\nu \gtrless 0$, after Fourier transformation to the time domain. We shall subsequently see that the quantum theory of coherence deals most naturally with analytic signals and that this formulation provides a natural bridge between the classical and quantum formulations.

The analytic signal, like its real part, must be properly regarded as a function of space and time, $V(\mathbf{r}, t)$. Since the wave equation is linear, it follows, e.g., that the amplitude at Q in the double-slit experiment (Fig. 1-1) is a linear combination of the appropriately time-delayed amplitudes of the two waves emergent from the slits S_1 and S_2. In the approximation that the field is constant over the slits S_1 and S_2, it is then plausible that the field at Q is given by an expression of the form

$$V(Q, t) = K_1 V(S_1, t - t_1) + K_2 V(S_2, t - t_2) \tag{1-7}$$

Here, K_1 and K_2 denote two time-independent propagation functions, about which we shall have more to say subsequently, and t_1 and t_2 denote the elapsed time to travel the distances S_1Q and S_2Q at the rate c, respectively. If, as we have motivated earlier, we define the intensity I at a point $(\mathbf{r}, t)$ by

$$I(\mathbf{r}, t) = V^*(\mathbf{r}, t) V(\mathbf{r}, t) \tag{1-8}$$

then it follows that the intensity at Q at time t is given by the absolute square of (1-7), namely, by

$$\begin{aligned} I(Q, t) &= K_1^* K_1 V^*(S_1, t - t_1) V(S_1, t - t_1) \\ &\quad + K_2^* K_2 V^*(S_2, t - t_2) V(S_2, t - t_2) \\ &\quad + K_1^* K_2 V^*(S_1, t - t_1) V(S_2, t - t_2) \\ &\quad + K_2^* K_1 V^*(S_2, t - t_2) V(S_1, t - t_1) \\ &= K_1^* K_1 V^*(S_1, t - t_1) V(S_1, t - t_1) \\ &\quad + K_2^* K_2 V^*(S_2, t - t_2) V(S_2, t - t_2) \\ &\quad + 2 \operatorname{Re}\{K_1^* K_2 V^*(S_1, t - t_1) V(S_2, t - t_2)\} \end{aligned} \tag{1-9}$$

1-3 STATISTICAL PICTURE OF PARTIALLY COHERENT LIGHT

As we have already argued, it is physically plausible to regard light from thermal sources as composed of essentially random contributions from myriads of atoms each contributing in varying degrees and from various positions within the source. Mathematically we are led to view such light waves as statistical variables, i.e., as fluctuating quantities. Depending on the details of the source, fluctuations may take place in the phase, the amplitude, the frequency, or in all three. Our basic viewpoint here is no different in principle from that held for the thermally generated noise in a radio receiver except that in the radio receiver case the fluctuations lie in a frequency range so as to make them more amenable to direct observation. Thus, we regard the scalar light amplitudes $V(\mathbf{r}, t)$ as members of a statistical ensemble, and we determine the quantities of interest by statistical averages. For the cases of usual concern, it is frequently suitable to make the simplifying assumption that the ensemble is *stationary*, which means that averages do not depend on the origin of time. If we denote statistical averages by angular brackets $\langle\cdot\ \cdot\ \cdot\rangle$, then the stationary property implies, for example, that

$$\langle V^*(\mathbf{r}_1, \tau_1 + t)V(\mathbf{r}_2, \tau_2 + t)\rangle = \langle V^*(\mathbf{r}_1, \tau_1)V(\mathbf{r}_2, \tau_2)\rangle \qquad (1\text{-}10)$$

independent of the time t.

With the aid of these notions, the expected intensity for a double-slit experiment is given by the mean of Eq. (1-9),

$$\begin{aligned}\langle I(Q, t)\rangle &= \langle I(Q)\rangle \\ &= K_1{}^*K_1\langle I(S_1)\rangle + K_2{}^*K_2\langle I(S_2)\rangle \\ &\quad + 2\,\mathrm{Re}\{K_1K_2{}^*\langle V^*(S_2, t - t_2)V(S_1, t - t_1)\rangle\}\end{aligned} \qquad (1\text{-}11)$$

In order to focus on the essentials in this expression, let us assume that the slits are of similar width and let us adopt the familiar Huygens approximation. Then, as we show later, the propagation factors K_1 and K_2 are such that $K_1K_2{}^*$ is real and $K_1K_2{}^* \simeq |K_1|^2 \simeq |K_2|^2 \equiv K^2$. Making this choice and setting $t = t_2$, we find

$$\langle I(Q)\rangle = K^2\{\langle I(S_1)\rangle + \langle I(S_2)\rangle + 2\,\mathrm{Re}\langle V^*(S_2, 0)V(S_1, t_2 - t_1)\rangle\} \qquad (1\text{-}12)$$

Let us define the fundamental quantity

$$\Gamma_{ij}(\tau) \equiv \langle V^*(\mathbf{r}_j, 0)V(\mathbf{r}_i, \tau)\rangle \qquad (1\text{-}13)$$

When $\mathbf{r}_i = \mathbf{r}_j$, Γ measures the autocorrelation of the signal $V(\mathbf{r}_i, t)$; when $\mathbf{r}_i \neq \mathbf{r}_j$, Γ measures the cross-correlation of the two signals. We shall call $\Gamma_{ij}(\tau)$ the *mutual coherence function*. If we set $I_1 = \Gamma_{11}(0)$ and

$I_2 = \Gamma_{22}(0)$, then we may rewrite Eq. (1-12) as

$$\langle I(Q)\rangle = K^2\{I_1 + I_2 + 2\,\mathrm{Re}\,\Gamma_{12}(t_2 - t_1)\} \tag{1-14}$$

Clearly

$$\mathrm{Re}\,\Gamma_{ij}(\tau) \leq |\Gamma_{ij}(\tau)| \leq (I_iI_j)^{1/2} \tag{1-15}$$

the latter statement following from the requirement that $\langle I(Q)\rangle \geq 0$ for any value of I_1/I_2; this result is, of course, just a statement of the Schwarz inequality. Thus, if we define

$$\gamma_{ij}(\tau) = \frac{\Gamma_{ij}(\tau)}{(I_iI_j)^{1/2}} \tag{1-16}$$

it follows that

$$\mathrm{Re}\,\gamma_{ij}(\tau) \leq |\gamma_{ij}(\tau)| \leq 1 \tag{1-17}$$

and

$$\langle I(Q)\rangle = K^2\{I_1 + I_2 + 2(I_1I_2)^{1/2}\,\mathrm{Re}\,\gamma_{12}(t_2 - t_1)\} \tag{1-18}$$

In units where the velocity of light $c = 1$, $t_j = s_j$, where s_j is the distance from S_j to Q. Equation (1-18) is the general interference law for partially coherent, stationary, optical fields and was developed first by Zernike [1-6].

To gain insight into the meaning of γ_{12}, let us first specialize to the idealized example of strictly monochromatic light with no statistical fluctuations. That is, let us put

$$V(S_j, t - t_j) = |A_j| \exp[-2\pi i\nu(t - t_j)] \tag{1-19}$$

so that from (1-13) and (1-16)

$$\gamma_{12}(t_2 - t_1) = \exp[-2\pi i\nu(t_2 - t_1)] \tag{1-20}$$

Therefore, in this special case,

$$I = K^2\{I_1 + I_2 + 2(I_1I_2)^{1/2}\cos[2\pi\nu(t_2 - t_1)]\} \tag{1-21}$$

which generates the ideal two-slit interference pattern of monochromatic light. Even if the cosine term vanishes at some point Q the light is still coherent, for by introducing idealized, uniform phase plates at either slit (which change the phase of a wave uniformly) the interference term would manifest itself.

As a next step in gaining insight into γ_{12} let us suppose we are dealing with so-called quasi-monochromatic light, which is composed of frequencies in a band $\Delta\nu$ which is very much smaller than the center frequency $\bar{\nu}$: $\Delta\nu/\bar{\nu} \ll 1$. On the basis of this assumption we may adopt the form

$$\gamma_{12}(t_2 - t_1) = |\gamma_{12}(t_2 - t_1)| \exp[-2\pi i\bar{\nu}(t_2 - t_1)] \tag{1-22}$$

in which the envelope $|\gamma_{12}|$ is a slowly varying function which remains substantially constant over many oscillations of the phase factor. In this case (1-18) leads to

$$I = K^2\{I_1 + I_2 + 2(I_1I_2)^{1/2}|\gamma_{12}(t_2 - t_1)| \cos[2\pi\bar{\nu}(t_2 - t_1)]\} \quad (1\text{-}23)$$

which over many cycles generates a pattern with a sinusoidal variation similar to that of the ideal two-slit interference pattern. The intensity maxima and minima in this pattern evidently occur when the cosine term assumes the values $+1$ and -1, respectively. Thus, the visibility for such a fringe pattern is given by

$$\mathcal{V} = \frac{I_{\max} - I_{\min}}{I_{\max} + I_{\min}} = \frac{2(I_1I_2)^{1/2}|\gamma_{12}(t_2 - t_1)|}{I_1 + I_2} \quad (1\text{-}24a)$$

which in the special case $I_1 = I_2$ becomes

$$\mathcal{V} = |\gamma_{12}(t_2 - t_1)| \quad (1\text{-}24b)$$

Thus, in this case, $|\gamma_{12}|$ is identical to the fringe visibility $\mathcal{V}$. If $|\gamma_{12}| = 1$, we have the maximum visibility of a coherent wave; if $|\gamma_{12}| = 0$, we have the absence of fringes of an incoherent wave; and if $0 < |\gamma_{12}| < 1$, we have the partial fringes of a partially coherent wave.

Although in the general case of (1-18) the observed intensity pattern may not exhibit a sinusoidal fringe pattern, it is still reasonable to regard $|\gamma_{12}|$ as a measure of the coherence of the wave fields. For, just as in the first case, uniform phase plates at either slit can convert $\mathrm{Re}\,\gamma_{12}(\tau)$ to any value lying within the extremes $\pm|\gamma_{12}(\tau)|$. If $|\gamma_{12}| = 1$, then the waves $V(S_1, \tau)$ and $V^*(S_2, 0)$ are as fully correlated as in (1-21) and may be called "coherent." If $\gamma_{12} = 0$ (not just $\mathrm{Re}\,\gamma_{12} = 0$), then these waves are uncorrelated and may be called "incoherent." Finally, if $0 < |\gamma_{12}| < 1$ the fields may be called "partially coherent." Thus in all cases we see that it is reasonable to define $\gamma_{12}(\tau)$ as the complex degree of coherence and to define $|\gamma_{12}(\tau)|$ as the *degree of coherence.*

As a first additional property of the mutual coherence function we note that $\Gamma_{12}(\tau)$ is an analytic signal in the sense of (1-4). This property is a consequence of the assumed stationarity of the ensemble of waveforms. To see this let us put

$$\begin{aligned}\Gamma_{12}(\tau) &= \langle V_2^*(t)V_1(t+\tau)\rangle \\ &= \int_0^\infty \int_0^\infty \exp\{-2\pi i[\nu_1(t+\tau) - \nu_2 t]\}\langle \tilde{V}_2^*(\nu_2)\tilde{V}_1(\nu_1)\rangle\, d\nu_1\, d\nu_2 \\ &= \int_0^\infty \int_0^\infty \exp\{-2\pi i[\nu_1\tau + t(\nu_1 - \nu_2)]\}\langle \tilde{V}_2^*(\nu_2)\tilde{V}_1(\nu_1)\rangle\, d\nu_1\, d\nu_2\end{aligned} \quad (1\text{-}25)$$

Then stationarity, which among other things implies that (1-25) does not depend on t, requires that the last indicated mean value have the form given by

$$\langle \tilde{V}_2^*(\nu_2)\tilde{V}_1(\nu_1)\rangle = \delta(\nu_1 - \nu_2)\tilde{\Gamma}_{12}(\nu_1) \tag{1-26}$$

where $\delta(\nu)$ is the Dirac delta function. As a consequence we learn that

$$\Gamma_{12}(\tau) = \int_0^\infty e^{-2\pi i\nu\tau}\tilde{\Gamma}_{12}(\nu)\, d\nu \tag{1-27}$$

which is clearly an analytic signal. It may be noted that $\Gamma_{12}(\tau)$ could still be an analytic signal in ensembles that are not stationary so long as the *specific mean* (1-25) turned out to be independent of t or, equivalently, that (1-26) holds true.

On the basis of interference measurements—either with idealized phase plates, or in the case of quasi-monochromatic light by measuring the visibility $\mathcal{V}$—the degree of coherence $|\gamma_{12}(\tau)|$ may be determined. However, the physically interesting spectral distribution $\tilde{\Gamma}_{12}(\nu)$ is directly related to the Fourier transform of $\gamma_{12}(\tau)$ and not in general to that of $|\gamma_{12}(\tau)|$. This raises the question whether and to what extent $|\gamma_{12}|$ can be used to determine

$$\gamma_{12}(\tau) = \exp[i\varphi_{12}(\tau)]|\gamma_{12}(\tau)| \tag{1-28}$$

This problem, known as the "phase problem," has been studied by Wolf [1-7], Kano and Wolf [1-8], Mehta [1-9], and Nussenzveig [1-10] among others. As a normalized form of the mutual coherence it follows that $\gamma_{12}(\tau)$ is an analytic signal, a property we may be able to put to use in determining the phase function $\varphi_{12}(\tau)$. For instance, if we make the assumption that $\gamma_{12}(\tau)$ has no zeros in the lower-half, complex τ plane, then the function

$$\ln \gamma_{12}(\tau) = \ln|\gamma_{12}(\tau)| + i\varphi_{12}(\tau) \tag{1-29}$$

remains analytic in the lower-half plane and is, therefore, an analytic signal. Hence, we may relate the real and imaginary parts of (1-29) by the Hilbert transform (1-6a), and we can determine $\varphi_{12}(\tau)$ by the relation

$$\varphi_{12}(\tau) = \frac{1}{\pi}\,\mathcal{P}\int_{-\infty}^{\infty} \frac{\ln|\gamma_{12}(\tau')|}{\tau' - \tau}\, d\tau' \tag{1-30}$$

provided that the integral converges.

The utility of this scheme lies in the assumption that $\gamma_{12}(\tau)$ has no zeros in the lower-half, complex, τ plane. If that assumption is false, then the expression for γ_{12} contains, as may be shown, an additional factor called the "Blashke factor"

$$\prod \left(\frac{\tau - \tau^{(j)}}{\tau - \tau^{(j)*}}\right) \tag{1-31}$$

where the product extends over all zeros $\tau^{(j)}$ of $\gamma_{12}(\tau)$ in the lower-half plane. Unless some additional physical information is available to pinpoint the location of the zeros of $\gamma_{12}(\tau)$ so as to compute the additional phase contributed by (1-31), the complex degree of coherence will be underdetermined. Nussenzveig [1-10] has examined several spectral distributions $\tilde{\Gamma}_{12}(\nu)$, which are frequently adopted on physical grounds, and has shown that in these cases the actual complex degree of coherence $\gamma_{12}(\tau)$ not only contains a large number of zeros in the lower-half plane but that the phase contributed by the Blashke factor tends to be comparable to the "minimal" phase term (1-30).

1-4 TEMPORAL AND SPATIAL PROPAGATION PROPERTIES OF THE MUTUAL COHERENCE FUNCTION

As a further property of the mutual coherence function we now show that it satisfies the same wave equation as the scalar fields themselves. In free space, both the real fields and their associated analytic signals satisfy the usual wave equation which in units where $c = 1$ reads

$$\left(\nabla^2 - \frac{\partial^2}{\partial t^2}\right) V(\mathbf{r}, t) = 0 \tag{1-32}$$

where

$$\nabla^2 = \frac{\partial^2}{\partial x^2} + \frac{\partial^2}{\partial y^2} + \frac{\partial^2}{\partial z^2}$$

denotes the Laplacian operator. If we multiply this equation by the complex conjugate solution $V^*(\mathbf{r}', t')$, it follows that

$$\left(\nabla^2 - \frac{\partial^2}{\partial t^2}\right) V(\mathbf{r}, t)V^*(\mathbf{r}', t') = 0 \tag{1-33}$$

Since (1-33) holds for each wave $V(\mathbf{r}, t)$ in the ensemble, it holds for the ensemble average thereof; namely,

$$\left(\nabla^2 - \frac{\partial^2}{\partial t^2}\right) \Gamma(\mathbf{r}, t; \mathbf{r}', t') = 0 \tag{1-34a}$$

If we take the complex conjugate of (1-34a) and interchange the primed and unprimed coordinates we similarly find that

$$\left(\nabla'^{\,2} - \frac{\partial^2}{\partial t'^{\,2}}\right) \Gamma(\mathbf{r}, t; \mathbf{r}', t') = 0 \tag{1-34b}$$

These wave equations for the mutual coherence function were first obtained by Wolf [1-11]. It is important to observe that for purposes of propagation the mutual coherence function acts as a wave, whereas for purposes of observation it behaves [through (1-14)] as an intensity. Neither the wave amplitude V nor the intensity I combines both of these useful properties.

Since the mutual coherence function satisfies the wave equations (1-34), Green's theorem may be used to generate an integral representation for Γ at arbitrary points just in terms of its values on some surface. To obtain such an integral representation for Γ, let us first eliminate t and t' from Γ in favor of ν, according to the equation

$$\Gamma(\mathbf{r}, t; \mathbf{r}', t') = \int_0^\infty \tilde{\Gamma}(\mathbf{r}, \mathbf{r}'; \nu) e^{-2\pi i\nu(t-t')}\, d\nu \tag{1-35}$$

which holds in virtue of the assumed stationarity of the ensemble. The resultant form of (1-34) becomes

$$(\nabla^2 + k^2)\tilde{\Gamma}(\mathbf{r}, \mathbf{r}'; \nu) = 0 \tag{1-36a}$$
$$(\nabla'^2 + k^2)\tilde{\Gamma}(\mathbf{r}, \mathbf{r}'; \nu) = 0 \tag{1-36b}$$

where $k = k(\nu) \equiv 2\pi\nu$. If $G(\mathbf{r}, \mathbf{s}) \equiv G(\mathbf{r}, \mathbf{s}, \nu)$ denotes a Green's function for (1-36a), then Green's theorem applied to this equation leads to

$$\tilde{\Gamma}(\mathbf{r}, \mathbf{r}'; \nu) = \int_S \left\{ G(\mathbf{r}, \mathbf{s}) \frac{\partial \tilde{\Gamma}}{\partial n}(\mathbf{s}, \mathbf{r}'; \nu) - \frac{\partial G}{\partial n}(\mathbf{r}, \mathbf{s}) \tilde{\Gamma}(\mathbf{s}, \mathbf{r}'; \nu) \right\} dS \tag{1-37}$$

as we shall review in some detail in Chapter 6. Here $\mathbf{s}$ denotes a point on the surface S, dS denotes a differential element of surface area, and $\partial/\partial n$ denotes a surface normal derivative. Green's function G may be chosen in a variety of ways. A particularly useful choice is one for which $G = 0$ if either argument is on S (as is, in fact $\mathbf{s}$). With this choice for G only the second term in (1-36) survives. We now employ Green's theorem again for the variable $\mathbf{r}'$ with a corresponding choice for Green's function to learn that

$$\tilde{\Gamma}(\mathbf{r}, \mathbf{r}'; \nu) = \int_S \int_S \frac{\partial G}{\partial n}(\mathbf{r}, \mathbf{s}) \frac{\partial G^*}{\partial n'}(\mathbf{r}', \mathbf{s}') \tilde{\Gamma}(\mathbf{s}, \mathbf{s}'; \nu)\, dS\, dS' \tag{1-38}$$

The essential fact here is that the value of $\tilde{\Gamma}$ at two general points in space is determined by a linear relation from the values $\tilde{\Gamma}$ assumes when confined to a surface S. Similar remarks apply of course to the time-dependent form in (1-35).

Suppose, for the sake of illustration, that the surface S corresponds to the plane $z = 0$, and that on this plane $\tilde{\Gamma}$ is nonvanishing over a region corresponding to a finite aperture. The appropriate Green's function G is readily found in terms of the *primitive* Green's function G_0 defined by

$$G_0(\mathbf{r}, \mathbf{r}') = \frac{e^{ik|\mathbf{r}-\mathbf{r}'|}}{4\pi|\mathbf{r} - \mathbf{r}'|} \tag{1-39}$$

In particular, guided by the method of images in electrostatics, we may choose

$$G(\mathbf{r}, \mathbf{r}') \equiv G_0(\mathbf{r}, x', y', z') - G_0(\mathbf{r}, x', y', -z') \tag{1-40}$$

where we have explicitly spelled out the coordinate dependence of $\mathbf{r}'$ on the right-hand side. Clearly $G = 0$, as desired, if the point $\mathbf{r}'$ lies on S, for then $z' = 0$ (or, as is easily seen, $G = 0$ if $\mathbf{r}$ lies on S).

The factors $\partial G/\partial n$ entering (1-38) determine the propagation factors K discussed in (1-7). The usual double-slit experiment corresponds to an "illuminated surface" S consisting of δ-function-like contributions, and to a quasi-monochromatic distribution of frequencies. That is, the spectral width of $\tilde{\Gamma}$ is very much smaller than the center frequency $\bar{\nu}$. If we set

$$R \equiv [(x - x')^2 + (y - y')^2 + z^2]^{1/2} \tag{1-41}$$

and suppose that $kR \gg 1$ over the spectral width of $\tilde{\Gamma}$, then

$$\begin{aligned} \frac{\partial G}{\partial n} = \frac{\partial}{\partial z}\left(\frac{e^{ikR}}{2\pi R}\right) &\simeq \frac{ikz}{2\pi R^2} e^{ikR} \\ &\simeq \frac{i\bar{k}z}{2\pi R^2} e^{ikR} \equiv K e^{ikR} \end{aligned} \tag{1-42}$$

Here, the second approximation makes use of the fact that the spectral width of Γ is assumed very narrow. Equation (1-42) serves to define the K of (1-7), while the remaining phase factor, $\exp(2\pi i\nu R)$, gives rise to the time-delay term appearing in (1-7). The stated properties of K necessary to derive (1-12) follow immediately.

A. van Cittert-Zernike Theorem

An important feature of the mutual coherence function is the acquisition of partial coherence by the very process of propagation. We may illustrate this most easily with the help of Eq. (1-38). Suppose, for example, that the surface S is that of the optical source itself and that the light is thermal-like in character, as from a star. As such, the field at $\mathbf{s}$ is likely to be independent of that at $\mathbf{s}'$ whenever $|\mathbf{s} - \mathbf{s}'|$ exceeds a "source coherence length," say a distance of no larger than a meter. Physically this simply means that the light sources are statistically independent over any macroscopic interval. It follows that $\tilde{\Gamma}(\mathbf{s}, \mathbf{s}'; \nu)$ would vanish unless

$|\mathbf{s} - \mathbf{s}'|$ is also sufficiently small. Whenever the remainder of the integrand in (1-38) is sufficiently slowly varying on such a scale, then we may adopt the relation

$$\tilde{\Gamma}(\mathbf{s}, \mathbf{s}'; \nu) = \delta_S(\mathbf{s} - \mathbf{s}')\tilde{\Gamma}(\mathbf{s}, \nu) \tag{1-43}$$

without loss of accuracy, where δ_S denotes a surface δ function. Consequently, under these assumptions, (1-38) becomes

$$\tilde{\Gamma}(\mathbf{r}, \mathbf{r}'; \nu) = \int_S \frac{\partial G}{\partial n}(\mathbf{r}, \mathbf{s}) \frac{\partial G^*}{\partial n}(\mathbf{r}', \mathbf{s})\tilde{\Gamma}(\mathbf{s}, \nu)\, dS \tag{1-44}$$

which in general need not vanish for $\mathbf{r} \neq \mathbf{r}'$. In other words, the field, which on the stellar surface, say, is statistically independent for different points acquires partial spatial coherence after propagation. The statement of the van Cittert-Zernike theorem makes the interesting point that Eq. (1-44) for the mutual coherence function may be "read" in a different fashion from that done so far. These authors noted that the formula for the mutual coherence function $\tilde{\Gamma}(\mathbf{r}, \mathbf{r}'; \nu)$ also corresponds to the field *amplitude* at the point $\mathbf{r}$, which is constructed via Huygen's principle as follows: (*1*) a point source is placed at $\mathbf{r}'$, the radiation from which then propagates $[\partial G^*/\partial n(\mathbf{r}', \mathbf{s})]$ to the various points $\mathbf{s}$ lying on the "aperture" determined by S; (*2*) this radiation then undergoes a reflection at each of the points $\mathbf{s}$ on S with a relative reflection coefficient $\tilde{\Gamma}(\mathbf{s}, \nu)$; and (*3*) finally it propagates $[\partial G/\partial n(\mathbf{r}, \mathbf{s})]$ from each point $\mathbf{s}$ in the aperture to the point of observation $\mathbf{r}$. The equivalence of the mutual coherence function and the wave amplitude constructed in the way described we shall call the "van Cittert-Zernike theorem." In certain cases, by carrying out a wave-front construction, the mutual coherence function can be determined without taking ensemble averages. Further discussion of the van Cittert-Zernike theorem can be found in Born and Wolf [1-1] and in Beran and Parrent [1-2].

It is interesting to pursue Eq. (1-44) one stage further to develop a far-field approximation especially suitable for the determination of stellar diameters. In this case we adopt (1-42) for $\partial G/\partial n$ and make the traditional far-field approximations: $\mathbf{r}^2 = \mathbf{r}'^2 = R^2 \gg \mathbf{s}^2$; $R^2 \gg (\mathbf{r} - \mathbf{r}')^2$. It then follows that the phase in (1-44) is given by

$$k(R - R') = k(|\mathbf{r} - \mathbf{s}| - |\mathbf{r}' - \mathbf{s}|) \simeq -\frac{k}{R}\mathbf{s} \cdot (\mathbf{r} - \mathbf{r}') \tag{1-45}$$

Combining these properties with (1-42), we find that

$$\begin{aligned}\tilde{\Gamma}(\mathbf{r}, \mathbf{r}'; \nu) &\equiv \tilde{\Gamma}(\mathbf{r} - \mathbf{r}', \nu) \\ &= |K|^2 \int_S \exp[-i(k/R)\mathbf{s} \cdot (\mathbf{r} - \mathbf{r}')]\tilde{\Gamma}(\mathbf{s}, \nu)\, dS\end{aligned} \tag{1-46}$$

which for all practical purposes introduces a spatial coherence governed by the Fourier transform of the intensity distribution of the source. If we apply this result to a star whose intensity has the constant value $\tilde{\Gamma}(\nu)$ over a circular disk of radius b, then setting $\mathbf{r}' = 0$, we may write

$$\begin{aligned}\tilde{\Gamma}(\mathbf{r}, \nu) &= |K|^2\tilde{\Gamma}(\nu) \int_0^b \int_0^{2\pi} e^{-i(k/R)sr\cos\varphi}\, s\, ds\, d\varphi \\ &= 2\pi|K|^2\tilde{\Gamma}(\nu) \int_0^b J_0(ksr/R)s\, ds \\ &= 2\pi(Rb/kr)|K|^2\tilde{\Gamma}(\nu)J_1(kbr/R) \qquad (1\text{-}47)\end{aligned}$$

where J_0 and J_1 are the usual Bessel functions. For quasi-monochromatic light such as we are assuming, the frequency dependence of (1-47) is governed by the function $\tilde{\Gamma}(\nu)$ while the other factors may be evaluated at the center frequency $\bar{\nu} = \bar{k}/2\pi$. Specifically, (1-47) leads to

$$\Gamma(\mathbf{r}, \tau) = 2\pi(Rb/\bar{k}r)|K|^2\Gamma(\tau)J_1(\bar{k}br/R) \qquad (1\text{-}48)$$

which on normalization becomes

$$\gamma(\mathbf{r}, \tau) = \gamma(\tau)\,\frac{J_1(x)}{x} \qquad (1\text{-}49)$$

where $x = \bar{k}br/R$ and $\gamma(\tau) = \Gamma(\tau)/\Gamma(0)$. The degree of coherence first vanishes, say, for a spatial separation r such that $\bar{k}br \simeq 3.83R$, a relation which permits the determination of the stellar radius b if its distance R from the earth is known. For a star the size of the sun ($b \simeq 10^{11}$ cm) at a distance of one light year ($R \simeq 10^{18}$ cm) and for a mean wave number $\bar{k} \simeq 10^5\ \text{cm}^{-1}$ ($\bar{\nu} \simeq 10^{15}$ cps), the separation distance r for γ to vanish is somewhat less than 4 m. Unfortunately this method is limited in its applicability by the fact that stellar light observed at two transverse points about 4 m apart is already considerably reduced in coherence by atmospheric distortion. One way to circumvent this difficulty is treated in Chapter 3.

Further discussion and numerous other topics in the classical theory of partial coherence can be found in the texts cited in the bibliography.

CHAPTER 2

PHOTOELECTRIC COUNTING DISTRIBUTIONS

The preceding chapter dealt with the description of partially coherent fields as statistical ensembles of fields. In this and the next chapter we take up a study of counting measurements through which the statistics of a partially coherent field may be studied.

2-1 FIXED INTENSITIES

There are several conventional mechanisms for the detection of light that make use of the interaction of radiation with matter. We have in mind photographic plates and photoelectric detectors, and our attention is primarily devoted to the "fast" detection by means of photoelectric detectors explicitly neglecting bandwidth limitations. It has been known since Einstein's original explanation that the photoelectric process is essentially quantum in nature. Its proper explanation involves the particle properties (i.e., photons) of the electromagnetic field and is thereby able to explain the statistical photoemission of photoelectrons.

However from a semiclassical point of view the incidence of the electromagnetic field may be regarded as modifying the statistics of the counter; a higher-intensity light beam resulting in a higher mean rate of photoemission.

A quantitative relationship between intensity and the probability of photoemission (and, hence, of counts) may be deduced from the conventional time-dependent perturbation theory of quantum mechanics. The result is in accord with our intuition, and it states that the differential probability dp that a count occurs in a time interval dt in a photoelectric counter on which radiation of intensity $I(t)$ falls is given by

$$dp(t) = \alpha I(t)\, dt = \alpha V^*(t)V(t)\, dt \tag{2-1}$$

The parameter α is a measure of the sensitivity of the detector, and it depends on the area of the detector, the mean spectral characteristics of the incident radiation, etc.

Suppose temporarily that there are *no* random fluctuations in the intensity $I(t)$. We then assume on plausible physical grounds, that the probability of counts in distinct time intervals are statistically independent. Combining this independence with the differential law (2-1), it is not difficult to deduce the resultant distribution. For clarity we include a plausibility derivation of this distribution.

A. Poisson Distribution

Since $1 - dp(t')$ represents the probability that *no* counts occur in the time interval dt' at t', the joint probability that no counts occur in an entire interval t to $t + T$ is, due to the assumed independence, given by a multiple product symbolically of the form

$$\text{“}\prod_{t}^{t+T} [1 - dp(t')]\text{”} \rightarrow \exp\left[-\int_t^{t+T} dp(t')\right]$$

the precise meaning of which, as given by the expression on the right, has also been indicated. Consequently, the probability for no counts in the indicated time interval is simply

$$P_0(0, T + t, t) = \exp\left[-\alpha \int_t^{t+T} I(t')\, dt'\right]$$

a result, we re-emphasize, which assumes there are no intensity fluctuations. Likewise the probability $P_0(1, T + t, t)$ that *one* count occurs between t and $t + T$ is given by

$$\text{“}\sum_{t''} dp(t'') \prod_{t}^{t+T}{}' [1 - dp(t')]\text{”} \rightarrow \int_t^{t+T} dp(t'') \exp\left[-\int_t^{t+T} dp(t')\right]$$

from which it follows that

$$P_0(1, T + t, t) = \alpha \int_t^{t+T} I(t')\, dt' \exp\left[-\alpha \int_t^{t+T} I(t')\, dt'\right]$$

Similar reasoning leads to the probability for n counts in the interval t to $t + T$, given a fixed intensity function $I(t')$, as

$$P_0(n, T + t, t) = \frac{1}{n!}\left(\alpha \int_t^{t+T} I(t')\, dt'\right)^n \exp\left[-\alpha \int_t^{t+T} I(t')\, dt'\right] \tag{2-2}$$

which is recognized as the familiar Poisson distribution. As we shall subsequently elaborate, the intensity does not fluctuate in an idealized laser, and (2-2) represents the counting distribution appropriate to such an idealized case.

If we introduce the abbreviation

$$\mu \equiv \alpha \int_t^{t+T} I(t')\, dt'$$

then the essence of (2-2) is given by

$$P_0(n, T + t, t) \equiv P_0(n, \mu) = \frac{\mu^n}{n!} e^{-\mu}$$

In terms of this expression it is simple to express several of the classic properties of the Poisson distribution. The mean number of counts $\bar{n}$ becomes

$$\begin{aligned}\bar{n} &= \sum_{n=0}^{\infty} nP_0(n, \mu) \\ &= \sum_{n=0}^{\infty} \frac{\mu^n}{(n-1)!} e^{-\mu} = \mu\end{aligned}$$

and the mean square number n^2 becomes

$$\begin{aligned}\overline{n^2} &= \sum_{n=0}^{\infty} n^2 P_0(n, \mu) \\ &= \sum_{n=0}^{\infty} \frac{n\mu^n}{(n-1)!} e^{-\mu} \\ &= \sum_{n=0}^{\infty} [(n-1) + 1] \frac{\mu^n}{(n-1)!} e^{-\mu} = \mu^2 + \mu\end{aligned}$$

An important property of any distribution is the *variance* $\sigma^2 = \overline{(n - \bar{n})^2} = \overline{n^2} - (\bar{n})^2$ which is a measure of *fluctuations* in n about its mean value $\bar{n}$; for the Poisson distribution

$$\sigma^2 = \mu^2 + \mu - \mu^2 = \mu = \bar{n}$$

A convenient way to summarize all the properties of a distribution is with the characteristic function, which for the Poisson distribution is defined by

$$C_0(s, \mu) \equiv \sum_{n=0}^{\infty} e^{ins} P_0(n, \mu) = \sum_{n=0}^{\infty} \frac{e^{ins}\mu^n}{n!} e^{-\mu} = \exp[(e^{is} - 1)\mu] \tag{2-3}$$

This function contains all the information about $P_0(n, \mu)$. For example, various moments may be obtained from (2-3) by repeated differentiation with respect to s evaluated at the origin. We shall have frequent occasion to study probability distributions by means of their characteristic functions.

2-2 RANDOM INTENSITIES

In the analysis of partially coherent light presented in Chapter 1 we interpreted the wave fields $V(t)$ and, thereby, the intensity $I(t)$ as random or stochastic variables. To account for this property of $I(t)$ we must take averages of the Poisson counting distribution $P_0(n, T + t, t)$ in the relevant distribution of the intensity. Now, in fact, only one combination of the intensity $I(t)$ enters into the computation of the moments, etc. Let us set

$$U = \int_t^{T+t} I(t')\, dt' \tag{2-4}$$

which, in virtue of the random nature of $I(t')$, is itself a random variable with some distribution $p(U)$. The modified counting distribution taking account of the variable U is then given by Mandel's [2-1] formula

$$P(n, T + t, t) \equiv \int_0^{\infty} \frac{(\alpha U)^n}{n!} e^{-\alpha U} p(U)\, dU \tag{2-5}$$

which is no longer a Poisson distribution. A useful *generating function* for the modified counting distribution is given by

$$Q(\lambda, T + t, t) = \sum_{n=0}^{\infty} (1 - \lambda)^n P(n, T + t, t) = \int_0^{\infty} e^{-\lambda\alpha U} p(U)\, dU \tag{2-6}$$

Evidently the generating function Q is essentially just the Laplace transform of $p(U)$. It follows from (2-5) and (2-6) that expansion of Q about the point $\lambda = 1$ leads to

$$P(n, T + t, t) = \frac{1}{n!} (-1)^n \frac{\partial^n}{\partial \lambda^n} Q(\lambda, T + t, t) \bigg|_{\lambda=1} \tag{2-7}$$

whereas expansion about the point $\lambda = 0$ yields

$$\begin{aligned} \overline{n(n-1) \cdots (n-k)} &\equiv \sum_{n=0}^{\infty} n(n-1) \cdots (n-k) P(n, T + t, t) \\ &= (-1)^k \frac{\partial^k}{\partial \lambda^k} Q(\lambda, T + t, t) \bigg|_{\lambda=0} \end{aligned} \tag{2-8}$$

$k = 1, 2, \ldots$, which are commonly called the "factorial moments." The closely related *characteristic function* for the counting distribution,

$$C(s, T + t, t) \equiv \sum_{n=0}^{\infty} e^{isn} P(n, T + t, t) \tag{2-9}$$

can likewise be useful. The counting distribution itself follows from a Fourier transform,

$$P(n, T + t, t) = \frac{1}{2\pi} \int_0^{2\pi} e^{-isn} C(s, T + t, t)\, ds \tag{2-10}$$

whereas multiple derivatives at the origin yield

$$\overline{n^k} \equiv \sum_{n=0}^{\infty} n^k P(n, T + t, t) = \left(-i \frac{\partial}{\partial s}\right)^k C(s, T + t, t) \bigg|_{s=0} \tag{2-11}$$

In spite of the relative simplicity of Eqs. (2-5) and (2-6), the distribution $p(U)$ like U itself is a derived quantity—a construct—not directly related to first principles. The basic physics of the problem resides not in U but rather in $V(t)$, the wave field. It is this latter quantity that enters into microscopic equations of motion, for example, the description of which, by an equivalent statistical problem, gives rise to the random features we seek to investigate. We shall examine some of these aspects more fully in other chapters in both a classical and quantum context.

We divide our present discussion of counting problems into two parts. For the remainder of this chapter, we deal directly with (2-5) and determine some general properties that hold whatever $p(U)$ may apply. This discussion does have one direct physically relevant application. Suppose that T is sufficiently short so that during the interval T, $I(t)$ remains sensibly constant, $I(t) \simeq I$. It, of course, depends on the nature of the source, but artificially synthesized thermal sources are available for which this approximation makes sense for times $T \lesssim 10^{-4}$ sec. If we assume the approximate constancy of I, we may put

$$U = \int_t^{T+t} I(t)\, dt = IT \tag{2-12}$$

and thus distributions in U become distributions in I about which we have greater physical insight. Our initial discussion will be addressed to this physical model.

In the next chapter we take up the counting distributions based on deeper physical models beginning with ensembles of wave fields $V(t)$, and treat their dependence on T, for example, more completely than is possible in the present chapter.

A. Short Measurement Time Formulation

For greater clarity in understanding the effect of random intensities in counting problems, we first discuss the case when (2-12) holds. If we regard the intensity value I as a random variable with distribution $p(I)$, then the counting distribution may be written

$$P(n, T) = \int_0^\infty \frac{(\alpha IT)^n}{n!} e^{-\alpha IT} p(I)\, dI \tag{2-13}$$

where we have suppressed an inessential t dependence.

One of the most important general properties of the modified distribution $P(n, T)$ is the *bunching of counts* as exemplified by an increased variance. Under the plausible physical assumption that $p(I)$ possesses the required moments, it follows that the modified mean count becomes

$$\begin{aligned}\bar{n} = \sum_{n=0}^{\infty} nP(n, T) &= \int_0^\infty \sum_{n=0}^{\infty} \frac{n(\alpha IT)^n}{n!} e^{-\alpha IT} p(I)\, dI \\ &= \int_0^\infty \alpha TIp(I)\, dI \equiv \alpha T\langle I\rangle\end{aligned}$$

where we define various intensity moments by

$$\langle I^n\rangle \equiv \int_0^\infty I^n p(I)\, dI \tag{2-14}$$

Similarly the modified mean square count becomes [cf. (2-6)]

$$\begin{aligned}\overline{n^2} = \sum_{n=0}^{\infty} n^2 P(n, T) &= \int_0^\infty [\alpha^2 T^2 I^2 + \alpha TI] p(I)\, dI \\ &= \alpha^2 T^2 \langle I^2\rangle + \alpha T\langle I\rangle\end{aligned}$$

Consequently the modified variance σ^2 becomes

$$\begin{aligned}\sigma^2 &= \overline{n^2} - (\bar{n})^2 \\ &= \alpha T\langle I\rangle + \alpha^2 T^2[\langle I^2\rangle - \langle I\rangle^2]\end{aligned} \tag{2-15}$$

which always exceeds $\bar{n}$ unless $p(I)$ is a Dirac δ function, $\delta(I - I_0)$. In the quantum analysis in Chapter 10 we shall learn that σ^2 can actually be less than $\bar{n}$.

An example of special physical significance for $p(I)$ is the *thermal distribution*

$$p(I) = I_0^{-1}\exp(-I/I_0) \tag{2-16}$$

for which the moments are given by

$$\begin{aligned}\langle I^n\rangle &= I_0^{-1}\int_0^\infty I^n \exp(-I/I_0)\,dI \\ &= I_0^n \int_0^\infty x^n e^{-x}\,dx = n!I_0^n\end{aligned} \tag{2-17}$$

Since $\bar{n} = \alpha T\langle I\rangle = \alpha T I_0$, Eq. (2-15) leads to the modified variance

$$\sigma^2 = \alpha T I_0 + \alpha^2 T^2[2I_0^2 - I_0^2] = \bar{n}(1 + \bar{n}) \tag{2-18}$$

which exceeds the value derived from a Poisson distribution.

From (2-6) we see that the generating function for this distribution is given simply by

$$\begin{aligned}Q(\lambda, T) &= I_0^{-1}\int_0^\infty \exp\left(-\lambda\alpha I T - \frac{I}{I_0}\right) dI \\ &= (1 + \lambda\alpha I_0 T)^{-1} = (1 + \lambda\bar{n})^{-1}\end{aligned} \tag{2-19}$$

Finally, the counting distribution for this example is given directly by (2-5) as

$$\begin{aligned}P(n, T) &= \frac{(\alpha T)^n}{I_0 n!}\int_0^\infty I^n \exp\left[-I\left(\alpha T + \frac{1}{I_0}\right)\right] dI \\ &= \frac{(\alpha T)^n}{I_0 n!}(\alpha T + 1/I_0)^{-(n+1)}\int_0^\infty x^n e^{-x}\,dx \\ &= (1 + \alpha I_0 T)^{-1}\left(1 + \frac{1}{\alpha I_0 T}\right)^{-n} = (1 + \bar{n})^{-1}(1 + \bar{n}^{-1})^{-n}\end{aligned} \tag{2-20}$$

using $\bar{n} \equiv \alpha I_0 T$.

The geometric series relation $P(n, T) \propto \gamma^n$, where $\gamma = (1 + \bar{n}^{-1})^{-1}$, that characterizes the present distribution has been verified in the photocounting experiments of Arecchi [2-4], which are arranged so that (2-12) is fulfilled. Arecchi has also shown that a Poisson distribution approxi-

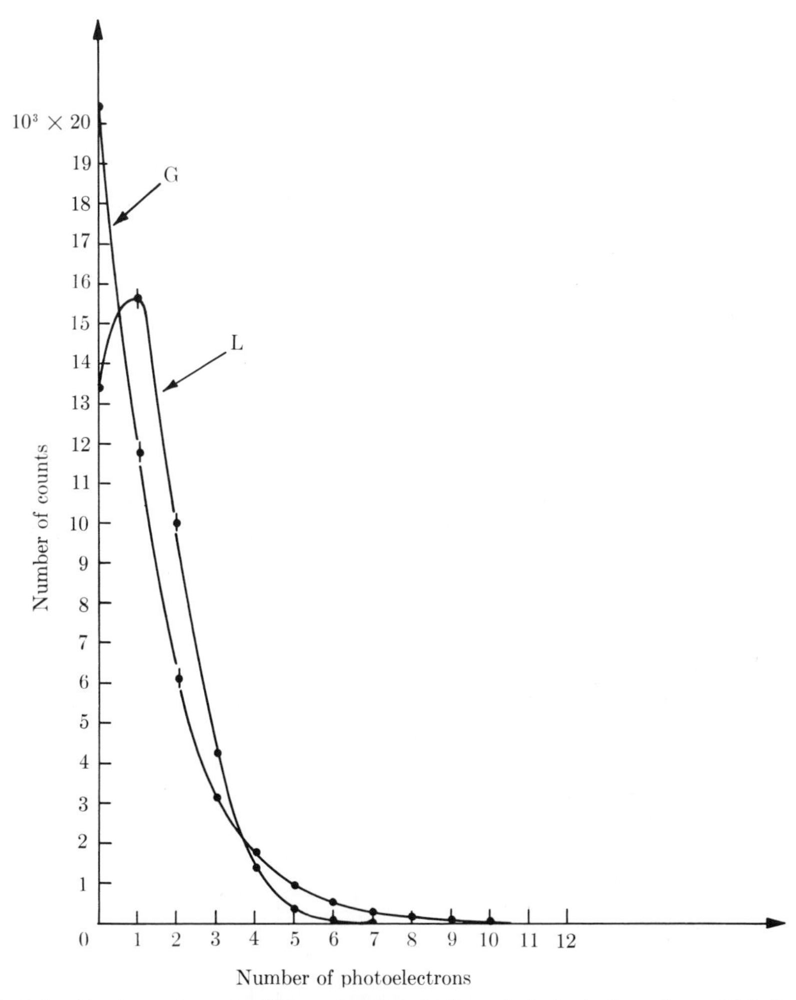

Fig. 2-1 Number of counts $F(n)$ versus the number of photoelectrons for artificially synthesized Gaussian light (G) and for laser light (L). The curve marked G interpolates an approximate geometric distribution with a mean count $\bar{n} = \{F(0)/F(1) - 1\}^{-1} \simeq 1.4$; the curve marked L interpolates an approximate Poisson distribution with a mean count $\bar{n} = F(1)/F(0) \simeq 1.2$. The observation time interval T was of the order of 3×10^{-5} sec in these experiments. [After F. T. Arecchi, *Phys. Rev. Letters* 15, 912 (1965); reprinted with permission.]

mately describes a highly stabilized laser (Fig. 2-1). Additional and more refined counting distributions not subject to the validity of (2-12) are discussed in the next chapter and in Chapter 9 in connection with our quantum treatment.

2-3 DETERMINATION OF THE INTENSITY DISTRIBUTION FROM THE COUNTING DISTRIBUTION

An important physical aspect of partially coherent radiation is the nature of the statistical ensemble. The question naturally arises, then, as to what extent the general distribution $p(U)$ in (2-5) is determined by observations of the counting distribution $P(n, T + t, t)$. We first demonstrate the important fact that the complete counting distribution uniquely determines $p(U)$.

The characteristic function for $p(U)$ is given by the Fourier transform

$$C(s) = \int_0^\infty e^{isU} p(U)\, dU \tag{2-21}$$

As in our previous cases, moments of the distribution $p(U)$, when they exist, can be found from $C(s)$ through differentiation. However, since intensities are never negative, we observe that $C(s)$ is actually the boundary value (i.e., as $t \to 0^+$) of an analytic function

$$C(s + it) \equiv \int_0^\infty e^{isU - tU} p(U)\, dU \tag{2-22}$$

analytic in the entire upper-half plane, $t > 0$. Partial information about this function in the upper-half plane is contained in the expression

$$\begin{aligned} C(i\lambda\alpha) &= \int_0^\infty e^{-\lambda\alpha U} p(U)\, dU \\ &= \sum_{n=0}^\infty (1 - \lambda)^n \int_0^\infty \frac{(\alpha U)^n}{n!} e^{-\alpha U} p(U)\, dU \\ &= \sum_{n=0}^\infty (1 - \lambda)^n P(n, T + t, t) \end{aligned} \tag{2-23}$$

for real λ in the interval $0 \leq \lambda \leq 1$. However, through the special properties of analytic functions, the partial information in (2-23) uniquely determines the function $C(s + it)$ in the entire upper-half plane. Thus the characteristic function, and thereby the distribution, is uniquely determined as was to be shown.

An explicit relation for the intensity distribution in terms of the counting distribution is given by a relation due to Widder [2-6] and discussed in the book of Shohat and Tamarkin [2-7]. We present a slightly modified form of the original analysis. For convenience, let us introduce the notation $y \equiv \alpha U$ and define $\hat{p}(y) = \alpha^{-1}p(U)$ so that

$$P(n, T + t, t) = \int_0^\infty \frac{y^n}{n!} \hat{p}(y)e^{-y}\, dy \tag{2-24}$$

This relation suggests the use of a form of Laguerre polynomials, $L_p(y)$, $p = 0, 1, 2, \ldots$, defined by

$$L_p(y) \equiv \frac{1}{p!} e^y \frac{d^p}{dy^p} y^p e^{-y} = \sum_{k=0}^{p} \binom{p}{k} \frac{(-y)^k}{k!} \tag{2-25}$$

which fulfill the orthogonality relation

$$\int_0^\infty L_p(y)L_q(y)e^{-y}\, dy = \delta_{pq} \tag{2-26a}$$

By a simple change of variables this orthogonality relation reads

$$2\int_0^\infty L_p(2y)L_q(2y)e^{-2y}\, dy = \delta_{pq} \tag{2-26b}$$

which we shall find more convenient. Let us now define the finite linear combinations of the counting distribution given by

$$\begin{aligned} \lambda_n &\equiv 2\int_0^\infty L_n(2y)\hat{p}(y)e^{-y}\, dy \\ &= 2\sum_{k=0}^{n} \binom{n}{k} (-2)^k P(k, T + t, t) \end{aligned} \tag{2-27}$$

for all n. Then we see that

$$\hat{p}(y) = \sum_{m=0}^{\infty} \lambda_m L_m(2y)e^{-y} \tag{2-28}$$

as a consequence of the orthogonality condition. Hence in our original notation

$$p(U) = \alpha \sum_{m=0}^{\infty} \lambda_m L_m(2\alpha U)e^{-\alpha U} \tag{2-29}$$

which is a determination of $p(U)$ from $P(k, T + T, t)$.

Several remarks are in order regarding Eq. (2-29), especially since these remarks apply to similar series we shall subsequently discuss. As with all orthogonal series expansions, care must be taken in interpreting (2-29). In order for the series (2-29) to converge at each point U, and so to define the function $p(U)$ pointwise, it suffices to have $\Sigma_{m=0}^{\infty} |\lambda_m| < \infty$, since for positive arguments αU the inequality $|L_m(2\alpha U)| \leq 1$ holds. When the sum of the coefficients λ_m is absolutely convergent, the function $p(U)$

given by (2-29) is actually continuous. However, it is often necessary or at least convenient, especially as an idealization for purposes of computation, to work with distributions $p(U)$ that are singular or discontinuous. An example frequently used is the rectangular distribution $p(U) = U_0^{-1}$ for $0 \le U \le U_0$, and $p(U) = 0$ for $U > U_0$. At a point U_0, where $p(U)$ is singular or discontinuous, the series representation (2-29) may not be literally valid. One must then invoke the more general interpretation of series such as (2-29), that of convergence "in the mean." In particular, if we introduce

$$p_M(U) \equiv \alpha \sum_{m=0}^{M} \lambda_m L_m(2\alpha U) e^{-\alpha U} \tag{2-30}$$

as the Mth partial sum, then (2-29) is a valid representation of an integrable $p(U)$ in the sense that

$$\lim_{M \to \infty} \int_0^\infty |p(U) - p_M(U)|\, dU = 0 \tag{2-31}$$

This type of convergence of the function sequence $p_M(U)$, $M = 1, 2, \ldots$, is often called L^1 convergence, and applies here since we are dealing with probability densities. Such convergence implies that the sequence of approximate mean values

$$b_M \equiv \int b(U) p_M(U)\, dU \qquad M = 1, 2, \ldots \tag{2-32a}$$

converges to the correct value

$$b \equiv \int b(U) p(U)\, dU \tag{2-32b}$$

for every bounded function $b(U)$. Examples for which the approximate mean values converge to the correct ones include: (1) $\exp(isU)$ for the characteristic function (2-21); (2) $\exp(-\lambda\alpha U)$ for the generating function (2-6); and (3) $(n!)^{-1}(\alpha U)^n \exp(-\alpha U)$ for the probability for n counts (2-5).

A. Independent Contributions and Associated Convolutions

We conclude this chapter by emphasizing the utility of studying a distribution by means of its generating function (or equally well by its characteristic function). Let us for convenience suppress all time dependencies and simply consider a pair of counting distributions and their associated generating functions

$$Q_j(\lambda) = \sum_{n=0}^{\infty} (1 - \lambda)^n P_j(n) \tag{2-33}$$

for $j = 1, 2$. If we form the product of Q_1 and Q_2 we discover that

$$\begin{aligned} Q(\lambda) &\equiv Q_1(\lambda)Q_2(\lambda) \\ &= \sum_{n_1,n_2=0}^{\infty} (1 - \lambda)^{n_1+n_2} P_1(n_1)P_2(n_2) \\ &\equiv \sum_{n=0}^{\infty} (1 - \lambda)^n P(n) \end{aligned} \tag{2-34}$$

where

$$P(n) \equiv \sum_{m=0}^{n} P_1(n - m)P_2(m) \tag{2-35}$$

Clearly each $P(n)$ is positive and their sum is unity so that (2-35) defines a valid distribution. Thus we see the important fact that the *product* of generating functions (or characteristic functions) leads to new distributions. Oftentimes, it is convenient to think of a distribution or to deduce new ones in this way, especially if there are several clear-cut independent origins to its statistical behavior.

In view of the direct connection between $Q(\lambda)$ and the characteristic function for $p(U)$, it follows that the intensity distribution in such a case is given by a convolution integral. In particular, we find again from (2-6) that

$$\begin{aligned} Q(\lambda) &= Q_1(\lambda)Q_2(\lambda) \\ &= \int_0^\infty \int_0^\infty \exp\left[-\lambda\alpha(U_1 + U_2)\right] p_1(U_1)p_2(U_2)\, dU_1\, dU_2 \\ &= \int_0^\infty e^{-\lambda\alpha U} p(U)\, dU \end{aligned} \tag{2-36}$$

where

$$p(U) \equiv \int_0^U p_1(U - W)p_2(W)\, dW \tag{2-37}$$

Physically this is the distribution for the random variable

$$U \equiv U_1 + U_2 \tag{2-38}$$

defined as the sum of two *independently* distributed variables U_1 and U_2 with distributions p_1 and p_2, respectively.

As a simple physical example of these formulas, let us again specialize to small times T such that $U_j = TI_j$ is a valid approximation. We may imagine that I_1 and I_2 represent the intensities for the two linearly independent modes of polarization of an incident wave. If these modes are independent and each is thermally distributed according to (2-16), then the appropriate generating function follows from (2-19) as

$$\begin{aligned} Q(\lambda, T) &= Q_1(\lambda, T)Q_2(\lambda, T) \\ &= (1 + \lambda\bar{n}_1)^{-1}(1 + \lambda\bar{n}_2)^{-1} \end{aligned} \tag{2-39}$$

where, for $j = 1, 2$, we have set

$$\bar{n}_j = \alpha T\langle I_j\rangle = \alpha T I_{0j} \tag{2-40}$$

Clearly an important parameter is given by

$$\mathcal{P} \equiv \left|\frac{\bar{n}_1 - \bar{n}_2}{\bar{n}_1 + \bar{n}_2}\right| = \left|\frac{I_{01} - I_{02}}{I_{01} + I_{02}}\right| \tag{2-41}$$

which, as we shall see in Chapter 5, may be identified with the degree of polarization of the incident radiation. With no loss of generality we may assume that $I_{01} \geq I_{02}$. It follows that

$$I_{01} = \tfrac{1}{2}(1 + \mathcal{P})I_0 \qquad \bar{n}_1 = \tfrac{1}{2}(1 + \mathcal{P})\bar{n} \tag{2-42a}$$

$$I_{02} = \tfrac{1}{2}(1 - \mathcal{P})I_0 \qquad \bar{n}_2 = \tfrac{1}{2}(1 - \mathcal{P})\bar{n} \tag{2-42b}$$

where

$$I_0 \equiv I_{01} + I_{02} \qquad \bar{n} \equiv \bar{n}_1 + \bar{n}_2 = \alpha T I_0 \tag{2-43}$$

The counting and intensity distributions that follow from (2-39) are simply obtained with the aid of the partial fraction expansion

$$\frac{1}{(1 + \lambda\bar{n}_1)}\,\frac{1}{(1 + \lambda\bar{n}_2)} = \frac{1}{(\bar{n}_1 - \bar{n}_2)}\left[\frac{\bar{n}_1}{(1 + \lambda\bar{n}_1)} - \frac{\bar{n}_2}{(1 + \lambda\bar{n}_2)}\right] \tag{2-44}$$

In particular (2-20) leads to the counting distribution

$$P(n, T) = \frac{1}{\mathcal{P}\bar{n}}\left\{\frac{1}{[1 + 2/(1 + \mathcal{P})\bar{n}]^{n+1}} - \frac{1}{[1 + 2/(1 - \mathcal{P})\bar{n}]^{n+1}}\right\} \tag{2-45}$$

whereas (2-16) leads to the intensity distribution

$$p(I) = \frac{1}{\mathcal{P}I_0}\left\{\exp\left[-\frac{2I}{(1 + \mathcal{P})I_0}\right] - \exp\left[-\frac{2I}{(1 - \mathcal{P})I_0}\right]\right\} \tag{2-46}$$

In addition, we note that the property $\overline{n^2} = \bar{n}(1 + 2\bar{n})$ for a thermal distribution coupled with (2-44) leads to the counting variance given by

$$\begin{aligned} \sigma_2 &= (\bar{n}_1 - \bar{n}_2)^{-1}[\bar{n}_1{}^2(1 + 2\bar{n}_1) - \bar{n}_2{}^2(1 + 2\bar{n}_2)] - \bar{n}^2 \\ &= [(\bar{n}_1 + \bar{n}_2) + (\bar{n}_1{}^2 + \bar{n}_2{}^2)] \\ &\equiv \bar{n}[1 + \epsilon\bar{n}] \end{aligned} \tag{2-47a}$$

where

$$\begin{aligned}\epsilon &\equiv (\bar{n})^{-2}[\bar{n}_1{}^2 + \bar{n}_2{}^2] \\ &= \tfrac{1}{2}(\bar{n})^{-2}[(\bar{n}_1 + \bar{n}_2)^2 + (\bar{n}_1 - \bar{n}_2)^2] \\ &= \tfrac{1}{2}[1 + \mathcal{P}^2] \qquad (2\text{-}47\text{b})\end{aligned}$$

The discussion of polarization in Chapter 5 shows that for polarized light $\mathcal{P} = 1$ and $\epsilon = 1$ [and σ^2 agrees with the result in (2-18)], and for unpolarized $\mathcal{P} = 0$ and $\epsilon = \frac{1}{2}$.

We note for $\mathcal{P} = 0$ that $Q(\lambda) = (1 + \lambda\bar{n}/2)^{-2}$. More generally, if

$$Q(\lambda) = (1 + \lambda\bar{n}/N)^{-N} \qquad (2\text{-}48)$$

corresponding to N independent, equally distributed "thermal" variables, then it follows that the counting variance reads

$$\begin{aligned}\sigma^2 &= \overline{n^2} - \bar{n}^2 = \overline{n(n-1)} + \bar{n}(1 - \bar{n}) \\ &= \bar{n}(1 - \bar{n}) + \frac{\partial^2}{\partial\lambda^2} Q(\lambda)\bigg|_{\lambda=0} \\ &= \bar{n}(1 - \bar{n}) + \left(1 + \frac{1}{N}\right)\bar{n}^2 \\ &= \bar{n}\left(1 + \frac{\bar{n}}{N}\right) \qquad (2\text{-}49)\end{aligned}$$

where we have used the second-order factorial moment defined in (2-8). For heuristic purposes it is often helpful to interpret a general distribution in the light of multiple, independent "thermal" distributions the number of which (N above) may evidently be read off directly from the variance. The degeneracy parameter δ (which is $\bar{n}/N$ above) is the mean occupancy per independent variable or per "cell," as it is frequently called.

If (2-48) is adopted as an adequate approximation for the complete characteristic function, it follows from (2-6) that the associated distribution for the variable U is given by

$$p(U) = \left(\frac{\alpha N}{\bar{n}}\right)\frac{U^{N-1}}{\Gamma(N)}\, e^{-\alpha N U/\bar{n}} \qquad (2\text{-}50)$$

In addition it follows from (2-7) that the associated counting distribution is given by

$$P(n) = \frac{\left(1 + \dfrac{\bar{n}}{N}\right)^{-N}}{n!}\left(\frac{\bar{n}}{\bar{n} + N}\right)^n \prod_{p=1}^{n} (p + N - 1) \qquad (2\text{-}51)$$

In later chapters we shall find it convenient to interpret several distributions from this viewpoint.

CHAPTER 3

SEMICLASSICAL TREATMENT OF PHOTOELECTRIC COUNTS

3-1 RANDOM WAVE FIELDS

We now take up the problem of photoelectric counting distributions with a general, partially coherent, light beam incident on the counters. For simplicity we shall continue to use the scalar optical wave field. In contrast to our preceding discussion we want to consider the wave field $V(\mathbf{r}, t)$ as the relevant random quantity in computing the counting distribution $P(n, T + t, t)$. Let us idealize to a point counter at $\mathbf{r}_i$ (a variable we presently suppress) and to a stationary distribution (so we may drop t). In such a case, Eq. (2-5) becomes

$$P(n, T) = \frac{1}{n!}\left\langle\left(\alpha \int_0^T V^*(t')V(t')\,dt'\right)^n \exp\left[-\alpha \int_0^T V^*(t')V(t')\,dt'\right]\right\rangle \tag{3-1}$$

where the angular brackets denote an average in the ensemble of fields V. From this relation it immediately follows that the mean count is

$$\bar{n} = \sum_{n=0}^{\infty} nP(n, T) = \left\langle \alpha \int_0^T V^*(t')V(t')\,dt' \right\rangle \tag{3-2}$$

and that the mean square count is

$$\begin{aligned}\overline{n^2} &= \sum_{n=0}^{\infty} n^2 P(n, T) \\ &= \left\langle \alpha^2 \int_0^T \int_0^T V^*(t')V(t')V^*(t'')V(t'')\,dt'\,dt'' \right\rangle + \bar{n}\end{aligned} \tag{3-3}$$

Consequently, we observe that to compute fully the mean square, $\overline{n^2}$, requires more than a knowledge of the mutual coherence function Γ defined in (1-13)—which was the only correlation function necessary to discuss interferometric effects in partial coherence—it requires a fourth-order correlation function. Higher-order counting moments require still higher-order correlation functions. As in Chapter 2 the counting moments may be conveniently collected in the generating function

$$\begin{aligned} Q(\lambda, T) &= \sum_{n=0}^{\infty} (1 - \lambda)^n P(n, T) \\ &= \left\langle \exp\left[-\lambda\alpha \int_0^T V^*(t')V(t')\, dt' \right] \right\rangle \end{aligned} \tag{3-4}$$

The proper calculation of either $P(n, T)$ or $Q(\lambda, T)$ requires correlation functions for the field $V(t')$ of arbitrarily high order.

The averages involved in (3-1) to (3-4) are intended to be over ensembles of random, complex *functions* $V(t)$ (rather than the single variable U of Chapter 2). Such averages are important in a number of physical and mathematical applications, and a considerable literature exists pertaining to their properties. In a general vein we may mention the works of Bartlett [3-4], Ramakrishnan [3-5], and the collection of articles edited by Wax [3-2]. The important works of Doob [3-7] and of Gelfand and Vilenkin [3-6] are more of a mathematical nature.

In the next section we want to give a brief review of properties and proper descriptive methods of stochastic processes (random functions) suitable for a systematic treatment of the counting distribution (3-1) or of its generating function (3-4). Our excursion into classical stochastic processes will not only have its immediate applications to our present analysis, but will be important for the quantum case as well.

3-2 STOCHASTIC PROCESSES

Recall that for a finite number n of random variables the common means to describe a probability distribution is to give the density function $\rho_n(x_1, x_2, \ldots, x_n)$ for the n variables x_j. A completely equivalent means to characterize the distribution is, as we remarked earlier, by means of the characteristic function [1]

$$C_n(s_1, s_2, \ldots, s_n) = \int \cdots \int \exp\,[i\Sigma x_j s_j]\rho_n(x_1, x_2, \ldots, x_n)\, dx_1 \cdots dx_n \tag{3-5}$$

[1] Integration limits will occasionally be left unspecified if they are generally clear from the context or, as here, they run from $-\infty$ to $+\infty$.

defined for all real values s_j, which is just the Fourier transform of ρ_n. No matter how badly ρ_n behaves, C_n is always continuous and uniquely determines ρ_n. Moreover, the mean value of any quantity that exists can always be found from C_n. These two properties are not generally found if one attempts to specify ρ_n through its moments. Not only may some or all of the moments be infinite, but even when all moments are finite their determination of ρ_n may not be unique.

As an example of a characteristic function, suppose ρ_n corresponds to an off-center Gaussian distribution,

$$\rho_n = \pi^{-n/2}(\det a_{jk})^{-1/2} \exp[-\tfrac{1}{2}\Sigma(x_j - b_j)a_{jk}(x_k - b_k)] \tag{3-6}$$

where each summation extends from 1 to n. Then a straightforward calculation yields

$$C_n \equiv \langle \exp(i\Sigma x_j s_j)\rangle = \exp(i\Sigma s_j b_j - \tfrac{1}{2}\Sigma s_j a_{jk}^{-1} s_k) \tag{3-7}$$

expressed in terms of the elements a_{jk}^{-1} of the matrix reciprocal to that with elements a_{jk}. Recognizing that only second-order terms appear in the exponent, we may note by expansion of each side of (3-7) that

$$\langle \Sigma x_j s_j \rangle = \Sigma s_j b_j \tag{3-8a}$$

$$\langle (\Sigma x_j s_j)^2 \rangle - \langle \Sigma x_j s_j \rangle^2 = \Sigma s_j a_{jk}^{-1} s_k \tag{3-8b}$$

Consequently, we can re-express C_n according to

$$\langle \exp(i\Sigma x_j s_j)\rangle = \exp(i\Sigma s_j\langle x_j\rangle - \tfrac{1}{2}\Sigma s_j\langle \Delta x_j\, \Delta x_k\rangle s_k) \tag{3-9}$$

where $\Delta x_j \equiv x_j - \langle x_j\rangle$. This functional relationship is *characteristic* of Gaussian distributions, and it may properly be taken as their *definition* in place of (3-6).

When we pass to an infinite number of random variables a corresponding probability density for all variables generally loses any but heuristic significance. On the other hand, the characteristic function (now a functional) remains a valid and useful concept. In particular, assuming the summation extends to infinity, we may already regard (3-9) as the characteristic functional for a Gaussian process with infinitely many random variables subject to one proviso. Whereas for finitely many degrees of freedom, the value of each variable s_j could be an arbitrary real number, there are now restrictions imposed on the set $\{s_j\}$. In order for desirable properties such as continuity and differentiability to be maintained, the allowed sequences s_j, $j = 1, 2, \ldots,$ must be chosen so that

$$\sum_{j=1}^{\infty} |s_j\langle x_j\rangle| < \infty \tag{3-10a}$$

$$\sum_{j,k=1}^{\infty} s_j\langle\Delta x_j\, \Delta x_k\rangle s_k < \infty \tag{3-10b}$$

for the mean and variance of the specific distribution under consideration. We may call sequences s_j fulfilling (3-10) *smooth* or *test* sequences to indicate their restricted nature. We shall have no need at the present to spell out in detail any particular set of smooth sequences. Indeed, in such problems many of the interesting results may be obtained without ever explicitly delineating the full set of suitable sequences. The important conceptual point is a recognition that *some* restrictive limitations must be imposed on the allowed s_j sequences, i.e., an appreciation that not every conceivable sequence s_j is allowed.

An alternative description to the sequence form just given is often convenient. Suppose the functions $u_j(t)$ form a complete orthonormal sequence of real functions of one variable. With their aid, and with the random variables x_j we can form a stochastic variable

$$x(t) = \sum_{j=1}^{\infty} x_j u_j(t) \tag{3-11}$$

which is our random function of time. Likewise with each of the smooth sequences we can associate a smooth test function

$$s(t) = \sum_{j=1}^{\infty} s_j u_j(t) \tag{3-12}$$

In terms of these two quantities we can re-express the characteristic functional for the Gaussian distribution as follows:

$$C\{s(t)\} = \langle \exp\,[i\textstyle\int s(t)x(t)\,dt]\rangle = \exp\,[i\textstyle\int s(t)\langle x(t)\rangle\,dt - \frac{1}{2}\int\!\!\int s(t')\langle \Delta x(t')\Delta x(t'')\rangle s(t'')\,dt'\,dt''] \tag{3-13}$$

The transcribed conditions that the smooth functions $s(t)$ must fulfill are evidently

$$\int |s(t)\langle x(t)\rangle|\,dt < \infty \tag{3-14a}$$

$$\int\!\!\int s(t')\langle \Delta x(t')\,\Delta x(t'')\rangle s(t'')\,dt'\,dt'' < \infty \tag{3-14b}$$

As with the sequences s_j, we need seldom specify the full set of smooth functions explicitly. For orientation purposes, let us note that in most problems of physical interest, one can assume that suitable smooth functions are infinitely differentiable and fall off as $t \rightarrow \pm\infty$ faster than any inverse power.

The time formulation such as in (3-13) is particularly convenient to discuss stationary distributions. For a stationary distribution it follows that

$$\langle x(t)\rangle = \langle x(0)\rangle = m \tag{3-15a}$$

and that

$$\langle \Delta x(t')\, \Delta x(t'')\rangle = \langle \Delta x(t' - t'')\, \Delta x(0)\rangle \tag{3-15b}$$

which can be expressed in the general form

$$\langle \Delta x(t')\, \Delta x(t'')\rangle = \int e^{-2\pi i\nu(t'-t'')}\tilde{\mu}(\nu)\, d\nu \tag{3-16}$$

where $\tilde{\mu}(\nu) \geq 0$. If we employ these relations and introduce

$$\tilde{s}(\nu) = \int e^{2\pi i\nu t}s(t)\, dt \tag{3-17}$$

as a smooth frequency-dependent function, then (3-13) becomes

$$C\{\tilde{s}(\nu)\} = \exp[im\tilde{s}(0) - \tfrac{1}{2}\int \tilde{s}^*(\nu)\tilde{\mu}(\nu)\tilde{s}(\nu)\, d\nu] \tag{3-18}$$

This result implies that each frequency component of a stationary Gaussian stochastic process is distributed as an independent Gaussian variable with (relative) variance $\tilde{\mu}(\nu)^{-1}$.

Summarizing this example, we note that all the information necessary to evaluate arbitrary mean values involving a real, stationary, Gaussian, stochastic process is contained in (3-18) and depends, therefore, on one number, m, and one function, $\tilde{\mu}(\nu)$. We note also the important fact that the conditions for stationarity could be deduced from (3-13) by simply requiring that $C\{s(t)\} = C\{s(t + t_0)\}$ for all t_0 and all smooth functions $s(t)$.

For applications to coherence theory it is convenient to work explicitly with random, analytic-signal wave fields rather than their real counterparts. Taking Eq. (1-3) into account for real time functions $S^{(r)}$ and $V^{(r)}$, we note first that

$$\begin{aligned}\tfrac{1}{2}\int S^{(r)}(t)V^{(r)}(t)\, dt &= \operatorname{Re}\int_0^\infty \tilde{S}^{(r)*}(\nu)\tilde{V}^{(r)}(\nu)\, d\nu \\ &\equiv \operatorname{Re}\int_0^\infty \tilde{S}^*(\nu)\tilde{V}(\nu)\, d\nu = \operatorname{Re}\int S^*(t)V(t)\, dt\end{aligned} \tag{3-19}$$

in terms of analytic-signal wave fields $V = \frac{1}{2}[V^{(r)} + iV^{(i)}]$ and analytic-signal smooth functions $S = \frac{1}{2}[S^{(r)} + iS^{(i)}]$. Consequently, the characteristic functional of interest may be expressed as

$$C\{S(t)\} \equiv \langle \exp[i\int S^{(r)}V^{(r)}\, dt]\rangle = \langle \exp[i\int (S^*V + SV^*)\, dt]\rangle \tag{3-20}$$

in terms of analytic signals $V(t)$ and $S(t)$ for whatever field distribution may apply. Stationarity of the underlying ensemble is ensured if we demand that

$$C\{S(t + t_0)\} = C\{S(t)\} \tag{3-21a}$$

for all t_0 and all $S(t)$. If the arguments are viewed as functions of frequency this condition reads

$$C\{\tilde{S}(\nu) \exp(-2\pi i\nu t_0)\} = C\{\tilde{S}(\nu)\} \tag{3-21b}$$

for all t_0 and all $\tilde{S}(\nu)$.

In order for each frequency component to be independently distributed it suffices that

$$C\{\tilde{S}_1(\nu) + \tilde{S}_2(\nu)\} = C\{\tilde{S}_1(\nu)\}C\{\tilde{S}_2(\nu)\} \tag{3-22}$$

for all $\tilde{S}_1(\nu)$ and $\tilde{S}_2(\nu)$ such that $\tilde{S}_1(\nu)\tilde{S}_2(\nu) = 0$.

Another condition that often occurs for complex wave fields is a lack of overall phase knowledge. Physically, this could arise, for example, when the fields $V(t)$ and $e^{i\varphi}V(t)$, φ a constant, are considered equally likely. If such is the case, we may secure this phase equality by asking that

$$C\{e^{-i\varphi}S(t)\} = C\{S(t)\} \tag{3-23}$$

for all real φ and $S(t)$. This condition may, in turn, be secured if

$$C\{S(t)\} = C_1\{S^*(t')S(t'')\} \tag{3-24a}$$

for some functional C_1. Expressed as a functional of smooth frequency functions, this relation reads

$$C\{\tilde{S}(\nu)\} = C_1\{\tilde{S}^*(\nu')\tilde{S}(\nu'')\} \tag{3-24b}$$

Lastly, we note that a simple (but not the only) way to satisfy both the phase-invariance condition and the stationarity condition is when

$$C\{\tilde{S}(\nu)\} = \bar{C}\{\tilde{S}^*(\nu)\tilde{S}(\nu)\} \tag{3-25}$$

for some suitable functional $\bar{C}$.

To see these conditions in concrete form, let us first look again at the Gaussian case. The characteristic functional for a complex, stationary, phase-uncertain Gaussian stochastic process is given by the obvious generalization of (3-13) as

$$\begin{aligned} C\{S(t)\} &= \exp[-\textstyle\int\int S^*(t')\langle V(t')V^*(t'')\rangle S(t'')\,dt'\,dt''] \\ &= \exp[-\textstyle\int\int S^*(t')\Gamma(t' - t'')S(t'')\,dt'\,dt''] \\ &= \exp[-\textstyle\int \tilde{S}^*(\nu)\tilde{\Gamma}(\nu)\tilde{S}(\nu)\,d\nu] \end{aligned} \tag{3-26}$$

which satisfies conditions (3-21) to (3-25). Physically, $\tilde{\Gamma}(\nu)$ represents the mean power at frequency ν contained in the wave fields that go to make up the specific Gaussian ensemble.

In Chapter 2 we formed new distributions by multiplying characteristic functionals. Here, let us illustrate that new distributions may also be formed by promoting some parameters of a given distribution to random variables and averaging the associated characteristic functional in an appropriate fashion.

To motivate the first example, suppose that $\tilde{\Gamma}(\nu)$ in (3-26) is written in the form

$$\tilde{\Gamma}(\nu) = \tilde{G}(\nu) + p\tilde{H}(\nu) \tag{3-27}$$

where all terms are positive. Let us regard $\tilde{G}$ and $\tilde{H}$ as fixed functions and view p as a new, discrete, random variable ($p = 0, 1, 2, \ldots$) with a Poisson distribution whose mean value $\langle p \rangle = \mu$. The resultant characteristic functional for the modified distribution (when we take account of the randomness of p) becomes

$$\begin{aligned} C\{S(t)\} &= \sum_{p=0}^{\infty} \frac{\mu^p}{p!} \exp\left[-\mu - \int |\tilde{S}|^2(\tilde{G} + p\tilde{H})\, d\nu\right] \\ &= \exp\left\{-\int |\tilde{S}|^2\tilde{G}\, d\nu - \mu\left[1 - \exp\left(-\int |\tilde{S}|^2\tilde{H}\, d\nu\right)\right]\right\} \end{aligned} \tag{3-28}$$

Although stationary, this example does not fulfill (3-22) so it does not correspond to an independent distribution for each frequency.

To obtain another related example, let us first express $\tilde{\Gamma}(\nu)$ in (3-26) in the form

$$\tilde{\Gamma}(\nu) = \tilde{G}(\nu) + \sum_{j=1}^{N} \tilde{K}(\nu_j)\, \delta(\nu - \nu_j) \tag{3-29}$$

where again all terms are positive. We assume that the functions $\tilde{G}$ and $\tilde{K}$ are fixed but we regard the ν_j as independent, random frequency variables each uniformly distributed in the interval $|\nu| \leq F/2$. Qualitatively speaking, $\tilde{\Gamma}(\nu)$ is a random variable with many, independent spikelike contributions (akin to shot noise) each entering with an amplitude determined by $\tilde{K}(\nu)$ and with a uniformly distributed center frequency. In the limit that $N \to \infty$, $F \to \infty$ such that $N/F = \rho$ is finite, the resultant modified distribution can be deduced from results quoted by Rice [3-3], and has a characteristic functional given by

$$C\{S(t)\} = \exp\{-\textstyle\int[|\tilde{S}|^2\tilde{G} + \rho(1 - \exp[-\tilde{K}|\tilde{S}|^2])]\, d\nu\} \tag{3-30}$$

which, like (3-26), is independently distributed for each ν.

This brief account should, at least, give the reader a rough feel for how random functions can be studied through the use of characteristic functionals. We shall on occasion introduce other random processes and associated characteristic functionals beyond those examples we have discussed here. In all cases, however, the basic concepts in the description remain unchanged.

3-3 APPLICATIONS TO PARTIAL COHERENCE

A. Single Counters

Let us return once again to the starting discussion of this chapter for the mean counting moments. According to (3-3), we can express $\overline{n^2}$ in terms of a fourfold correlation the precise value of which depends on the statistics in question.

Suppose we are dealing with radiation from a thermal source (lamp, star, etc.)—but *not* that from a laser—for which a stationary, phase-uncertain Gaussian distribution is generally appropriate. A straightforward expansion of (3-26), which contains all relevant information about the ensemble, shows that

$$\frac{2^4}{4!}\left\langle\left(\mathrm{Re}\int S^*(t)V(t)\,dt\right)^4\right\rangle = \frac{1}{2!}\left\{\iint S^*(t')\langle V(t')V^*(t'')\rangle S(t'')\,dt'\,dt''\right\}^2 \tag{3-31}$$

This relation holds for arbitrary smooth functions $S(t)$. On equating appropriate coefficients we find that to fulfill (3-31) we must have [2]

$$\langle V^*(t_1)V(t_2)V^*(t_3)V(t_4)\rangle = \langle V^*(t_1)V(t_2)\rangle\langle V^*(t_3)V(t_4)\rangle + \langle V^*(t_1)V(t_4)\rangle\langle V^*(t_3)V(t_2)\rangle \tag{3-32}$$

Thus for the case of particular interest to compute $\overline{n^2}$ we find that

$$\begin{aligned}\langle V^*(t')V(t')V^*(t'')V(t'')\rangle &= \langle V^*(t')V(t')\rangle\langle V^*(t'')V(t'')\rangle \\ &\quad + \langle V^*(t')V(t'')\rangle\langle V^*(t'')V(t')\rangle \\ &\equiv \langle I(t')\rangle\langle I(t'')\rangle + |\Gamma(t'-t'')|^2\end{aligned} \tag{3-33}$$

where we have introduced

$$\Gamma(t'-t'') = \langle V^*(t'')V(t')\rangle \tag{3-34}$$

which is the autocorrelation function of the ensemble for the point $\mathbf{r}_i$ [called $\Gamma_{ii}(t'-t'')$ in Chapter 1]. From (3-2) and (3-3) the variance

[2] More generally, (3-26) leads to

$$\left\langle\prod_{p=1}^{n} V^*(t_{2p-1})V(t_{2p})\right\rangle = \sum_P \prod_{p=1}^{n} \langle V^*(t_{2p-1})V(t_{2P(p)})\rangle$$

a sum over the $n!$ permutations P on the integers $p \to P(p)$, $p = 1, \ldots, n$.

becomes

$$\sigma^2 = \overline{n^2} - (\bar{n})^2$$
$$= \alpha^2 \int_0^T \int_0^T |\Gamma(t' - t'')|^2 \, dt' \, dt'' + \bar{n} \tag{3-35}$$

There is, therefore, an excess counting or a bunching of counts which depends on T through the mutual coherence function Γ.

As in Chapter 1, let us introduce the normalized function γ (called γ_{ii} in Chapter 1) defined by

$$\gamma(t' - t'') = \Gamma(t' - t'')/\Gamma(0) \tag{3-36}$$

which according to (1-17) fulfills the condition $|\gamma(t' - t'')| \leq 1$. Following Mandel [2-1], let us define

$$\xi(T) \equiv \frac{1}{T} \int_0^T \int_0^T |\gamma(t' - t'')|^2 \, dt' \, dt''$$
$$= \frac{2}{T} \int_0^T (T - \tau)|\gamma(\tau)|^2 \, d\tau \tag{3-37}$$

The function $\xi(T)$ has the units of time and is a convenient nondecreasing measure of the cumulative temporal evolution of the signal coherence.

It follows from the relation $|\gamma(t)| \leq 1$ that $\xi(T) \leq T$. If for some initial time interval $\gamma(t)$ is sensibly 1, then $\xi(T) \simeq T$. Whenever $\xi(T) < T$ it reflects the presence of an intervening period of partial coherence. If $\gamma(t)$ falls to zero in a *characteristic time* $\mathfrak{T}$ (e.g., as in the functions $e^{-t/\mathfrak{T}}$ or $\exp[-\frac{1}{2}(t/\mathfrak{T})^2]$), the precise functional form being not too important, then for large T, $T \gg \mathfrak{T}$, $\xi(T)$ becomes sensibly constant and has the value

$$\xi(T) = \frac{2}{T} \int_0^T (T - \tau)|\gamma(\tau)|^2 \, d\tau$$
$$\simeq 2\mathfrak{T}\left(\int_0^\infty |\gamma(\mathfrak{T}x)|^2 \, dx\right)$$

In other words, $\xi(T) \simeq c\mathfrak{T}$, where c is a constant of order unity, provided, of course, that the integrals converge. The limiting value

$$\xi(\infty) = 2 \int_0^\infty |\gamma(\tau)|^2 \, d\tau \tag{3-38}$$

is a possible measure of the *coherence time* which we shall adopt.

Since

$$\bar{n} = \alpha \int_0^T \langle V^*(t')V(t')\rangle \, dt' = \alpha T\Gamma(0) \tag{3-39}$$

in virtue of the stationarity, we can rewrite our basic variance (3-35) in the form

$$\sigma^2 = \bar{n}\{1 + [\xi(T)/T]\bar{n}\} \tag{3-40}$$

with $\xi(T)$ given by (3-37). From the discussion in Chapter 2, and in particular Eq. (2-49), we note that this variance is the same as that which would arise for the distribution of photons which are partitioned into $T/\xi(T)$ independent "time cells" each of which is thermally distributed with a mean occupancy per cell, or degeneracy parameter, given by $\delta = \bar{n}/[T/\xi(T)] = \bar{n}\xi(T)/T$. In the context of photocounts for stationary Gaussian ensembles it has been argued by Mandel [3-12] that for sufficiently long T it is, in fact, suitable to assume that a mean of δ photons within an interval corresponding to a coherence time are thermally distributed and that neighboring intervals are statistically independent. Under these assumptions the counting distribution (3-1) becomes that of (2-51) with the identification $N = T/\xi(T)$. More refined approximations for stationary Gaussian ensembles and long measuring times T are developed in Chapter 9 in conjunction with our quantum discussion.

The results of the calculation we have carried out in the Gaussian case for the bunching of counts are in essence quite general. Any classical distribution yields an excess counting over the Poisson case and, thus, a bunching just as in (3-40). For comparison we state the results of a calculation similar to that carried out above but now for the wave-field distribution characterized by (3-28). In this case, the mean count is

$$\bar{n} = \alpha T[G(0) + \mu H(0)] \tag{3-41}$$

while the counting variance is

$$\sigma^2 = \bar{n} + 2\alpha^2 \int_0^T (T - \tau)|G(\tau) + \mu H(\tau)|^2 \, d\tau + \alpha^2\mu \left[T^2H^2(0) + 2\int_0^T (T - \tau)|H(\tau)|^2 \, d\tau \right] \tag{3-42}$$

This expression for σ^2 always contains a term proportional to T^2 whereas (3-40) asymptotically grows at most linearly with T, so long as the coherence time is finite. Clearly the two results agree in the limit $\mu \to 0$ as they must.

B. Several Detectors

Instead of considering the fluctuations in the counts in a single detector, we may alternatively consider the correlation between counts in two or more distinct detectors illuminated by light which exhibits partial coherence. In particular, suppose that $V(\mathbf{r}, t)$ represents the wave field from an extended source as a function of space and time. Then it is reasonable to expect that correlations in the statistics of $V(\mathbf{r},t)$ may persist when the various signals which are compared pertain to spatially separated points. Let us assume that we have two "fast" detectors located, respectively, at $\mathbf{r}_1$ and $\mathbf{r}_2$, and let us put

$$V_i(t) = V(\mathbf{r}_i, t) \tag{3-43}$$

and

$$I_i(t) = V_i^*(t)V_i(t) \tag{3-44}$$

The counting distribution appropriate to a fixed intensity at $\mathbf{r}_i$ is just like that given in (2-2), namely

$$P_{0i}(n_i, T) = \frac{1}{n_i!}\left(\alpha_i \int_0^T I_i(t)\,dt\right)^{n_i} \exp\left[-\alpha_i \int_0^T I_i(t)\,dt\right] \tag{3-45}$$

Consequently, when the intensities are viewed as random, the mean counting cross-correlation, for example, is given by

$$\begin{aligned}\overline{n_1n_2} &= \sum_{n_1,n_2} n_1n_2\langle P_{01}(n_1, T)P_{02}(n_2, T)\rangle \\ &= \alpha_1\alpha_2 \int_0^T \int_0^T \langle I_1(t')I_2(t'')\rangle\,dt'\,dt''\end{aligned} \tag{3-46}$$

the precise value of which depends on the statistics.

For the sake of illustration, let us assume a stationary, phase-uncertain Gaussian distribution for the complex wave field $V(\mathbf{r}, t)$. Extending the discussion given earlier in this chapter, we can characterize such a distribution by a characteristic functional of complex smooth functions $S(\mathbf{r}, t)$ depending on both space and time, and for which

$$\begin{aligned}C\{S(\mathbf{r}, t)\} = \exp\{-\textstyle\int\int S^*(\mathbf{r}_1, t_1)\langle V(\mathbf{r}_1, t_1) \\ \times V^*(\mathbf{r}_2, t_2)\rangle S(\mathbf{r}_2, t_2)\,d^3r_1\,d^3r_2\,dt_1\,dt_2\}\end{aligned} \tag{3-47}$$

Specialized to localized detectors at $\mathbf{r}_1$ and $\mathbf{r}_2$, we may instead simply use $S_i(t) = S(\mathbf{r}_i, t)$, $i = 1, 2$, and adopt

$$C\{S_i(t)\} = \exp\left\{-\sum_{i,j} \int\int S_i^*(t_1)\langle V_i(t_1)V_j^*(t_2)\rangle S_j(t_2)\,dt_1\,dt_2\right\} \tag{3-48}$$

All cross-correlation quantities may be found from Eq. (3-48). In particular, it follows that

$$\begin{aligned}\langle V_1^*(t')V_1(t')V_2^*(t'')V_2(t'')\rangle &= \langle V_1^*(t')V_1(t')\rangle\langle V_2^*(t'')V_2(t'')\rangle \\ &\quad + \langle V_1^*(t')V_2(t'')\rangle\langle V_2^*(t'')V_1(t')\rangle\end{aligned} \tag{3-49}$$

On application to (3-46) we find that

$$\overline{n_1n_2} = \bar{n}_1\bar{n}_2 + \alpha_1\alpha_2 \int_0^T \int_0^T |\Gamma_{12}(t' - t'')|^2\,dt'\,dt'' \tag{3-50}$$

where, just as in (1-13),

$$\Gamma_{12}(t' - t'') \equiv \langle V_2^*(t'')V_1(t')\rangle \tag{3-51}$$

denotes a cross-correlation function of the ensemble, and

$$\bar{n}_i = \alpha_i \int_0^T \langle V_i^*(t')V_i(t')\rangle\, dt' \equiv \alpha_i T\Gamma_{ii}(0) \tag{3-52}$$

Let us introduce the normalized function

$$\gamma_{12}(\tau) = \Gamma_{12}(\tau)/\{\Gamma_{11}(0)\Gamma_{22}(0)\}^{1/2} \tag{3-53}$$

and the quantity

$$\xi_{12}(T) \equiv \frac{2}{T}\int_0^T (T - \tau)|\gamma_{12}(\tau)|^2\, d\tau \tag{3-54}$$

which, as before, is a useful measure of the cumulative temporal behavior of the mutual coherence of the signals. In terms of these quantities the excess counting correlation is given by

$$\overline{n_1 n_2} - \bar{n}_1\bar{n}_2 = \bar{n}_1\bar{n}_2[\xi_{12}(T)/T] \tag{3-55}$$

which thus exhibits that intensity correlations may exist in spatially separated counters.

In addition to the temporal behavior of the joint counting correlation it is useful to display explicitly the spatial dependence of the right-hand side of (3-55). Suppose for simplicitly we deal with an ensemble that is not only stationary but over reasonable distances it is also independent of the spatial origin. In these circumstances it follows that we may set

$$\langle V^*(\mathbf{r}_2, t_2)V(\mathbf{r}_1, t_1)\rangle = \Gamma(\mathbf{r}_1 - \mathbf{r}_2, t_1 - t_2) \tag{3-56}$$

so that, in particular, Eq. (3-52) leads to

$$\bar{n}_i = \alpha_i \int_0^T \Gamma(0,0)\, dt' = \alpha_i T\Gamma(0,0) \tag{3-57}$$

independent of the detector location. If we set $\mathbf{r}_1 - \mathbf{r}_2 = \mathbf{r}$, then the spatial and temporal dependence of the excess counting correlation is explicitly displayed by

$$\overline{n_1 n_2} - \bar{n}_1\bar{n}_2 = \bar{n}_1\bar{n}_2[\xi(\mathbf{r}, T)/T] \tag{3-58}$$

where

$$\xi(\mathbf{r}, T) = \frac{2}{T}\int_0^T (T - \tau)|\gamma(\mathbf{r}, \tau)|^2\, d\tau \tag{3-59}$$

and

$$\gamma(\mathbf{r}, \tau) = \Gamma(\mathbf{r}, \tau)/\Gamma(0,0) \tag{3-60}$$

For simplicity let us imagine that T is small compared to the coherence time $\xi(\mathbf{r}, \infty)$ for the range of spatial separations of interest. Then we may set

$$\frac{\xi(\mathbf{r}, T)}{T} \simeq |\gamma(\mathbf{r}, 0)|^2 \tag{3-61}$$

which gives rise to the relation

$$\overline{n_1 n_2} - \bar{n}_1 \bar{n}_2 = \bar{n}_1 \bar{n}_2 |\gamma(\mathbf{r}, 0)|^2 \tag{3-62}$$

for the excess counting correlation as a function of counter separation $\mathbf{r}$ expressed in terms of the degree of coherence.

Although our examples have been carried out for a Gaussian model characterized by (3-48) it is clear from (3-46) that a temporal and spatial counting correlation exists for any ensemble having suitable intensity correlations.

INTENSITY INTERFEROMETRY. The measurement of counting correlations gives rise to a kind of "intensity interferometry." In application to stellar measurements, as discussed by Hanbury Brown and Twiss [3-9], there are sometimes definite advantages in intensity interferometry as compared to traditional (amplitude) interferometry. Suppose, on the one hand, we compare the *amplitudes* of stellar light at $\mathbf{r}_1$ and $\mathbf{r}_2$, where $\mathbf{r}_1 - \mathbf{r}_2 = \mathbf{r}$, and test these waves for spatial coherence, say by placing at these two points the slits of a two-slit interferometer. Specifically, this means we study the function (3-56) or more precisely, according to (1-14), its real part. As the stellar light passes through the atmosphere, turbulence in the air may, through changes in the index of refraction, modify the observed signal by a random, rapidly varying, phase factor. This effect may be characterized by the transition

$$V_j(t) \rightarrow V_j(t) \exp[i\varphi_j(t)] \tag{3-63}$$

where $\varphi_j(t) = \varphi(\mathbf{r}_j, t)$ denotes the phase factor at detector j. Consequently, the *observed* mutual coherence function differs from that characteristic of the *source,*

$$\Gamma_{\text{obs}}(\mathbf{r}, t'', t') = \exp\{i[\varphi_1(t') - \varphi_2(t'')]\}\, \Gamma_{\text{source}}(\mathbf{r}, t' - t'') \tag{3-64}$$

which is in general no longer a function of the time difference. Even worse, Re Γ_{obs} is in general not equal to Re Γ_{source}.

This phase distortion is very serious in precise optical measurements and is responsible for the limitations that apply to the measurement of stellar diameters with the Michelson interferometer discussed at the end of Chapter 1. Even when $t' = t''$, the rapidly varying phase factor in

(3-64) need not vanish since the functions φ_1 and φ_2 could be different and largely independent, as happens for a spatial interval greater than about 5 or 6 m.

In intensity interferometry, on the other hand, it is the intensities at spatially separated points rather than the amplitudes, which are tested for coherence. In virtue of (3-46) this may be done by measuring the excess counting correlation (3-55) for a time interval T, in which the quantity of direct interest which enters is the degree of coherence. It follows from (3-64) that

$$|\gamma_{\text{obs}}(\mathbf{r}, \tau)| = |\gamma_{\text{source}}(\mathbf{r}, \tau)| \tag{3-65}$$

so that the phase distortions between the separate observation points that plague amplitude interferometry are rendered harmless. Thus, with intensity interferometry it becomes possible to explore wave-field correla-

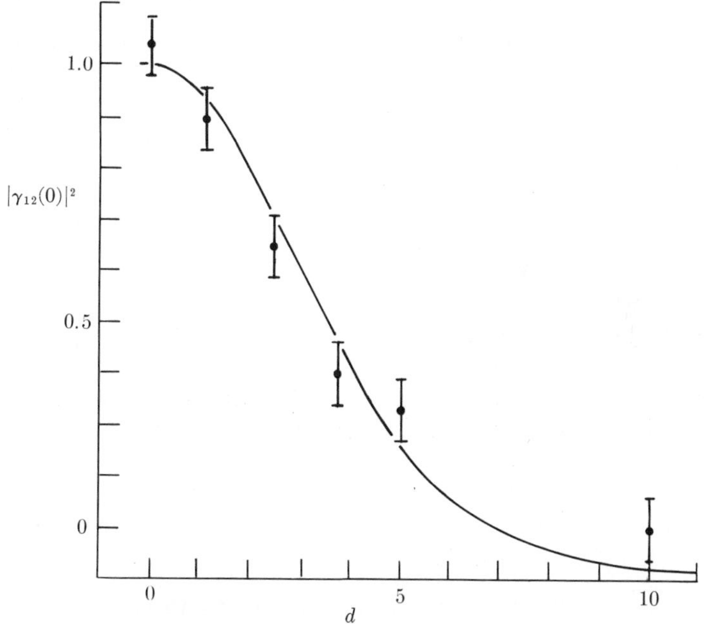

Fig. 3.1 The square of the degree of coherence $|\gamma_{12}(0)|^2$ versus photodetector separation d measured in millimeters. This figure which shows the theoretical and experimental confirmation of the Hanbury Brown-Twiss effect was made, not for a stellar image, but for a mercury arc lamp. The experimental results are indicated by dots and vertical error bars, while the solid curve denotes the theoretical prediction making due allowance for the spectral distribution of the light and for the characteristics of the electronic circuits. (After R. Hanbury Brown and R. Q. Twiss, *Proc. Roy. Soc. London* A243, 291 (1957); reprinted with permission.)

tions characteristic of the source over much greater separations than was possible before.

More specifically, let us suppose that T is short compared to the coherence time and that (3-62) applies. If, as in Chapter 1, we deal with quasi-monochromatic radiation from a uniformly illuminated disk in the far-field approximation, we may adopt Eq. (1-49) for the (complex) degree of coherence. For a star of radius b, which lies a distance R from the earth and which is radiating at a mean frequency $\bar{\nu} = \bar{k}/2\pi$, it follows that the excess counting correlation for a counter separation r is given by

$$\overline{n_1 n_2} - \bar{n}_1\bar{n}_2 = \bar{n}_1\bar{n}_2 \left(\frac{J_1(x)}{x}\right)^2 \tag{3-66}$$

where $x = \bar{k}br/R$. From measurements of the cross-correlation (3-66) as a function of r, the stellar size may be deduced if the distance R is known. This cross-correlation first vanishes at a spatial interval r such that $\bar{k}br \simeq 3.83R$. By techniques essentially of this type, Hanbury Brown and Twiss [3-9] have extended the "baseline" of their "interferometer" to about 600 ft which is a factor 30 times larger than is practical with a Michelson interferometer due to atmospheric degradation. Results of an analogous experiment are shown in Fig. 3-1.

C. Bandwidth, Counter Size, and the Significance of Smoothing Functions

The preceding discussion has been based on idealized fast detectors which can be localized at a point. Account for bandwidth effects and finite size can be readily included at least in a reasonably approximate fashion. Suppose that $\tilde{S}^*(\nu)$ denotes the admittance function for the detector, i.e., relative amplitude and phase modification at frequency ν for the wave field $V(\mathbf{r}, t)$. Similarly let $a_i(\mathbf{r})$ denote the spatial admittance function for detector i, i.e., relative amplitude and phase modification at position $\mathbf{r}$ for $V(\mathbf{r}, t)$. Then we may assume that the *effective* wave field, $V_i^{\text{eff}}(t)$, at detector i is given by

$$V_i^{\text{eff}}(t) = \int a_i(\mathbf{r}) S^*(t - t') V(\mathbf{r}, t')\, d^3r\, dt' \tag{3-67}$$

where $S^*(t)$, the Fourier transform of $\tilde{S}^*(\nu)$, is just the impulse response function. In turn, we may assume that the effective intensity $I_i^{\text{eff}}(t)$, which enters the determination of the counting rate for detector i, is given by

$$I_i^{\text{eff}}(t) = |V_i^{\text{eff}}(t)|^2 \tag{3-68}$$

To see the nature of the modifications introduced through (3-67), let us consider the simpler case of bandwidth limitations alone [i.e., setting

$a_i(\mathbf{r}) = \delta(\mathbf{r} - \mathbf{r}_i)]$ on the Gaussian distribution for the *single*-counter example discussed earlier. From (3-32) we learn that

$$\langle V_e^*(t_1)V_e(t_2)V_e^*(t_3)V_e(t_4)\rangle = \langle V_e^*(t_1)V_e(t_2)\rangle\langle V_e^*(t_3)V_e(t_4)\rangle + \langle V_e^*(t_1)V_e(t_4)\rangle\langle V_e^*(t_3)V_e(t_2)\rangle \quad (3\text{-}69)$$

where for simplicity we have introduced the abbreviation

$$V_e(t) \equiv V_i^{\text{eff}}(t) = \int S^*(t - t')V(\mathbf{r}_i, t')\,dt' \quad (3\text{-}70)$$

If we likewise set $I_e = |V_e|^2$, then the first two counting moments read

$$\bar{n} = \alpha \int_0^T \langle I_e(t')\rangle\,dt' \quad (3\text{-}71\text{a})$$

$$\overline{n^2} = \alpha^2 \int_0^T \int_0^T \langle I_e(t')I_e(t'')\rangle\,dt'\,dt'' + \bar{n} \quad (3\text{-}71\text{b})$$

Using these, we find the modified expressions for mean and variance given by

$$\begin{aligned}\bar{n} &= \alpha \int_0^T dt \iint S^*(t - t_1)S(t - t_2)\Gamma(t_1 - t_2)\,dt_1\,dt_2 \\ &= \alpha T \int |\tilde{S}(\nu)|^2\tilde{\Gamma}(\nu)\,d\nu\end{aligned} \quad (3\text{-}72)$$

and

$$\begin{aligned}\sigma^2 &= \overline{n^2} - (\bar{n})^2 \\ &= \alpha^2 \int_0^T \int_0^T dt'\,dt'' \iiiint S^*(t' - t_2)S(t' - t_1)S^*(t'' - t_4)S(t'' - t_3) \\ &\quad \times \Gamma(t_2 - t_3)\Gamma(t_4 - t_1)\,dt_1\,dt_2\,dt_3\,dt_4 + \bar{n} \\ &= \alpha^2 \int_0^T \int_0^T dt'\,dt'' \left| \int e^{-2\pi i\nu(t'-t'')}\,|\tilde{S}(\nu)|^2\tilde{\Gamma}(\nu)\,d\nu \right|^2 + \bar{n}\end{aligned} \quad (3\text{-}73)$$

Clearly, the formulas for counting moments when bandwidth effects are included are qualitatively similar to those obtained earlier. We note moreover that if $\tilde{S}(\nu) \simeq 1$ over the essential spectral width of the mutual coherence function $\tilde{\Gamma}(\nu)$, then the counting moments are the same as for a fast detector. On the other hand, if $\tilde{S}(\nu)$ is *narrow* compared to $\tilde{\Gamma}(\nu)$ then the counting statistics are determined largely by the detector response characteristics and very little by the source. Similar remarks apply when allowance for a spatial size is made with the aid of $a_i(\mathbf{r})$.

In the general case, the wave-field modifications required by (3-67) are clearly just those introduced by the special smoothing functions

$$S_{i,t}^*(\mathbf{r}, t') \equiv a_i(\mathbf{r})S^*(t - t') \quad (3\text{-}74)$$

as would appear, e.g., in the characteristic functions (3-47). In consequence, we can interpret the smooth functions $S(\mathbf{r}, t')$ as representing the combined spatial and bandwidth limitations inherent in any measurement process. Far from being purely formal, the description of stochastic variables by characteristic functionals and smooth test functions that we have employed has an important physical basis!

3-4 CONCLUDING REMARKS

In this and the preceding chapters we have discussed the description of partially coherent optical phenomena and, especially, the associated counting moments from a combined classical and semiclassical point of view. The essential ingredients, as we presented it, included an ensemble of classical, analytic-signal, wave fields $V(\mathbf{r}, t)$ each obeying the wave equation. Although we treated mainly stationary and phase-uncertain distributions, these special conditions are by no means essential. We shall have occasion to employ ensembles that relax both conditions in later chapters.

The extension of our discussion to the proper vector fields of optics theory is straightforward. In our quantum treatment we shall have occasion to make reference to all of the features attributable to the vector character of the radiation field. Interested readers may find appropriate vector generalizations of our classical and semiclassical discussions in Born and Wolf [1-1], Mandel [2-1], O'Neill [1-3], Beran and Parrent [1-2] and Mandel and Wolf [3-11].

Many other interesting topics arise in classical partial coherence theory. Notable among these is the relation of the formal Bose-Einstein distribution of photoelectric counts and coherence time, etc., to similar concepts in statistical mechanics and information theory. For a discussion of these topics we may refer the reader to the article of Gabor [3-8] and to the literature cited therein.

CHAPTER 4

DYNAMICAL DETERMINATION OF STATISTICAL DESCRIPTION

4-1 STATEMENT OF DYNAMICAL PROBLEM

In the previous chapters we have argued that partial coherence theory and semiclassical counting statistics can be viewed as applications of the theory of stochastic processes. From a physical point of view the question remains as to the choice of a relevant random description. In many ways this is the heart of the problem, and very few generally applicable rules can be given. Instead, each problem must be examined separately in the light of its physical origin.

In the present chapter we should like to give a glimpse at a variety of generic problems and indicate how one would formulate equations leading to their solutions. Rather than get bogged down in the details of a solution for a specific, nontrivial problem, we feel it to be far more preferable to discuss certain general features common to a great variety of stochastic problems and to formulate a common framework in which they may be studied. Although our discussion is given here in the classical framework, many of the techniques and formal relations have their exact analogs in a quantum analysis.

In the simplification of a scalar wave field $V(\mathbf{r}, t) \equiv V(x)$ it is useful to consider the following general type of equations:[1]

$$\Box V(x) = j(x) = j(x; V, \{\psi_k\}) \tag{4-1a}$$
$$\Box \psi_k(x) = F_k(x) = F_k(x; V, \{\psi_l\}) \tag{4-1b}$$

The physical content of these equations is simply this: The field $V(x)$ is dynamically responsive to the source $j(x)$, which, in turn, is determined by

[1] We abbreviate the d'Alembertian by $\Box \equiv \nabla^2 - \partial^2/\partial t^2$.

the field V itself and a finite number of other fields $\{\psi_k\}$. A similar interpretation applies to the second set of equations. We may loosely call the ψ_k "matter or source fields" for the "radiation field" V.

An implicit assumption in (4-1) is the local dependence of j and F_k—at least local in time—on the fields V or ψ_k. With this understanding $V(x)$ is responsive to the source $j(x)$ which, in turn, is determined by the field values at the same space–time point. Further problems of the general type (4-1) can be roughly divided into the following categories:

A. Origins of Stochastic Behavior

1. Suppose we consider the field V in a region devoid of sources. Then we recover the free-field equation

$$\Box V(x) = 0 \tag{4-2}$$

discussed in Chapter 1. As a second-order, hyperbolic, differential equation it is plausible that $V(x)$ has a unique solution determined by its initial conditions. However, we may be ignorant of precise features of those initial conditions, and we are thus free to draw valid conclusions only about certain restricted questions. For example, in an oscillator emitting a pure sine wave we cannot expect our solution to have information about the present value of the phase if we were completely ignorant about the phase at the outset.

We may restate the case under examination by the remark that the solution to (4-2)

$$V(x) \equiv V(x; V_0) \tag{4-3}$$

where V_0 signifies the (set of) initial conditions, is a random variable with a distribution governed by that for the "primary" random variable V_0.

2. The uncertainty introduced via the initial conditions may be extended to the full set of coupled equations (4-1). In the same vein as above, let us assume that

$$V(x) = V(x; V_0, \{\psi_{k0}\}) \tag{4-4a}$$
$$\psi_k(x) = \psi_k(x; V_0, \{\psi_{l0}\}) \tag{4-4b}$$

represents the solution to the coupled equations. If all, or a portion of the initial conditions are uncertain, then we may interpret $V(x)$ and each $\psi_k(x)$ as random processes with distributions governed by those for the "primary" random variables V_0 and $\{\psi_{k0}\}$.

In turn, we may consider the source $j(x)$ as a secondary random process,

$$j(x) = j(x; V, \{\psi_k\}) \tag{4-5}$$

governed by the random processes for V and all ψ_k.

3. Considerable formal simplification in the foregoing picture occurs in special cases. It may well happen that the number of contributions that go to make up the source $j(x)$ are so vast in number that the statistics of $j(x)$ as defined by (4-5) are insensitive to a wealth of the details of the many distributions characterizing the variables V and ψ_k. We have in mind, for example, the well-known central limit theorem—or "law of large numbers"—which, roughly speaking, says that the sum of a vast number of independent variables assumes a Gaussian distribution. We shall examine this theorem in greater detail especially in its quantum analog in Chapter 9. Here we wish only to make plausible the notion that some sort of simplification in the properties of $j(x)$ may occur. In such circumstances it is physically reasonable to assume that the "basic equation" reads

$$\Box V(x) = j(x) \tag{4-6}$$

and that the solution

$$V(x) = V(x; j) \tag{4-7}$$

(omitting explicit reference to V_0) is a random process determined by that for the (now!) primary process $j(x)$. Equations of the type (4-6) are called "fluctuation" equations. A physical problem in which the present simplification is justified would be thermal radiation emitted from a vast multitude of atomic radiators as in a lamp or in a star.

Although there is no requirement that the statistics of $j(x)$ are Gaussian, such a random source is often loosely referred to as a "thermal bath" or "reservoir." The independence of $j(x)$ on the response $V(x)$ is indicative of the imperturbable nature characteristic of a reservoir.

The special circumstances under discussion differ in two ways from the preceding examples: On the one hand, there is a considerable simplification because V is related to j by a linear transformation [since (4-6) is a linear equation]. On the other hand, the primary stochastic variable $j(x)$ has become a random function of space *and time,* whereas in the former cases (with random initial conditions only) the primary variables were random functions of space alone. Sometimes this is a high price to pay.

4. In a number of cases, where the previous simplification is too restrictive, it is possible that the source may be insensitive to details of the distribution of *some* of the random variables $\{\psi_k\}$. Specifically, let us assume that only two source fields are present so that the equations of interest read

$$\Box V(x) = j(x; V, \psi_1, \psi_2) \tag{4-8a}$$
$$\Box \psi_1(x) = F_1(x; V, \psi_1, \psi_2) \tag{4-8b}$$
$$\Box \psi_2(x) = F_2(x; V, \psi_1, \psi_2) \tag{4-8c}$$

As they stand these may be assumed to be deterministic and subject only to fluctuations in their initial conditions. Suppose ψ_2 describes a field characteristic of a "reservoir": unperturbed by the distribution of $V(x)$ or $\psi_1(x)$ and leading to sources for V and ψ_1 the statistics of which are largely insensitive to the details of their initial configuration. Let us imagine that we can solve the last equation for ψ_2 with V and ψ_1 fixed and let us call the solution $f(x)$. As a reservoir variable the quantity $f(x)$ is by assumption independent of $V(x)$ and $\psi_1(x)$. On substituting into (4-8) we generate the basic set of fluctuation equations

$$\Box V(x) = j(x; V, \psi_1, f) \tag{4-9a}$$
$$\Box \psi_1(x) = F_1(x; V, \psi_1, f) \tag{4-9b}$$

which has the following interpretation. The field V is determined as the solution of a coupled system of equations in which the source terms depend not only on the dependent variables V and ψ_1 but on an "external" random function $f(x)$. There is, of course, no difficulty in extending these equations to several random contributions $f_1(x)$ and $f_2(x)$ or in assuming that each field has its own reservoir.

As in the preceding examples, the basic equations may well depend on the entire space–time history of the random contribution $f(x)$. Not only may the distribution of $f(x)$ be complicated, but, in general, we have lost the possibility of a simple linear relation between $V(x)$ and the primary random process $f(x)$.

5. As a final example we briefly remark on the issue of atmospheric turbulence raised in Chapter 3. We may consider effects of this type as being due to random refraction indices which affect not the source terms but the propagation aspects. In a manner of speaking the d'Alembertian operator $\Box$ becomes random since the velocity of propagation in the medium undergoes fluctuations. This problem may be viewed in the manner illustrated in Chapter 3 in which the equation is "solved" for a fixed history of the refraction index $n(x)$,

$$V(x) = V(x; n) \tag{4-10}$$

and treated as a random variable based on the primary variable $n(x)$. In the form of (4-10) this problem is no more general than those implicit in (4-9), although it should be emphasized that the origin of the stochastic behavior is physically different in the two cases.

Generic Form. As a generic form for further discussion let us assume we are dealing with equations of the general type of (4-9). To be specific one may consider the equations

$$\Box V(x) = V^3(x) + \psi^2(x) + f(x) \tag{4-11a}$$
$$\Box \psi(x) = V(x)\psi(x) + g(x) \tag{4-11b}$$

Here we have dropped the subscript 1 on the "matter" field ψ and have introduced two random driving forces f and g (which may be the same!). These equations are not unlike those that arise in classical electrodynamics or in a medium with nonlinear dielectrics, etc. The essential features for our illustrative purposes are the nonlinearity of the equations and the presence of random contributions.

In certain cases it may be possible to linearize these equations about their "operating point"; i.e., consider the set of linear equations that pertain to small deviations

$$v(x) \equiv V(x) - V_0(x) \tag{4-12a}$$
$$\varphi(x) \equiv \psi(x) - \psi_0(x) \tag{4-12b}$$

where $V_0(x)$ and $\psi_0(x)$ are fixed, nonrandom functions. However, we shall not explicitly examine the rather straightforward features that result in such cases.

4-2 REFORMULATION OF THE FLUCTUATION EQUATIONS

A. Mean Equations for the Moments

Equations (4-9) and (4-11) are not "ordinary" partial differential equations in view of the random source terms. To solve these equations in the classic sense would first of all require that an explicit solution for $V(x) = V(x;f)$ be found where $f(x)$ is prescribed. In practice, this is both prohibitively difficult as well as being far too luxurious. The observables or meaningful questions regarding the solution depend on averages over the random source term $f(x)$. We may convert (4-9) or (4-11) to conventional partial differential equations dealing (ostensibly!) with observables by considering the mean equations

$$\langle \Box V(x)\rangle = \Box\langle V(x)\rangle = \langle j(x; V, \psi_1, f)\rangle \tag{4-13a}$$
$$\langle \Box \psi_1(x)\rangle = \Box\langle \psi_1(x)\rangle = \langle F_1(x; V, \psi_1, f)\rangle \tag{4-13b}$$

The cost of this procedure is vividly displayed if we specifically consider the mean equations for (4-11). These read

$$\Box\langle V(x)\rangle = \langle V^3(x)\rangle + \langle \psi^2(x)\rangle + \langle f(x)\rangle \tag{4-14a}$$
$$\Box\langle \psi(x)\rangle = \langle V(x)\psi(x)\rangle + \langle g(x)\rangle \tag{4-14b}$$

Although this is an equation without fluctuations, it is underdetermined since, e.g., $\langle V(x)\rangle$ depends on $\langle V^3(x)\rangle$ about which we really have no knowledge without a solution in hand.

To focus on the essentials of this problem, let us adopt as our fluctuation equation the single nonlinear equation

$$\Box V(x) = V^3(x) + f(x) \tag{4-15}$$

where $f(x)$ is a stochastic driving force. To gain information about $\langle V^3(x)\rangle$ we could consider the equation obtained by multiplying (4-15) by $V(y)V(z)$ followed by an ensemble average. Specifically,

$$\langle[\Box_x V(x) - V^3(x) - f(x)]V(y)V(z)\rangle = 0$$

which otherwise states that

$$\Box_x\langle V(x)V(y)V(z)\rangle = \langle V^3(x)V(y)V(z)\rangle + \langle f(x)V(y)V(z)\rangle \tag{4-16}$$

Thus to learn about the third-order moment or correlation requires knowledge of the fifth-order correlation; and so on *ad infinitum*!

We can systemize these equations somewhat by introducing the sequence of functions

$$G_{rs}(x_1, \ldots, x_r; y_1, \ldots, y_s) = \langle f(x_1) \cdots f(x_r)V(y_1) \cdots V(y_s)\rangle \tag{4-17}$$

(clearly symmetric in the x and y variables separately), which are interrelated by the fundamental dynamical equations

$$\begin{aligned}\Box_{y_1}G_{rs}(x_1, \ldots, x_r; y_1, \ldots, y_s) &= G_{rs+2}(x_1, \ldots, x_r; y_1, \ldots, y_s, y_1, y_1) \\ &\quad + G_{r+1s-1}(x_1, \ldots, x_r, y_1; y_2, \ldots, y_s)\end{aligned} \tag{4-18}$$

for all r and s. In this way we have recast our original problem into an infinite sequence of coupled equations. Quite clearly an analogous set of coupled equations holds for the more complicated interaction in (4-11).

Similar equations to (4-18) apply in many branches of physics: nonlinear optics, statistical mechanics, turbulence, etc. Moreover, essentially identical equations arise for the mean values of operator products in quantum problems as well. A brief guide to the literature dealing with such problems, equations, and their approximate solutions is given in the bibliography.

B. Mean Equation for the Characteristic Functional

An especially convenient formal summary of the heirarchy of coupled equations (4-18) can be given with the aid of the appropriate characteristic functional. For simplicity let us regard $V(x)$ and $f(x)$ as real fields.

Then the appropriate generating functional may be taken as

$$C\{S, s\} = \langle \exp\{i\int [S(y)V(y) + s(y)f(y)]\, d^4y\}\rangle \tag{4-19}$$

By hypothesis the statistics of the driving force are assumed known. That is, the quantity

$$C\{0, s\} = \langle \exp[i\int s(y)f(y)\, d^4y]\rangle \tag{4-20}$$

may be assumed known. On the other hand, the desired physical quantities are given in terms of $V(x)$ and, thus, we seek to find

$$C\{S, 0\} = \langle \exp[i\int S(y)V(y)\, d^4y]\rangle \tag{4-21}$$

Both the "known" and "desired" distributions are determined as special cases of the joint mean (4-19). This is an important and general feature of the study of the fluctuation equations through the relevant characteristic functional.

We may deduce an equation for $C\{S, s\}$ with the aid of suitable *functional derivatives.* These derivatives are most properly introduced as weight functions associated with "directional derivatives." That is, the functional derivatives

$$\frac{\delta C\{S, s\}}{\delta S(x)} \qquad \frac{\delta C\{S, s\}}{\delta s(x)}$$

are defined through the relations

$$\int E(x)\, \frac{\delta C\{S, s\}}{\delta S(x)}\, d^4x \equiv \frac{d}{d\tau}\, C\{S + \tau E, s\}\bigg|_{\tau=0} \tag{4-22a}$$

$$\int e(x)\, \frac{\delta C\{S, s\}}{\delta s(x)}\, d^4x \equiv \frac{d}{d\tau}\, C\{S, s + \tau e\}\bigg|_{\tau=0} \tag{4-22b}$$

where $E(x)$ and $e(x)$ denote fixed, but general, smooth functions. As we remarked in the last chapter it is generally necessary to restrict attention to suitable smooth functions as the arguments for characteristic functionals.

As a simple example of functional derivatives let us first consider

$$C_1\{S\} \equiv \int S^2(x)\, d^4x$$

Then

$$\frac{d}{d\tau}\, C_1\{S + \tau E\}\bigg|_{\tau=0} = \frac{d}{d\tau}\left\{\int [S^2 + 2\tau SE + \tau^2E^2]\, d^4x\right\}\bigg|_{\tau=0}$$

$$= 2\int E(x)S(x)\, d^4x$$

a calculation which implicitly assumes that both E and S are square integrable. For this example, therefore,

$$\frac{\delta C_1\{S\}}{\delta S(x)} = 2S(x)$$

Just as in classical analysis, certain functionals may not, strictly speaking, be differentiable. For example, in a formal manner we see that

$$\begin{aligned}\frac{\delta}{\delta S(x')}\frac{\delta}{\delta S(x)}C_1\{S\} &= 2\frac{\delta}{\delta S(x')}S(x)\\ &= 2\frac{d}{d\tau}[S(x)+\tau\,\delta(x-x')]\bigg|_{\tau=0}\\ &= 2\,\delta(x-x')\end{aligned} \tag{4-23}$$

and in particular, therefore,

$$\frac{\delta^2}{\delta S(x)^2}C_1\{S\} = 2\,\delta(0) = \infty$$

However, two functional derivatives at the same point need not yield infinity as is shown by the example

$$C_2\{S\} = (\textstyle\int E_0(x)S(x)\,d^4x)^2$$

where $E_0(x)$ is a fixed smooth function, which leads to

$$\frac{\delta^2 C_2\{S\}}{\delta S(x)^2} = 2E_0{}^2(x)$$

Since we are only trying to make these procedures plausible we shall assume our functionals have the requisite differentiability.

It is now a simple matter to cast our basic equation (4-15) into one for the characteristic functional. Since

$$\left(-i\frac{\delta}{\delta S(x)}\right)^p C\{S,s\} = \left\langle V^p(x)\exp\left\{i\int[S(y)V(y)+s(y)f(y)]\,d^4y\right\}\right\rangle \tag{4-24a}$$

$$\left(-i\frac{\delta}{\delta s(x)}\right)^q C\{S,s\} = \left\langle f^q(x)\exp\left\{i\int[S(y)V(y)+s(y)f(y)]\,d^4y\right\}\right\rangle \tag{4-24b}$$

are elementary consequences of (4-19) it is evident that C fulfills the relation

$$-i\Box\frac{\delta}{\delta S(x)}C = \left[\left(-i\frac{\delta}{\delta S(x)}\right)^3 + \left(-i\frac{\delta}{\delta s(x)}\right)\right]C$$

which, on eliminating a common factor i, becomes

$$\Box \frac{\delta}{\delta S(x)} C\{S, s\} = \left[-\frac{\delta^3}{\delta S(x)^3} + \frac{\delta}{\delta s(x)} \right] C\{S, s\} \tag{4-25}$$

The solution we seek satisfies (4-20) and is well behaved for large $S(x)$. This functional differential equation summarizes the infinite heirarchy of coupled equations given in (4-18). Indeed, these coupled equations may be recovered directly from (4-25) by expanding the exponentials in (4-19) in a power series and equating appropriate powers after carrying out the required functional differentiations.

From a practical point of view there are very few nonlinear equations that are explicitly soluble either in the form (4-18) or (4-25). Equations (4-18) are generally preferred for it is easier to butcher the infinite chain of equations to get a soluble approximation. The state of the art in solving functional differential equations such as (4-25) is not so highly developed!

4-3 MARKOFFIAN AND NON-MARKOFFIAN PROCESSES

A. Definitions and Distinctions

In stochastic processes there are problems which admit a description very much like that of the Hamiltonian formulation of classical mechanics or classical field theory. One characteristic feature of this viewpoint is a set of N equations that are first order in time and, thus, which have solutions determined uniquely by the same number of initial conditions. To win such equations it is usually necessary to double the number of basic variables, just as in classical mechanics where the number of coordinates x_k is doubled in passing to phase-space variables x_k and p_k. For present purposes we may write such first-order equations in the generic form

$$\dot{\psi}_k = F_k(\{\psi_l\}, \{f_m\}, t) \tag{4-26}$$

where $k = 1, \ldots, N$. Here we have absorbed the field of interest V and its time derivative as two of the collection of fields $\{\psi_k\}$. The f_m represent the phenomenological random driving forces. In the spirit of the Hamiltonian approach we assume that all arguments of F_k are taken at the same *time* (although they may involve different space regions). In our discussion we focus on the temporal behavior of Eq. (4-26).

Although for a fixed set of driving forces, Eq. (4-26) leads to a unique future determination of the variables ψ_k from their values at an earlier time, there is no guarantee, after the stochastic behavior of the forces $\{f_m\}$ is accounted for, that the future behavior of the *distribution* for the variables ψ_k is determined solely by the distribution of values for ψ_k at some earlier time. In order to make this remark more explicit let us first introduce

$$\psi_k(t) \equiv \Psi_k(t, \{f_m\}; \{\varphi_l\}, \tau) \tag{4-27}$$

as the solutions of (4-26) for given, fixed, driving force histories $\{f_m\}$ and subject to the initial condition at $t = \tau$ that

$$\psi_k(\tau) = \varphi_k \tag{4-28}$$

independent of $\{f_m\}$. Then an important distribution for the variables ψ_k at time t is given by the formal relation

$$p(\{\psi_k\}, t|\{\varphi_k\}, \tau) \equiv \langle \Pi_k\, \delta[\psi_k - \psi_k(t)]\rangle = \langle \Pi_k\, \delta[\psi_k - \Psi_k(t, \{f_m\}; \{\varphi_l\}, \tau)]\rangle \tag{4-29}$$

At $t = \tau$, this distribution becomes simply

$$p(\{\psi_k\}, \tau|\{\varphi_k\}, \tau) = \langle \Pi_k\, \delta(\psi_k - \varphi_k)\rangle = \Pi_k\, \delta(\psi_k - \varphi_k) \tag{4-30}$$

which motivates our referring to (4-29) as a conditional distribution (see also the discussion in the next chapter). For times $t > \tau$ the distribution p will reflect details of the ensemble of driving forces $\{f_m\}$ in virtue of the defining relation (4-29). Although each solution (4-27) depends on the driving forces only between τ and t, these "present" values may be correlated with or determined by events in the "past" (i.e., for times less than τ). In such a case $p(\{\psi_k\}, t|\{\varphi_k\}, \tau)$ depends on unspecified past properties of the ensemble and not just on the initial conditions $\{\varphi_k\}$ at time τ.

To test for such dependencies we may imagine *selectively tampering* with the ensemble of random driving forces by *removing* histories which violate one or another set of conditions in the past and then recomputing the mean (4-29) in the modified ensemble. The extent to which $p(\{\psi_k\}, t|\{\varphi_l\}, \tau)$ is independent of such tamperings is a measure of its independence on the past details of the ensemble of random forces.

The important processes for which the distribution (4-29) is *totally independent* of such tamperings with the ensemble in the past are called Markoffian. All other cases are called non-Markoffian. In certain instances the number of initial conditions may be increased so that an otherwise non-Markoffian system becomes Markoffian. As an example consider a box of colliding gas molecules. The position of a single particle may be determined from the equation

$$m\ddot{x}(t) = f(t) \tag{4-31}$$

where f is the stochastic force representing the influence of the other particles. Clearly, the future behavior of $x(t)$ depends on the past history of the stochastic force to the extent that a molecule in a box is always in interaction with all the other molecules. However, this problem can surely be made Markoffian if we are willing to introduce the roughly 10^{23} variables necessary to specify the distribution of initial conditions for all the molecules.

Of course, in practice, we circumvent this difficulty by *assuming* the collisions are *impulsive* and that the stochastic force has no memory. For instance, the classic random walk problem (Weiner process) is determined by (4-31) under the assumption that $f(t)$ is characterized by

$$\langle \exp[i \int s(t')f(t')\, dt'] \rangle = \exp[-\tfrac{1}{2}a \int \dot{s}^2(t')\, dt'] \tag{4-32}$$

which is of the form (3-18) with $m = 0$ and $\tilde{\mu}(\nu) = 4\pi^2 a \nu^2$. The classic Brownian motion is also based on (4-31) coupled with an alternate stochastic process characterized by

$$\langle \exp[i \int s(t')f(t')\, dt'] \rangle = \exp[-\tfrac{1}{2}b \int s^2(t')\, dt'] \tag{4-33}$$

for which $\tilde{\mu}(\nu) = b$. This process with a flat distribution is often called "white noise." As far as the variable x is concerned, a random walk is Markoffian whereas Brownian motion is not. To make Brownian motion into a Markoffian process requires that we consider conditional distributions for both position and velocity. The distinctions in each of these cases are, of course, physically clear. However, we emphasize that if the process $f(t')$ has any nontrivial memory [as arises, for example, if we filter the force and thereby change its spectrum such that $\int \tilde{\mu}(\nu)\, d\nu < \infty$], then the x process is never Markoffian and no finite number of initial conditions will make it so.

Sometimes, the physical problem under consideration justifies a Markoffian assumption or idealization regarding the driving forces. However, when this is not the case the problem should properly be treated in the context of a non-Markoffian process allowing for the correct memory effects in operation between system and reservoir. Some of the most fascinating of stochastic problems are those corresponding to non-Markoffian processes.

B. Special Relations for Markoffian Processes

In the special cases where the processes are Markoffian, several important relations for the conditional distribution may be deduced. Suppose we consider Eq. (4-29) again, but now we tamper with the ensemble in the past by considering the mean

$$\langle \Pi_k\, \delta[\psi_k - \Psi_k(t, \{f_m\}; \{\varphi_l\}, \tau)] \Pi_l\, \delta[\varphi_l - \Psi_l(\tau, \{f_m\}; \{\lambda_r\}, 0)] \rangle \tag{4-34}$$

Here we have imposed as a restriction on the past behavior of the driving forces that they be compatible with the evolution of the field variables from $\{\lambda_r\}$ at time zero to the values $\{\varphi_l\}$ at time τ. According to our Markoffian hypothesis this tampering should not influence the result (4-29) except for the possible appearance of a numerical factor A since we may not have recomputed the average in a normalized ensemble. Thus (4-34) must have the form

$$p(\{\psi_k\}, t | \{\varphi_l\}, \tau) A \tag{4-35}$$

on the basis of the Markoffian property. In turn, if we set $t = \tau$ and use (4-28) [cf. (4-30)], then we readily deduce that

$$A \equiv p(\{\varphi_l\}, \tau | \{\lambda_r\}, 0) \tag{4-36}$$

When we now integrate (4-34) over the variables $\{\varphi_l\}$ and exploit the δ functions in the integrand we find the important relation ($d^N\varphi_l \equiv \Pi_l \, d\varphi_l$)

$$\begin{aligned} \int \cdots \int p(\{\psi_k\}, t | \{\varphi_l\}, \tau) p(\{\varphi_l\}, \tau | \{\lambda_r\}, 0) \, d^N\varphi_l \\ = \langle \Pi_k \, \delta[\psi_k - \Psi_k(t, \{f_m\}; \{\lambda_r\}, 0]\rangle \\ = p(\{\psi_k\}, t | \{\lambda_r\}, 0) \end{aligned} \tag{4-37}$$

which is known as the Chapman-Kolmogorov equation. In differential form this equation reads

$$\frac{\partial p(\{\psi_k\})}{\partial t} = \int \cdots \int K(\{\psi_k\}, \{\varphi_l\}) p(\{\varphi_l\}) \, d^N\varphi_l \tag{4-38}$$

where we have suppressed irrelevant arguments and have introduced the integral kernel

$$K(\{\psi_k\}, \{\varphi_l\}) \equiv \frac{\partial}{\partial t} p(\{\psi_k\}, t | \{\varphi_l\}, \tau) \Big|_{\tau = t} \tag{4-39}$$

In a stationary distribution, K is independent of time.

Alternative to (4-38) we may represent the action of the integral kernel K by means of a differential operator, which may, in certain cases, be adequately approximated by one of finite order. A general expression for this differential operator may be found as follows. If we denote the characteristic function of $p(\{\psi_k\})$ by

$$\begin{aligned} C(\{s_k\}) &\equiv \exp\,[W(\{s_k\})] \\ &= \langle \exp(i\Sigma s_k\psi_k)\rangle = \int \cdots \int \exp(i\Sigma s_k\psi_k) p(\{\psi_k\}) \, d^N\psi_k \end{aligned} \tag{4-40}$$

then we may set

$$p(\{\psi_k\}) = (2\pi)^{-N} \int \cdots \int \exp[-i\Sigma s_k\psi_k + W(\{s_k\})] \, d^N s_k \tag{4-41}$$

From this relation it immediately follows that

$$\frac{\partial p(\{\psi_k\})}{\partial t} \equiv \dot{p}(\{\psi_k\}) = (2\pi)^{-N} \int \cdots \int \dot{W}(\{s_k\}) \exp\left[-i \sum s_k\psi_k + W(\{s_k\})\right] d^N s_k$$

$$= \dot{W}(\{i\,\partial/\partial\psi_k\})(2\pi)^{-N} \int \cdots \int \exp\left[-i \sum s_k\psi_k + W(\{s_k\})\right] d^N s_k$$

$$= \dot{W}(\{i\,\partial/\partial\psi_k\})p(\{\psi_k\}) \tag{4-42}$$

where $\dot{W}$ is short for $(\partial/\partial t)W$. As in the Hamiltonian formulation of mechanics this equation determines the future distribution for p from given initial conditions. Moreover, in a stationary distribution $\dot{W}$ is a constant operator independent of time.

It is conventional to express W through the cumulants of the distribution (also called "semi-invariants" or "linked moments") which are expressed as nonlinear combinations of various moments of the random variables. The simplest expression relating the ordinary and linked moments obtains for the generating functional which reads

$$\exp[W(\{s_k\})] = \langle \exp(i\Sigma s_k\psi_k)\rangle \equiv \exp\{\langle[\exp(i\Sigma s_k\psi_k) - 1]\rangle_L\} \tag{4-43}$$

where $\langle\cdot\ \cdot\ \cdot\rangle$ and $\langle\cdot\ \cdot\ \cdot\rangle_L$ denote the ordinary and linked moments, respectively. It follows from this relation that W admits the series expansion given by

$$W(\{s_k\}) = \langle[\exp(i\Sigma s_k\psi_k) - 1]\rangle_L$$

$$= \sum_{n=1}^{\infty} \frac{(i)^n}{n!} \sum_{k_1,\ldots,k_n} s_{k_1} \cdots s_{k_n} \langle\psi_{k_1} \cdots \psi_{k_n}\rangle_L \tag{4-44}$$

The coefficients in this series are the cumulants and their expression in terms of ordinary moments also follows from (4-43). In particular, by expansion in powers of s_1, the first few cumulants are given (for a single variable $\psi_1 \equiv \psi$) as

$$\langle\psi\rangle_L = \langle\psi\rangle \tag{4-45a}$$
$$\langle\psi^2\rangle_L = \langle\psi^2\rangle - \langle\psi\rangle^2 \tag{4-45b}$$
$$\langle\psi^3\rangle_L = \langle\psi^3\rangle - 3\langle\psi^2\rangle\langle\psi\rangle + 2\langle\psi\rangle^3 \tag{4-45c}$$
$$\langle\psi^4\rangle_L = \langle\psi^4\rangle - 3\langle\psi^2\rangle^2 - 4\langle\psi^3\rangle\langle\psi\rangle + 12\langle\psi^2\rangle\langle\psi\rangle^2 - 6\langle\psi\rangle^4 \tag{4-45d}$$

In Gaussian processes all cumulants higher than the second order vanish. If approximations to the distribution (4-41) are required it is physically preferable to set higher cumulants, rather than higher moments, equal to zero, for this corresponds to the proper treatment of lower-order correlations and a neglect of intrinsic higher-order correlations. Frequently, such a description is adequate or at least provides a convenient starting point [although, strictly speaking, if $W(\{s_k\})$ is a polynomial it must be of second degree in order that (4-43) correspond to a true characteristic function].

In either the exact or approximate cases we may combine (4-42) and (4-44) to write

$$\frac{\partial p(\{\psi_k\})}{\partial t} = \sum_{n=1}^{\infty} \frac{(-1)^n}{n!} \sum_{k_1, \ldots, k_n} \left(\frac{\partial}{\partial \psi_{k_1}} \cdots \frac{\partial}{\partial \psi_{k_n}} \right) \times \left\{ \frac{\partial}{\partial t} \langle \psi_{k_1} \cdots \psi_{k_n} \rangle_L \right\} p(\{\psi_k\}) \quad (4\text{-}46)$$

which is known as the stochastic equation. In cases when the series terminates with $n = 2$, then (4-46) is the well-known Fokker-Planck equation. In the diffusion approximation all terms higher than $n = 2$ are dropped thus leading to a Fokker-Planck equation.

4-4 CONCLUDING REMARKS

In conclusion we want to stress again the generality of the approach to fluctuation equations that is possible with characteristic functionals. Even in the "pure" cases [(1) and (2) above], subject only to uncertainty in the initial conditions, these techniques lead to quite general solutions.

For example, with

$$C\{s\} \equiv \langle e^{i\int s(t')x(t')\,dt'} \rangle \quad (4\text{-}47)$$

the simple equation $\ddot{x} = 0$ takes the form

$$\frac{d^2}{dt^2} \frac{\delta C\{s\}}{\delta s(t)} = 0 \quad (4\text{-}48)$$

To find the general solution to this relation we note: (*1*) that we may restrict our attention to argument functions $s(t')$ which vanish for sufficiently large positive and negative values of t'; (*2*) that such functions determine and are determined uniquely by their moments

$$s_p \equiv \int t'^{\,p} s(t')\,dt' \quad (4\text{-}49)$$

and (3) that we can regard C as a function of the variables s_p, $p = 0, 1, 2, \ldots$ From the chain rule of differentiation

$$\frac{\delta}{\delta s(t)} C = \sum_{p=0}^{\infty} \frac{\delta s_p}{\delta s(t)} \frac{\partial C}{\partial s_p} = \sum_{p=0}^{\infty} t^p \frac{\partial C}{\partial s_p} \tag{4-50}$$

which expresses the full time dependence of this relation. In view of (4-48) it follows that C can only depend on s_0 and s_1, and in particular since C is a characteristic functional that

$$\begin{aligned} C\{s\} &= C(\textstyle\int s(t')\,dt', \int t's(t')\,dt') \\ &\equiv \textstyle\int \exp\{i[x_0 \int s(t')\,dt' + v_0 \int t's(t')\,dt']\} p(x_0, v_0)\,dx_0\,dv_0 \end{aligned} \tag{4-51}$$

The interpretation of x_0 and v_0 as initial position and velocity is self-evident. In particular, we note that

$$C\{s\} = \exp[-a(\textstyle\int s(t')\,dt')^2 - b(\int t's(t')\,dt')^2] \tag{4-52}$$

is a solution of (4-48) corresponding to an independent normal distribution in x_0 and v_0.

Although the free particle is an extremely elementary example, we emphasize that the general solution of (4-48) which we found yielded all solutions with arbitrary, initial value distributions. All temporal correlations of interest can be deduced from the solution given as a characteristic functional as well. Furthermore, this is the quantity of ultimate interest even when the particle is subjected to random forces as we discussed earlier. It may also be pointed out that the device of restricting attention to a suitable subclass of smooth functions and focusing on a suitable parameterization (e.g., $\{s_p\}$) may be useful in more general problems as well.

We shall return to dynamical equations and their analysis with the help of characteristic functions in Chapter 9.

CHAPTER 5

STATISTICAL STATES IN QUANTUM THEORY

5-1 INTRODUCTION

Up to this point, the analysis of the electromagnetic field (or rather its idealization in terms of the real scalar field $V^{(r)}$) has been purely classical. The statistical ensemble, giving rise to partially coherent interference phenomena as well as to non-Poissonian counting statistics, has been of strictly classical origin. Indeed, the predictions of the classical formulation of partial coherence are experimentally well satisfied, and, in addition, the qualitative features of correlation and fluctuations of photoelectric counts may be satisfactorily accounted for in the classical theory. But a proper treatment must surely take into account the known quantum nature of the radiation field. Consequently, the quantum formulation to which we are driven by logical necessity, must in the end lead to qualitatively similar results as the classical theory. Not only will we show the qualitative similarity of the quantum and classical results, but we will demonstrate in the course of the next several chapters a virtual *identity in formulation*, which, under a suitable reinterpretation scheme, permits us to interpret our previous classical results in a quantum context.

To lay the ground work for such a demonstration, we carefully review in this chapter some basic concepts of quantum mechanics, such as Hilbert space, linear operators, and calculation of the trace, with an emphasis directed toward the statistical description of quantum states. Examples are given for systems with a finite number of states, for systems pertaining to one degree of freedom and to a finite number of degrees of freedom, and finally for some systems with an infinite number of degrees of freedom as is necessary for the radiation field.

5-2 QUANTUM FORMALISM AND NOTATION

The formulation of quantum theory—be it for the most elementary or the most complicated system—entails the representation of observables and various dynamical variables as linear operators acting as transformations on a Hilbert space of vectors. In turn, the vectors themselves essentially correspond to the pure states of the system.

A. Hilbert Space

A Hilbert space is in many ways analogous to the familiar three-dimensional Euclidean space of vector analysis. In the elegant notation of Dirac [5-1], the vectors of Hilbert space are denoted by "kets," such as $|\psi\rangle$, with various distinguishing labels. As in ordinary, conventional vector analysis, we may add different Hilbert space vectors or multiply them by (complex) scalars to obtain new vectors. The number of linearly independent vectors determines the dimension D of Hilbert space, which may be finite or (countably) infinite. For every pair of vectors $|\psi\rangle$ and $|\lambda\rangle$ a complex number is defined, denoted by

$$\langle\lambda|\psi\rangle \tag{5-1}$$

and called the "inner product," which is analogous to the "dot product" of vector analysis. The inner product is linear in the vector $|\psi\rangle$ and obeys the two conditions

$$\langle\lambda|\psi\rangle = \langle\psi|\lambda\rangle^* \qquad \langle\psi|\psi\rangle \geq 0 \tag{5-2}$$

equality holding in the last condition if and only if $|\psi\rangle = 0$, the zero vector. Schwarz's inequality implies that

$$|\langle\lambda|\psi\rangle|^2 \leq \langle\lambda|\lambda\rangle\langle\psi|\psi\rangle \tag{5-3}$$

equality holding if and only if $|\lambda\rangle = \alpha|\psi\rangle$ for some complex α. If $|\psi\rangle = 0$, $\langle\lambda|\psi\rangle = 0$ for all $|\lambda\rangle$, and conversely. If instead $\langle\lambda|\psi\rangle = 0$ for fixed $|\lambda\rangle$ and $|\psi\rangle$, neither of which are the zero vector, then these vectors are called "orthogonal." The length or norm of every vector is finite and is given by

$$\|\,|\psi\rangle\| \equiv \langle\psi|\psi\rangle^{1/2} \geq 0 \tag{5-4}$$

If the norm is 1, the vector is said to be normed or normalized. An elementary consequence of (5-3) is the triangle inequality which reads

$$\|\,|\lambda\rangle + |\psi\rangle\| \leq \|\,|\lambda\rangle\| + \|\,|\psi\rangle\| \tag{5-5}$$

Every Hilbert space admits (numerous!) "complete orthonormal bases," namely, a set of vectors $\{|n\rangle\}$, $n = 1, 2, \ldots, D$ for which

$\langle n|m\rangle = \delta_{nm}$, and which span the Hilbert space. As analogs of an orthonormal basis in conventional vector analysis the set $\{|n\rangle\}$ gives rise to the expansion

$$|\psi\rangle = \sum_{n=1}^{D} \psi_n |n\rangle = \sum_{n=1}^{D} |n\rangle\langle n|\psi\rangle \tag{5-6}$$

for every vector $|\psi\rangle$. In terms of the coefficients in this expansion the norm-square reads

$$\langle\psi|\psi\rangle = \sum_{n=1}^{D} |\psi_n|^2 = \sum_{n=1}^{D} \langle\psi|n\rangle\langle n|\psi\rangle \tag{5-7}$$

If $D < \infty$, the ψ_n can be arbitrary complex numbers. In order that the norm be finite when $D = \infty$, however, it is necessary that the coefficients $\{\psi_n\}$ be square summable. We remark that the completeness property of Hilbert space demands that there be a vector $|\psi\rangle$ in Hilbert space for *every* square summable sequence and that this class of vectors exhausts Hilbert space.

This last remark is the key point behind the representation of the abstract Hilbert space vectors by means of sequences of complex numbers, which, indeed, was the original mathematical form studied by Hilbert and the original quantum mechanical form used by Heisenberg. It may be said that the basis vectors $|n\rangle$ "generate" a representation of $|\psi\rangle$ by sequences of complex numbers $\psi_n = \langle n|\psi\rangle$. In the slick notation of Dirac, the inner product reads

$$\langle\lambda|\psi\rangle = \sum_{n=1}^{D} \langle\lambda|n\rangle\langle n|\psi\rangle \tag{5-8}$$

analogous to the dot product expressed in terms of components.

B. Linear Operators

Observables and dynamical quantities are represented by linear operators, i.e., linear transformations that change one vector into another vector. Specifically, if A denotes an operator then $A|\psi\rangle$ denotes the transformed vector, and $\langle\lambda|A|\psi\rangle$ the corresponding new inner product with $|\lambda\rangle$. Operators may be added together as well as multiplied by complex numbers or by other operators to yield new operators. The identity operator I leaves all vectors and operators unchanged. Frequently, we shall loosely write the numerical coefficient c when we really mean the operator cI. [1]

[1] It is convenient to refer to dynamical quantities as "q-numbers" or "c-numbers" in their quantum or classical applications, respectively. Frequently a multiple of the identity operator is also called a c number.

If $|\langle\lambda|A|\psi\rangle| \leq b < \infty$ for all normed vectors $|\lambda\rangle$ and $|\psi\rangle$, then the operator A is said to be bounded. The least such b is called $\|A\|$, the norm of A. In a finite-dimensional Hilbert space, every operator is bounded, but this is not so in an infinite-dimensional space. The detailed study of unbounded operators is a serious mathematical enterprise, and we shall generally be forced to treat such operators heuristically being guided mostly by physical intuition. (The vague qualification "suitably many" appearing below is an allusion to complications arising from unbounded operators.)

In the representation of Hilbert space by sequences $\{\psi_n\}$, the operator A is represented by a matrix $\{A_{mn}\}$ with elements

$$A_{mn} = \langle m|A|n\rangle \tag{5-9}$$

which may be interpreted as the mth element of the vector $A|n\rangle$. In turn, the vector $A|\psi\rangle$ has the sequence representation $\{(A\psi)_m\}$, where

$$\begin{aligned}(A\psi)_m = \langle m|A|\psi\rangle &= \sum_{n=1}^{D} \langle m|A|n\rangle\langle n|\psi\rangle \\ &= \sum_{n=1}^{D} A_{mn}\psi_n\end{aligned} \tag{5-10}$$

as follows from (5-6) and (5-9). For example, it is evident that the identity operator I is represented by the unit matrix since $\langle m|I|n\rangle = \langle m|n\rangle = \delta_{mn}$.

At the heart of a full exploitation of the Dirac notation is the repeated use of the fundamental relation

$$I = \sum_{n=1}^{D} |n\rangle\langle n| \tag{5-11}$$

which is called a "resolution of the identity." A vector $|n\rangle$ written as $\langle n|$ is called a "bra" or adjoint vector. The notation $A = |n\rangle\langle m|$, e.g., is meant to be suggestive of the definition $\langle\lambda|A|\psi\rangle \equiv \langle\lambda|n\rangle\langle m|\psi\rangle$. Both Eqs. (5-8) and (5-10) are simple identities that follow from an insertion of the identity operator in the above form. Equation (5-11) is valid for an *arbitrary*, complete, orthonormal basis $\{|n\rangle\}$.

The adjoint $A^\dagger$ of an operator A is defined as that operator for which

$$\langle\lambda|A^\dagger|\psi\rangle = \langle\psi|A|\lambda\rangle^* \tag{5-12}$$

for all (or suitably many) $|\lambda\rangle$ and $|\psi\rangle$. If $AA^\dagger = A^\dagger A = I$, then $A^\dagger = A^{-1}$ and A is unitary. For a unitary operator A, $\|A|\psi\rangle\| = \|\,|\psi\rangle\|$ for all $|\psi\rangle$.

If $A^\dagger = A$, then we call A Hermitian. It follows from (5-12) that the value of $\langle\psi|A|\psi\rangle$ is always real for an Hermitian operator. An Hermitian operator A that satisfies $\langle\psi|A|\psi\rangle \geq 0$ for all (or suitably many) $|\psi\rangle$ is called "positive." In a finite-dimensional Hilbert space, every Hermitian operator has a complete set of orthonormal eigenvectors and real eigenvalues such that

$$A|a_n\rangle = a_n|a_n\rangle \tag{5-13}$$

If, in fact, A is positive, then $a_n \geq 0$. In the basis $|a_n\rangle$, A is diagonal for $\langle a_m|A|a_n\rangle = a_n\,\delta_{nm}$. For an infinite-dimensional Hilbert space not every Hermitian operator (even if it is bounded!) can be so diagonalized.

Two technical points regarding the Hermitian operators we shall use are worthy of comment. We shall assume that all the Hermitian operators we deal with possess complete spectral resolutions and are, thus, what are called "self-adjoint" in the mathematical literature. This property ensures that a Hermitian operator A is the generator of a unitary transformation $U(s) = \exp(isA)$, s real, and that $\langle\psi|\exp(isA)|\psi\rangle$ admits the representation

$$\langle\psi|e^{isA}|\psi\rangle = \int e^{isa}\,d\sigma(a) \tag{5-14}$$

for some (probability) measure σ determined by $|\psi\rangle$ and A. One need only examine the operator $-i\hbar\,\partial/\partial x$ on the Hilbert space of functions $f(x)$ defined for $x > 0$ to find an example of an operator which is Hermitian in the elementary sense but does not fulfill (5-14). It is common in physics texts to introduce nonnormalizable eigenvectors (δ-function normalization) $|A'\rangle$ for Hermitian operators A for a point A' in the continuous spectrum. We shall make no use of such vectors except to point out that an incautious use can occasionally lead to trouble. For example, let A and B be Hermitian operators that fulfill the relation $AB = BA + iB$, and let $A|A'\rangle = A'|A'\rangle$ for some real A'. Then it follows that $B|A'\rangle$ is also an eigenvector of A with the *complex* eigenvalue $A' + i$, contradicting the Hermitian nature of A. To avoid this dilemma, either $|A'\rangle$ or $B|A'\rangle$ are unnormalizable thus invalidating the argument.

Suppose we deal with a positive Hermitian operator in the infinite-dimensional case ($D = \infty$) that *does* have a complete set of eigenvectors and eigenvalues as in (5-13). Then we can represent A as

$$A = \sum_{n=1}^{\infty} |a_n\rangle a_n\langle a_n| \tag{5-15}$$

with real coefficients $a_n \geq 0$. If $a_n \leq b < \infty$, then A is bounded, otherwise not. An important special subcase of the bounded operators occurs when

$$\sum_{n=1}^{\infty} a_n < \infty \tag{5-16}$$

In this case the trace of A exists, namely,

$$\mathrm{Tr}(A) \equiv \sum_{n=1}^{\infty} \langle a_n|A|a_n\rangle = \sum_{n=1}^{\infty} a_n < \infty \tag{5-17}$$

and A is called "traceable." It is a medium-deep mathematical theorem that for positive, Hermitian operators A, the value of $\mathrm{Tr}(A)$ is independent of *which* complete orthonormal basis is used to evaluate the sum (e.g., not necessarily its own eigenvectors). Thus $\mathrm{Tr}(A)$ is an *intrinsic* property of A itself. Finally, a deeper mathematical theorem says that if A is positive, Hermitian, and $\mathrm{Tr}(A)$ is finite, then A *necessarily* has a complete orthonormal set of eigenvectors and associated eigenvalues such that (5-15) and (5-16) are true.

In the infinite-dimensional case, the class of operators for which $\mathrm{Tr}(A)$ exists is not limited to the special positive Hermitian operators we have indicated. However, every traceable operator T has a "polar decomposition," $T = VA$, where A is a positive, Hermitian, traceable operator of the form (5-15) and V is isometric, i.e., $V^\dagger V = I$; such a decomposition is the analog of the polar form $z = e^{i\varphi}r$ which holds for a general complex number z. The operator V has the property that it maps any orthonormal set $\{|\psi_n\rangle\}$ into another orthonormal set $\{|\lambda_n\rangle\}$, which on combination with the form of (5-15) leads to the fact that every traceable operator T has a *canonical decomposition* given by

$$T = \sum_{n=1}^{\infty} |\lambda_n\rangle\beta_n\langle\psi_n| \tag{5-18}$$

where we have used the real parameters $\beta_n \geq 0$ satisfying $\Sigma_{n=1}^{\infty}\beta_n < \infty$ and where $\{|\lambda_n\rangle\}$ and $\{|\psi_n\rangle\}$ are two, complete, orthonormal bases. Alternatively, Eq. (5-18) may be taken as the canonical *definition* of those operators for which the trace can be uniquely and unambiguously defined. In particular, it follows that

$$\mathrm{Tr}(T) = \sum_{n=1}^{\infty} \beta_n\langle\psi_n|\lambda_n\rangle \tag{5-19}$$

This series is absolutely convergent and in virtue of Schwarz's inequality

(5-3) is bounded by

$$|\mathrm{Tr}(T)| \leq \sum_{n=1}^{\infty} \beta_n \equiv \|T\|_1$$

an expression which defines a useful "trace-class norm" to attach to the traceable operator T (and which differs from the operator norm $\|T\|$). For positive, Hermitian, traceable operators, Eq. (5-17) shows that $\mathrm{Tr}(A) = \|A\|_1$, but otherwise the inequality holds. We shall have occasion to use the canonical decomposition (5-18) and the trace-class norm $\|T\|_1$ in our analysis in Chapter 8.

Of course, in a finite-dimensional Hilbert space (with dimension $D < \infty$), every operator is traceable. Consequently, every operator has a canonical decomposition identical to (5-18) in which only the first D terms appear.

C. Statistical States

Pure States. In quantum theory, the normalized vectors $|\psi\rangle$ of Hilbert space correspond to pure states of the system. If the Hermitian operator $\mathcal{O}$ denotes an observable, then the mean observed value for $\mathcal{O}$ in the state $|\psi\rangle$ is given by the real number

$$\langle \mathcal{O} \rangle \equiv \langle \psi | \mathcal{O} | \psi \rangle \tag{5-20}$$

In turn, higher observed mean moments of $\mathcal{O}$ are given by the real expressions

$$\langle \mathcal{O}^n \rangle \equiv \langle \psi | \mathcal{O}^n | \psi \rangle \tag{5-21}$$

If $\mathcal{O}$ is unbounded, then $\langle \mathcal{O}^n \rangle$ may be undefined for certain states. Just as in classical probability theory, however, the characteristic function for the distribution of $\mathcal{O}$ in the state $|\psi\rangle$, given by

$$C_{\mathcal{O}}(s) = \langle \psi | e^{is\mathcal{O}} | \psi \rangle \tag{5-22}$$

where $\exp(is\mathcal{O})$ is unitary, is *always* defined for any choice of $\mathcal{O}$ and $|\psi\rangle$.

As usual, each characteristic function $C_{\mathcal{O}}(s)$ is a continuous function of s and is the Fourier transform of the distribution of observed values corresponding to $\mathcal{O}$. These observed values will have a spread, i.e., a nonzero variance, so long as the state $|\psi\rangle$ is not an eigenvector of $\mathcal{O}$. However, even if $|\psi\rangle$ is an eigenvector for one observable it cannot be an eigenvector for *all* observables simultaneously (since they do not all commute). Hence, for any pure state, there are always some observables with a spread in their distribution, and, thus, a probabilistic interpretation is inescapable.

Two states are considered physically equivalent if the mean values for all observables (or if all their characteristic functions) are the same. Since all Hermitian operators are potential observables, it follows that $|\psi_1\rangle$ and $|\psi_2\rangle$ correspond to the same state if and only if $|\psi_1\rangle = e^{i\varphi}|\psi_2\rangle$. That is, $|\psi_1\rangle$ and $|\psi_2\rangle$ are identical except for a possible scalar factor of modulus one.

An alternate description of a pure state is by means of the density operator

$$\rho = |\psi\rangle\langle\psi| \tag{5-23}$$

with the rule for computing mean values given by

$$\begin{aligned}\langle \mathcal{O} \rangle \equiv \mathrm{Tr}(\rho\mathcal{O}) &= \sum_{n=1}^{\infty} \langle n|\psi\rangle\langle\psi|\mathcal{O}|n\rangle \\ &= \langle\psi|\mathcal{O}|\psi\rangle\end{aligned} \tag{5-24}$$

as in (5-20). Clearly ρ is Hermitian, positive, and traceable since it is of the form (5-15). Moreover,

$$\rho^2 = |\psi\rangle\langle\psi|\psi\rangle\langle\psi| = |\psi\rangle\langle\psi| = \rho \tag{5-25}$$

since $|\psi\rangle$ is normalized. The density operators for two physically equivalent pure states are strictly identical: $\rho_1 = |\psi_1\rangle\langle\psi_1| = |\psi_2\rangle\langle\psi_2| = \rho_2$. In summary we note that each pure state of the system can be identified with a positive, Hermitian, density operator ρ for which $\rho^2 = \rho$ and $\mathrm{Tr}(\rho) = 1$.

Mixed States. In the general theory of probability, one commonly deals with a multitude of conditional distributions. Suppose, by way of illustration, we denote by $p(T|S, M, H)$ the conditional distribution of outdoor temperatures T for the state S of the United States, during the month M and during the hour H of the day. If, however, "blurred" statistics are available pertaining to temperatures T only in the morning $\mathfrak{M}$, during the summer $\mathcal{S}$, and for the New England States $\mathfrak{NE}$ as a whole, then the relevant distribution (still conditional!) is a suitable average:

$$p(T|\mathfrak{NE}, \mathcal{S}, \mathfrak{M}) = \left\{\begin{matrix}\text{Average over New England} \\ \text{States in the summer months} \\ \text{and the morning hours.}\end{matrix}\right\} p(T|S, M, H)$$

Such an averaging, or blurring, of the purer conditions leads inevitably to a distribution which is "broader" than otherwise.

A more specific example may prove instructive. The photoelectric counting distributions discussed in Chapters 2 and 3 were derived in a two-step argument. First, in Eq. (2-2), we determined the counting distribution conditional on the intensity having the value $I(t)$ indicated. The final counting distribution was found subsequently by averaging the conditional distribution with the relevant distribution of intensities as in (2-10) or (3-1). As noted several times, the counting variance always increases after such an intensity average.[2]

The procedure used for the counting distributions illustrates a convenient conceptual way to determine any probability distribution: First, determine the *pure* distributions, i.e., those conditional distributions in which every other significant parameter is held fixed; second, introduce a subsequent average over the distribution of the other parameters.

Let us apply this prescription to determine the distribution for the observed values of an arbitrary observable $\mathcal{O}$ in quantum theory. Each of the pure distributions, as represented by its characteristic function, is given by the relation

$$C_{\mathcal{O}}(s|\rho_\alpha) = \mathrm{Tr}(\rho_\alpha e^{is\mathcal{O}}) = \langle\psi_\alpha|e^{is\mathcal{O}}|\psi_\alpha\rangle \tag{5-26}$$

which as the notation implies is conditional on the state of the system being given by ρ_α (or by $|\psi_\alpha\rangle$). If "pure" knowledge of the state is unavailable, then we must average (5-26) over various ρ_α. Let α denote the set of variables of uncertainty in ρ_α and let $\mu(\alpha)$—with possible δ functions—be the normalized distribution of α values. Then, using the linear property of the trace, it follows that the relevant (and still conditional!) characteristic function is

$$\begin{aligned} C_{\mathcal{O}}(s) \equiv C_{\mathcal{O}}(s|\rho) &= \int \mu(\alpha)\, d\alpha\, \mathrm{Tr}(\rho_\alpha e^{is\mathcal{O}}) \\ &= \mathrm{Tr}([\textstyle\int \mu(\alpha)\rho_\alpha\, d\alpha] e^{is\mathcal{O}}) \\ &\equiv \mathrm{Tr}(\rho e^{is\mathcal{O}}) \end{aligned} \tag{5-27}$$

where

$$\rho \equiv \int \mu(\alpha)\rho_\alpha\, d\alpha \tag{5-28}$$

Now, no matter what the variables α actually are, or what sort of distribution $\mu(\alpha)$ is adopted, a remarkable property always holds for ρ. Clearly, ρ is positive, Hermitian, and fulfills $\mathrm{Tr}(\rho) = 1$. Thus, according to the remarks made in connection with Eq. (5-15), we see that ρ *always has the canonical decomposition*

$$\rho = \sum_{n=1}^{\infty} |\psi_n\rangle\beta_n\langle\psi_n| \tag{5-29}$$

where $\beta_n \geq 0$, $\Sigma_{n=1}^{\infty}\, \beta_n = 1$, and $\{|\psi_n\rangle\}$ forms a complete orthonormal basis.

[2] In addition, the distributions defined in (4-29) and (4-30) are also conditional distributions of a self-explanatory nature.

In summary, we remark that the general state of a system corresponds to a density operator ρ of the form (5-29). Average values of the Hermitian observable $\mathcal{O}$ are given by $\langle \mathcal{O} \rangle = \mathrm{Tr}(\rho \mathcal{O})$, whereas the characteristic function for the distribution of observed values for $\mathcal{O}$ is given by

$$C_{\mathcal{O}}(s) = \mathrm{Tr}(\rho e^{is\mathcal{O}}) \tag{5-30}$$

Pure states fulfill the condition $\rho^2 = \rho$, but mixed states [in which more than one term appears in the sum (5-29)] do not. For a finite-dimensional Hilbert space, the only change in the foregoing summary is that the sum in (5-29) has a finite number of terms.

A few examples may help make these features clearer!

5-3 EXAMPLES OF STATISTICAL STATES IN QUANTUM THEORY

A. Polarization States of a Monochromatic Light Beam

As an example of a system with a finite number of linearly independent states, let us consider the polarization states of a light beam. In this example we idealize the problem by fixing the additional optical degrees of freedom corresponding to direction and color (frequency). Such a beam of light, then, has two independent states, which may be taken as two linear polarizations. The polarization directions are transverse to the propagation direction, as will be explicitly demonstrated in the following chapter.

Statistical states of our idealized system need not correspond to polarized light. On one extreme, a zero polarization, in which no directions are favored, corresponds to a mixed state. On the other extreme are the pure states of 100% polarization. From our general discussion we can determine the mixed states from the pure ones.

Since there are only two independent states of polarization, we may adopt a Hilbert space of only two dimensions, $D = 2$, and, thus, we may represent a pure state by a normalized two-component vector

$$|\psi\rangle = \begin{pmatrix} u_1 \\ u_2 \end{pmatrix} \qquad \langle \psi | \psi \rangle = |u_1|^2 + |u_2|^2 = 1 \tag{5-31}$$

The values of u_j correspond to the relative amounts of polarization. For example, if $u_1 = 0$, $u_2 \neq 0$ (or vice versa), then the light is linearly polarized. If $u_1 = \pm i u_2$, then the light is circularly polarized. In the general case, when neither of the above special conditions hold, the light is elliptically polarized.

The density matrix for the pure state (5-31) is a 2×2 Hermitian matrix of trace 1:

$$\rho = |\psi\rangle\langle\psi| = \begin{pmatrix} u_1 \\ u_2 \end{pmatrix} (u_1{}^* \; u_2{}^*) = \begin{pmatrix} u_1{}^*u_1 & u_2{}^*u_1 \\ u_1{}^*u_2 & u_2{}^*u_2 \end{pmatrix} \tag{5-32}$$

An especially convenient parameterization for ρ that holds for the mixed as well as the pure states is given in terms of the Stokes parameters.[3] For the pure state (5-31) these parameters are defined by

$$s_0 = u_1{}^*u_1 + u_2{}^*u_2 = 1 \tag{5-33a}$$
$$s_1 = u_1{}^*u_2 + u_2{}^*u_1 \tag{5-33b}$$
$$s_2 = i(u_2{}^*u_1 - u_1{}^*u_2) \tag{5-33c}$$
$$s_3 = u_1{}^*u_1 - u_2{}^*u_2 \tag{5-33d}$$

In any case—and in particular the pure state case—we put

$$\rho = \frac{1}{2}\begin{pmatrix} s_0 + s_3 & s_1 - is_2 \\ s_1 + is_2 & s_0 - s_3 \end{pmatrix} \tag{5-34}$$

If we introduce the usual Pauli matrices

$$\sigma_1 = \begin{pmatrix} 0 & 1 \\ 1 & 0 \end{pmatrix} \quad \sigma_2 = \begin{pmatrix} 0 & -i \\ i & 0 \end{pmatrix} \quad \sigma_3 = \begin{pmatrix} 1 & 0 \\ 0 & -1 \end{pmatrix}$$

and denote the identity matrix by σ_0, then we may write

$$\begin{aligned} \rho &= \tfrac{1}{2}(s_0\sigma_0 + s_1\sigma_1 + s_2\sigma_2 + s_3\sigma_3) \\ &\equiv \tfrac{1}{2}(1 + \mathbf{s} \cdot \boldsymbol{\sigma}) \end{aligned} \tag{5-35}$$

In turn, we may determine s_j, $j = 0, 1, 2, 3$, from ρ through the relation

$$s_j = \mathrm{Tr}(\rho\sigma_j) \tag{5-36}$$

We also note that (5-34) leads to

$$\det(\rho) = \tfrac{1}{4}(s_0{}^2 - \mathbf{s}^2) \tag{5-37}$$

In the Stokes notation the pure states are represented by *unit* vectors $\mathbf{s}$, $\mathbf{s}^2 = 1$. This condition is a consequence of the vanishing of the determinant of ρ in (5-32), which from (5-37) implies that $\mathbf{s}^2 = s_0{}^2 = 1$.

The mixed states follow in turn from the pure states. Let ρ_α denote a family of pure states determined by an associated family of unit vectors $\mathbf{s}_\alpha = \mathrm{Tr}(\rho_\alpha\boldsymbol{\sigma})$. Then, as in the general formulation in (5-28)

$$\begin{aligned} \rho = \int \mu(\alpha)\rho_\alpha \, d\alpha &= \tfrac{1}{2}[1 + \boldsymbol{\sigma} \cdot \textstyle\int \mu(\alpha)\mathbf{s}_\alpha \, d\alpha] \\ &\equiv \tfrac{1}{2}(1 + \mathbf{s} \cdot \boldsymbol{\sigma}) \end{aligned} \tag{5-38}$$

As an average over different unit vectors the resultant $\mathbf{s}$ in (5-38) will always satisfy $\mathbf{s}^2 < 1$, which is the distinguishing property of impure

[3] See Born and Wolf [1-1], Chapter X.

states. It should be clear that different $\mu(\alpha)$ may give rise to the same $\mathbf{s}$ and thus the same ρ. In short, the same state may arise for different reasons.

An intrinsic degree of polarization $\mathcal{P}$, independent of the kind of polarization (linear, circular, etc.), is given by

$$\mathcal{P}^2 \equiv \mathbf{s}^2 \tag{5-39a}$$

Alternatively, if ρ_1 and ρ_2 denote the eigenvalues of ρ, then the relations $\mathrm{Tr}(\rho) = \rho_1 + \rho_2 = 1$ and $\det(\rho) = \rho_1\rho_2$, coupled with (5-37), imply that

$$\mathcal{P}^2 = 1 - 4\det(\rho) = (\rho_1 + \rho_2)^2 - 4\rho_1\rho_2 = (\rho_1 - \rho_2)^2 \tag{5-39b}$$

If we set $\rho_i = \bar{n}_i/(\bar{n}_1 + \bar{n}_2)$, $i = 1, 2$, then (5-39b) shows that the parameter defined in (2-41) can be viewed as the degree of polarization for that particular example.

Quite generally, for a pure state $\mathcal{P} = 1$, while for an impure state $\mathcal{P} < 1$. The most impure state has $\mathcal{P} = 0$ and corresponds to the density matrix

$$\rho = \frac{1}{2}\begin{pmatrix} 1 & 0 \\ 0 & 1 \end{pmatrix} \tag{5-40}$$

Such light may be decomposed into any two independent polarizations with equal probability. Other effects being equal, light from a thermal source is unpolarized in the sense that $\mathcal{P} = 0$.

B. Statistical States of an Harmonic Oscillator

So central is the harmonic oscillator to quantum mechanics in general and to quantum optics in particular that we want to discuss this example in some detail. The basic operators that are introduced are the Hermitian "coordinate" operator Q and its conjugate, the Hermitian "momentum" operator P, which fulfill the canonical commutation relation

$$[Q, P] \equiv QP - PQ = i\hbar \tag{5-41}$$

Of course, these operators characterize a single degree of freedom quite generally and are not limited to oscillators.

CREATION AND ANNIHILATION OPERATORS. An especially convenient way to study the properties of Q and P is through the annihilation and creation operators, a and $a^\dagger$ defined, respectively, by

$$a \equiv (\omega/2\hbar)^{1/2}Q + i(1/2\omega\hbar)^{1/2}P \tag{5-42a}$$
$$a^\dagger \equiv (\omega/2\hbar)^{1/2}Q - i(1/2\omega\hbar)^{1/2}P \tag{5-42b}$$

For oscillator problems, ω has the interpretation of the angular frequency of the oscillator in question. From (5-41) it follows that

$$[a, a^\dagger] = aa^\dagger - a^\dagger a = 1 \tag{5-43}$$

which is likewise a classic form of the commutation relations. Multiplication by a from the right or by $a^\dagger$ from the left yields the two relations

$$Na = a(N - 1) \tag{5-44a}$$
$$Na^\dagger = a^\dagger(N + 1) \tag{5-44b}$$

where we have introduced the "number operator"

$$N \equiv a^\dagger a \tag{5-45}$$

which is clearly positive and Hermitian. Repeated use of these relations leads to

$$Na^m = a^m(N - m) \tag{5-46a}$$
$$Na^{\dagger m} = a^{\dagger m}(N + m) \tag{5-46b}$$

for all $m = 0, 1, 2, \ldots$. Furthermore it follows that

$$a^{\dagger m}a^m = N(N - 1)(N - 2) \cdots (N - [m - 1]) \tag{5-47}$$

for all $m \geq 1$. The obvious positive nature of the left side of (5-47) for all m rules out the possibility that the number operator N has any continuous distribution for its eigenvalues. For, if there were any continuous spectrum, there would be approximate eigenstates of N for which none of the factors on the right side of (5-47) would vanish, whereas, for suitable m, some (e.g., one) could be made negative.

Suppose, then, as it must, that N has *one* normalized eigenstate $|n\rangle$

$$N|n\rangle = n|n\rangle \tag{5-48}$$

for some real number n. Again it follows from (5-47) that a contradiction exists unless n is a nonnegative integer. To show that, in fact, all such n occur, let us for convenience start with $n = 0$ and the "ground state" $|0\rangle$. It follows from (5-46b) that

$$N(a^{\dagger m}|0\rangle) = a^{\dagger m}(N + m)|0\rangle = m(a^{\dagger m}|0\rangle) \tag{5-49}$$

so that $a^{\dagger m}|0\rangle$ is proportional to $|m\rangle$ for each $m \geq 1$. That this statement is not empty follows from the nonzero normalization condition

$$\langle 0|a^m a^{\dagger m}|0\rangle = m! \tag{5-50}$$

which is a consequence of the more general relation

$$a^m a^{\dagger m} = (N + 1)(N + 2) \cdots (N + m) \tag{5-51}$$

for $m \geq 1$. Hence we may adopt

$$|n\rangle = \frac{1}{\sqrt{n!}} a^{\dagger n}|0\rangle \tag{5-52}$$

as normalized eigenvectors of N with eigenvalue n. These are interconnected, for example, by the relations

$$a^{\dagger}|n\rangle = \sqrt{n+1}\,|n+1\rangle \tag{5-53a}$$
$$a|n\rangle = \sqrt{n}\,|n-1\rangle \tag{5-53b}$$

which are called "raising" and "lowering," respectively.

The final clincher in our initial discussion of N involves another assumption. Suppose there were an additional degeneracy parameter, which, for example, specified that there were L linearly independent ground states $|0, l\rangle$, $l = 1, 2, \ldots, L$, for all of which $N|0, l\rangle = 0$. Then there would exist L complete ladders of states $|n, l\rangle$, as follows from our previous construction, but the operators a and $a^{\dagger}$ could never mix states with different l's. To eliminate the possibility of such degeneracy, one may postulate that *every* operator must be represented as a function of a and $a^{\dagger}$. In other words, the quantization involves, by assumption, an *irreducible* representation of the operators Q and P (as the usual Schrödinger representation x and $-i\hbar\,\partial/\partial x$ automatically yields). So saying, there can then be only *one* ladder, $|n\rangle$, $n = 0, 1, 2, \ldots$, which thus forms a complete orthonormal basis for the (infinite-dimensional) Hilbert space. It is conventional in discussions of the oscillator to label the states with eigenvalues of the number operator N which thus begin with zero. This leads to an obvious and trivial modification of the formulas given in our general discussion.

STATISTICAL STATES. An important set of pure-state density matrices are those based on eigenstates of N, namely, $\rho_n = |n\rangle\langle n|$. In turn, an important set of mixed states are given by

$$\rho = \sum_{n=0}^{\infty} \beta_n |n\rangle\langle n| \tag{5-54}$$

For an harmonic oscillator in thermal equilibrium at temperature T—or reciprocal temperature $\beta \equiv 1/\kappa T$ (where κ is Boltzmann's constant)—the weight

$$\beta_n = (1 - e^{-\beta\hbar\omega})e^{-n\beta\hbar\omega} \tag{5-55}$$

since (as we shall elaborate further in the next chapter) the energy operator or Hamiltonian $\mathcal{H} = \hbar\omega N$ and so the energy eigenvalues are just

$E_n = \hbar\omega n$. The mean occupancy in the thermal state is found to be

$$\langle N \rangle = \text{Tr}(\rho N) = \sum_{n=0}^{\infty} ne^{-n\beta\hbar\omega}(1 - e^{-\beta\hbar\omega})$$
$$= \frac{1}{e^{\beta\hbar\omega} - 1} \tag{5-56}$$

where, in terms of $y = \exp(-\beta\hbar\omega)$, we have used the relation

$$(1 - y) \sum_{n=0}^{\infty} ny^n = (1 - y)y \frac{d}{dy} \sum_{n=0}^{\infty} y^n$$
$$= (1 - y)y \frac{d}{dy} \frac{1}{1 - y} = \frac{y}{1 - y} = \frac{1}{y^{-1} - 1}$$

As a consequence we find that

$$\bar{E} = \hbar\omega\langle N \rangle = \frac{\hbar\omega}{e^{\beta\hbar\omega} - 1} \tag{5-57}$$

The characteristic function for the distribution of N is

$$C_N(s) = \text{Tr}(\rho e^{isN}) = \sum_{n=0}^{\infty} (1 - e^{-\beta\hbar\omega})e^{-n(\beta\hbar\omega - is)}$$
$$= \frac{1 - e^{-\beta\hbar\omega}}{1 - e^{-\beta\hbar\omega + is}} \tag{5-58}$$

In subsequent chapters we shall also be interested in cases where the β_n in (5-54) correspond to a Poisson distribution, namely, when

$$\beta_n = \frac{1}{n!} \mu^n e^{-\mu} \tag{5-59}$$

In such a case the mean number is

$$\langle N \rangle = \text{Tr}(\rho N) = \sum_{n=0}^{\infty} \frac{n}{n!} \mu^n e^{-\mu} = \mu \tag{5-60}$$

and the characteristic function for N becomes

$$C_N(s) = \text{Tr}(\rho e^{isN}) = \sum_{n=0}^{\infty} \frac{1}{n!} \mu^n e^{isn} e^{-\mu}$$
$$= \exp[(e^{is} - 1)\mu] \tag{5-61}$$

for which the similarity with the completely classical expression (2-8) may be noted.

There are numerous other density operators of potential interest. Although all such operators have a canonical decomposition (5-29), it is sometimes convenient to have another formulation in terms of the physically important eigenstates $|m\rangle$ of the number operator. Each $|\psi_n\rangle$ appearing in (5-29) admits the expansion

$$|\psi_n\rangle = \sum_{m=0}^{\infty} \psi_{n,m}|m\rangle \tag{5-62}$$

so that

$$\begin{aligned}\rho &= \sum_{n=1}^{\infty} |\psi_n\rangle\beta_n\langle\psi_n| \\ &= \sum_{n=1}^{\infty} \sum_{m,m'=0}^{\infty} \psi_{n,m}|m\rangle\beta_n\langle m'|\psi^*_{n,m'} \\ &= \sum_{m,m'=0}^{\infty} |m\rangle\rho(m,m')\langle m'|\end{aligned} \tag{5-63}$$

where clearly

$$\rho(m, m') = \sum_{n=1}^{\infty} \psi_{n,m}\beta_n\psi^*_{n,m'} = \langle m|\rho|m'\rangle \tag{5-64}$$

The latter form in Eq. (5-63) holds, of course, for very general operators. To ensure that ρ is, in fact, a density operator it suffices to require: Hermiticity, $\rho(m', m) = \rho(m, m')^*$; positivity

$$\sum_{m,m'=0}^{\infty} c_m{}^*\rho(m, m')c_{m'} \geq 0 \tag{5-65}$$

for square summable $\{c_m\}$; and traceability, in particular, that

$$\sum_{m=0}^{\infty} \rho(m, m) = 1 \tag{5-66}$$

If $\rho(m, m') = \beta_m\delta_{m,m'}$, we recover the special case of (5-54) discussed above.

C. *Statistical States for Several Oscillators*

Assume that we deal with K independent oscillators with angular frequencies ω_k, $k = 1, 2, \ldots, K$. Each oscillator is described by its "coordinate" and "momentum" operators, Q_k and P_k, which fulfill

$$[Q_k, Q_{k'}] = [P_k, P_{k'}] = 0 \tag{5-67a}$$
$$[Q_k, P_{k'}] = i\hbar\, \delta_{kk'} \tag{5-67b}$$

We can introduce annihilation and creation operators for each oscillator by

$$a_k = (\omega_k/2\hbar)^{1/2}Q_k + i(1/2\omega_k\hbar)^{1/2}P_k \tag{5-68a}$$
$$a_k^\dagger = (\omega_k/2\hbar)^{1/2}Q_k - i(1/2\omega_k\hbar)^{1/2}P_k \tag{5-68b}$$

and associated number operators

$$N_k \equiv a_k^\dagger a_k \qquad k = 1, 2, \ldots, K \tag{5-69}$$

The entire analysis of the preceding section applies to each and every one of the present oscillators. An important point is that the eigenvectors of any *one* N_k do not by themselves span Hilbert space (since the representation for any one Q_k and P_k is now reducible!). Rather, if we assume that the collection of Q_k, P_k, $k = 1, 2, \ldots, K$ are irreducible, then the collection of simultaneous unit eigenvectors of all the N_k, denoted by

$$|n_1, n_2, \ldots, n_K\rangle \equiv |\{n_k\}\rangle \tag{5-70}$$

do form a complete orthonormal basis. [4]

Many of the single oscillator results are readily generalized. Pure states of fixed numbers are given by

$$\rho_{\{n_k\}} = |\{n_k\}\rangle\langle\{n_k\}| \tag{5-71}$$

while a special class of density operators is of the form

$$\rho = \sum_{\{n_k\}=0}^{\infty} \beta_{\{n_k\}} |\{n_k\}\rangle\langle\{n_k\}| \tag{5-72}$$

This form is, of course, equivalent to our general prescription (5-29) since the collection of all sequences $\{n_k\}$ is countable.

Of special interest is the thermal distribution for K independent oscillators for which the Hamiltonian is

$$\mathcal{H} = \sum_{k=1}^{K} \hbar\omega_k a_k^\dagger a_k = \sum_{k=1}^{K} \hbar\omega_k N_k \tag{5-73}$$

[4] Another way of stating these notions is that $N_1, N_2, \ldots, N_K$ form a "complete set of commuting observables" (CSCO). A simultaneous eigenvector of a CSCO is uniquely specified (up to an unimportant overall phase factor) by the set of relevant eigenvalues.

In this case

$$\beta_{\{n_k\}} = \prod_{k=1}^{K} (1 - \exp[-\beta\hbar\omega_k]) \exp(-n_k\beta\hbar\omega_k) \tag{5-74}$$

In consequence, it follows that

$$\bar{E} = \mathrm{Tr}(\rho\mathcal{H}) = \sum_{k=1}^{K} \frac{\hbar\omega_k}{\exp(\beta\hbar\omega_k) - 1} \tag{5-75}$$

which is just the sum of (5-57) for the different frequencies involved. The characteristic function for energy values E is

$$C_E(s) = \mathrm{Tr}(\rho e^{is\mathcal{H}}) = \prod_{k=1}^{K} \frac{1 - \exp(-\beta\hbar\omega_k)}{1 - \exp[-\hbar\omega_k(\beta - is)]} \tag{5-76}$$

the product form being indicative of the independent contribution from each oscillator.

For a multiple Poisson distribution, for which

$$\beta_{\{n_k\}} = \prod_{k=1}^{K} \frac{1}{n_k!} \mu_k^{n_k} \exp(-\mu_k) \tag{5-77}$$

the mean occupancies are clearly $\langle N_k \rangle = \mu_k$. Hence, if we again adopt (5-73), then

$$\bar{E} = \mathrm{Tr}(\rho\mathcal{H}) = \hbar \sum_{k=1}^{K} \omega_k\mu_k \tag{5-78}$$

while the characteristic function for E becomes

$$C_E(s) = \mathrm{Tr}(\rho e^{is\mathcal{H}}) = \exp\left[\sum_{k=1}^{K} (\exp[i\hbar\omega_k s] - 1)\mu_k\right] \tag{5-79}$$

We may develop a formula like (5-63) for several oscillators by use of the resolution of the identity

$$I = \sum_{\{n_k\}=0}^{\infty} |\{n_k\}\rangle\langle\{n_k\}| \tag{5-80}$$

Consequently, any ρ may be expressed in the form

$$\rho = \sum_{\{m_k\},\{m_k'\}=0}^{\infty} |\{m_k\}\rangle \rho(\{m_k\}, \{m_k'\}) \langle \{m_k'\}| \tag{5-81}$$

where, in fact,

$$\rho(\{m_k\}, \{m_k'\}) \equiv \langle \{m_k\}|\rho|\{m_k'\}\rangle \tag{5-82}$$

These coefficients fulfill obvious Hermiticity, positivity, and traceability requirements that follow by analogy from (5-65) and (5-66).

D. Statistical States for Infinitely Many Oscillators

We now take up the transition ($K \to \infty$) to an infinite number of oscillator degrees of freedom Q_k, P_k, $k = 1, 2, \ldots$, under the physically reasonable hypothesis that the total number operator

$$N = \sum_{k=1}^{\infty} N_k \tag{5-83}$$

and the total energy operator,

$$\mathcal{H} = \sum_{k=1}^{\infty} \hbar\omega_k N_k \tag{5-84}$$

remain well defined. For this to be true it suffices that a complete orthonormal basis for Hilbert space now consist of the simultaneous number eigenvectors,

$$|n_1, n_2, \ldots\rangle \equiv |\{n_k\}\rangle \tag{5-85}$$

for each of which the eigenvalues satisfy

$$\sum_{k=1}^{\infty} n_k < \infty \tag{5-86}$$

This implies that for any such basis vector $|\{n_k\}\rangle$, only a finite number of $n_k > 0$. Such sequences $\{n_k\}$ are again countable, and our general formulation applies.

It must be emphasized, in spite of (5-86), that there nevertheless exist other vectors in Hilbert space that have nonvanishing occupancy for every oscillator. For example, if $\{n_k\} = \{\delta_{kl}\}$ (i.e., $n_l = 1$, all other n_k vanishing), then

$$|\psi\rangle = \sum_{l=1}^{\infty} \frac{1}{l} |\{\delta_{kl}\}\rangle \tag{5-87}$$

is a valid normalizable vector for which

$$\langle N_k \rangle \equiv \langle \psi | N_k | \psi \rangle = \frac{1}{k^2} > 0 \tag{5-88}$$

for all $k \geq 1$. It is, of course, not necessary that $\langle N_k \rangle \to 0$ for large k. To illustrate a counter example, it suffices to replace δ_{kl} by $l^4 \, \delta_{kl}$ in the above example. For such a state, $\langle N_k \rangle = k^2$ and, thus, $\langle N \rangle = \infty$.

Let us note again that for any density operator ρ and Hermitian observable $\mathcal{O}$, the associated characteristic function (5-30) is continuous in s. Applied to the number operator N this requires that

$$C_N(s) = \mathrm{Tr}(\rho e^{isN}) \tag{5-89}$$

be a continuous function of s. In turn, this property may put constraints on the set of parameters that describe a given density operator. In the special case of a multiple Poisson distribution it follows that

$$\begin{aligned} C_N(s) &= \exp\left[\sum_{k=1}^{\infty} (e^{is} - 1)\mu_k\right] \\ &\equiv \exp[(e^{is} - 1)\langle N \rangle] \end{aligned} \tag{5-90}$$

which to be continuous simply requires that

$$\langle N \rangle \equiv \sum_{k=1}^{\infty} \mu_k < \infty \tag{5-91}$$

Thus not every sequence $\{\mu_k\}$ of mean (Poisson) occupancies leads to a density operator, but only those fulfilling (5-91).

In turn, to ensure that

$$C_E(s) = \mathrm{Tr}(\rho e^{is\mathcal{H}}) \tag{5-92}$$

be continuous in s for a multiple Poisson distribution, we must examine

$$C_E(s) = \exp\left[\sum_{k=1}^{\infty} (\exp[i\hbar\omega_k s] - 1)\mu_k\right] \tag{5-93}$$

It follows from the inequality

$$\begin{aligned} \left| \sum_{k=1}^{\infty} (\exp[i\hbar\omega_k s] - 1)\mu_k \right| &\leq \sum_{k=1}^{\infty} |\exp[i\hbar\omega_k s] - 1|\mu_k \\ &\leq 2 \sum_{k=1}^{\infty} \mu_k = 2\langle N \rangle < \infty \end{aligned} \tag{5-94}$$

that the constraint (5-91) also ensures the continuity of (5-93). We note this condition does not require that

$$\bar{E} = \hbar \sum_{k=1}^{\infty} \omega_k \mu_k$$

be finite, although, for physical cases no doubt $\bar{E} < \infty$ as well.

Qualitatively similar conditions apply for the thermal distribution of an infinite number of oscillators. For the characteristic function of N we find from (5-58) that

$$C_N(s) = \prod_{k=1}^{\infty} \frac{(1 - \exp[-\beta\hbar\omega_k])}{(1 - \exp[-\beta\hbar\omega_k + is])} \tag{5-95}$$

The continuity of $C_N(s)$ is assured if the product converges to a nonzero value. To test the convergence we may use a von Neumann theorem which states that a product $\Pi_{k=1}^{\infty} z_k$, for which no $z_k = 0$, converges to a nonzero value if and only if the sum

$$\sum_{k=1}^{\infty} |1 - z_k| < \infty$$

Since $\omega_k > 0$, no factor in (5-95) vanishes and the theorem applies. Convergence of the related sum is secured if

$$\sum_{k=1}^{\infty} \left| 1 - \frac{1 - \exp(-\beta\hbar\omega_k)}{1 - \exp(-\beta\hbar\omega_k + is)} \right| = \sum_{k=1}^{\infty} \frac{\exp(-\beta\hbar\omega_k)|1 - e^{is}|}{|1 - \exp(-\beta\hbar\omega_k + is)|}$$
$$\leq 2 \sum_{k=1}^{\infty} \exp(-\beta\hbar\omega_k) < \infty \tag{5-96}$$

which is clearly seen to be necessary as well as sufficient. As we shall show in the next chapter, Eq. (5-96) can be well fulfilled for the radiation field oscillators.

Finally, to ensure the continuity of the characteristic function for energy, which reads

$$\begin{aligned} C_E(s) &= \mathrm{Tr}(\rho e^{is\mathcal{H}}) \\ &= \prod_{k=1}^{\infty} \frac{(1 - \exp[-\beta\hbar\omega_k])}{(1 - \exp[-(\beta - is)\hbar\omega_k])} \end{aligned} \tag{5-97}$$

it is necessary and sufficient that

$$\sum_{k=1}^{\infty} \exp(-\beta\hbar\omega_k) < \infty \tag{5-98}$$

be true again, as a calculation patterned after (5-96) quickly shows.

Numerous other density operators exist besides the examples discussed, and we shall discuss some of them in subsequent chapters. For present purposes, we note that, with the understanding of (5-85) and (5-86), we may reinterpret Eqs. (5-80) to (5-82) so as to describe a general density matrix in terms of an occupation number representation.

5-4 CONCLUDING REMARKS

The moral of our discussion and especially of our last example is twofold. First, not only for one or for several degrees of freedom, but even in the case of an infinite number of degrees of freedom, the traditional, separable, Hilbert space (with a countable basis), which we have defined, is completely adequate and suitable for quantum theory. Despite occasional statements in the literature to the contrary, nonseparable spaces (with noncountable bases) are unnecessary for quantum fields, at least insofar as the class of problems we treat are concerned. The second moral is that if one attempts to extend a sequence of density operators, say $\rho_{(K)}$, each pertaining to the first K degrees of freedom, to the limit $K = \infty$, then constraints on the parameters involved may be expected so that the limit operator is actually a density operator. For instance, the simplest example of this type that we discussed was the multiple Poisson distribution, for which the necessary constraint is (5-91).

The lesson to be learned here may be restated quite generally. The limit of density operators need no longer be a density operator in the traditional sense that physical limits are taken, namely, through limits of expectation values for certain operators. This feature is by no means restricted to problems with an infinite number of degrees of freedom but occurs in the most elementary of situations. Consider a particle free to move within a box of volume $\Omega < \infty$ and whose Hamiltonian is $\mathcal{H}_\Omega = p^2/2m$. For every value of Ω, the thermal distribution

$$\rho_\Omega = \exp(-\beta\mathcal{H}_\Omega) \tag{5-99}$$

is a density matrix (unnormalized but traceable), but the limiting operator

$$\lim_{\Omega\to\infty} \rho_\Omega \equiv \rho_\infty = \exp(-\beta\mathcal{H}_\infty) \tag{5-100}$$

is not a traceable operator even though it is bounded

Any physical system possessing complete, spatial, translational invariance can never have a precise thermal distribution described by a density operator. One such system of special interest to us is the free radiation field defined over all space. To give such a system a physically meaningful thermal distribution—a task which is explicitly of interest to us—two routes are open. On the one hand, we could define the radiation field throughout *all* space but require that it be thermal only over a finite region (e.g., over the Milky Way!) and vacuum-like elsewhere. On the other hand, we may imagine a finite quantization volume $\Omega \equiv L^3$—a cubic "box"—with periodic boundary conditions, which, then, effectively becomes the entire physical space of the problem. As is conventional, we shall adopt the second route of "putting the system into a box" for our subsequent analysis and description. It is in this sense that the radiation field will fulfill Eq. (5-98) in order to possess a thermal distribution given by a density operator.

For an enormous quantization box the appropriate density operator permits the calculation of numerous physical mean values which are for all practical purposes independent of the box size. For such questions (e.g., the mean thermal energy per unit volume) the results are meaningful and frequently simplified by passing to the limit of an infinite volume. Some of our results dealing with expectation values are quoted in a form appropriate to an infinite quantization volume.

Finally, let us note that modern mathematical methods [5] currently under study in quantum statistical mechanics do permit a direct consideration of thermal states in infinite volumes, etc., by generalizing the notion of "state" of a system to include not only those described by true density operators but those attainable through a sequence of true density operators appropriate to finite volumes. The physical interpretation determined by this prescription is identical to that obtained from the more familiar device which we follow, of first evaluating various expectation values as though the system were in a large box and, subsequently, passing to the limit of infinite volume.

[5] The idea of generalized states for quantum systems has been put forth by Segal [5-8]. A discussion of these modern mathematical methods (C^* algebras) and their application to quantum theory is also given by Haag and Kastler [5-9].

CHAPTER 6

EQUATIONS OF MOTION OF THE ELECTROMAGNETIC FIELD

6-1 TIME DEVELOPMENT IN QUANTUM THEORY

As we have seen in detail in the last chapter, the state of a quantum mechanical system is determined by a density operator ρ, and various probability distributions are determined with the aid of ρ. The density operator ρ may depend parametrically on a number of quantities, such as the temperature, the time, and the volume of the system container. These parameters refer to the conditional aspects of the density operator, just as similar parameters label conditional variables in classical probability densities.

As we emphasized in Chapter 4, Markoff processes play an important role in classical probability theory. For such cases the future distribution function is determined in a linear fashion just from the present distribution. In other words, the distribution function obeys a linear differential equation—the stochastic equation—which is first order in time.

In quantum mechanics, Markoffian systems are equally fundamental. For these cases the state of the system obeys a linear, first-order equation, which is just the usual Schrödinger equation. In particular, for the state $|\psi\rangle = |\psi(t)\rangle$, Schrödinger's equation reads

$$i\hbar \frac{\partial}{\partial t} |\psi\rangle = \mathcal{H}|\psi\rangle \tag{6-1}$$

where $\mathcal{H}$ is the system Hamiltonian operator, which is Hermitian and assumed (for now) to be time independent. For a pure-state density operator, $\rho = |\psi\rangle\langle\psi|$, it follows that

$$i\hbar \frac{\partial}{\partial t} \rho = [\mathcal{H}, \rho] \tag{6-2}$$

By linearity, it is immediately seen that all (or suitably many) density operators obey the same linear equation of motion (6-2).

The symbolic integrated solution to (6-1) is given by

$$|\psi(t)\rangle = e^{-it\mathcal{H}/\hbar}|\psi(0)\rangle \equiv U(t)|\psi(0)\rangle \tag{6-3}$$

Since the Hamiltonian is Hermitian, the evolution operator $U(t)$, which transforms the initial state $|\psi(0)\rangle$ into $|\psi(t)\rangle$, is unitary and so preserves its norm. From our formal solution we easily determine for a pure-state density operator that

$$\begin{aligned} \rho(t) = |\psi(t)\rangle\langle\psi(t)| &= U(t)|\psi(0)\rangle\langle\psi(0)|U(t)^{-1} \\ &= U(t)\rho(0)U(t)^{-1} \end{aligned} \tag{6-4}$$

From linearity it follows that the solution for a general density operator is similarly given by the relation

$$\rho(t) = U(t)\rho(0)U(t)^{-1} \tag{6-5}$$

We remark that this viewpoint of the state of the system evolving in time is called the "Schrödinger picture" and is the viewpoint most in accord with classical probability concepts.

There is, however, an alternative way to account for time evolution which is sometimes convenient. This prescription has its origin in the fact that the experimental predictions of the theory are determined solely by the mean values of various operators in the appropriate statistical state. With this in mind, we may re-express the time-dependent mean value for a general observable $\mathcal{O}$ according to the relation

$$\begin{aligned} \langle\mathcal{O}(t)\rangle \equiv \mathrm{Tr}[\rho(t)\mathcal{O}] &= \mathrm{Tr}[U(t)\rho U(t)^{-1}\mathcal{O}] \\ &= \mathrm{Tr}[\rho U(t)^{-1}\mathcal{O}U(t)] \equiv \mathrm{Tr}[\rho\mathcal{O}(t)] \end{aligned} \tag{6-6}$$

making use of the invariance of the trace under cyclic operator permutation. Here we have simply set $\rho = \rho(0)$, and we have defined the time-dependent operator observable $\mathcal{O}(t)$ by means of the relation

$$\mathcal{O}(t) = U^{-1}(t)\mathcal{O}U(t) \tag{6-7}$$

Consequently, all mean values are properly represented if instead of assuming that the *one* operator ρ evolves according to (6-5), we assume that *every* observable $\mathcal{O}$ evolves according to (6-7). This viewpoint of time evolution in quantum mechanics is called the "Heisenberg picture."

The difference in the two evolution equations should be carefully noted. In differential form these equations read

$$i\hbar \frac{\partial}{\partial t} \rho = [\mathcal{H}, \rho] \tag{6-8}$$

$$-i\hbar \frac{\partial}{\partial t} \mathcal{O} = [\mathcal{H}, \mathcal{O}] \tag{6-9}$$

Only one of these holds true in a given instance depending on the picture adopted. For our later applications in this chapter we shall adopt the Heisenberg picture.

If the Hamiltonian is time dependent—as may well happen in the presence of external sources—then nearly all of the foregoing equations hold true if $\mathcal{H}$ is understood as $\mathcal{H}(t)$. The only basic change is the definition of the evolution operator $U(t)$ in terms of $\mathcal{H}(t)$. For simplicity, let it be imagined that $\mathcal{H}(t)$ is piecewise constant; i.e.,

$$\mathcal{H}(t) = \mathcal{H}(t_j) \quad t_j \leq t < t_{j+1} \quad t_{j+1} - t_j \equiv \Delta_j \tag{6-10}$$

Then the correct unitary evolution operator $U(t)$, $t_l \leq t < t_{l+1}$, reads

$$U(t) = \exp[-i(t - t_l)\mathcal{H}_l/\hbar] \prod_{j=0}^{l-1} \exp(-i\, \Delta_j \mathcal{H}_j/\hbar) \tag{6-11}$$

which is generally different from

$$U'(t) = \exp\left[-i(t - t_l)\mathcal{H}_l/\hbar - i \sum_{j=0}^{l-1} \Delta_j \mathcal{H}_j/\hbar\right] \tag{6-12}$$

The proper solution (6-11) satisfies

$$i\hbar \frac{\partial}{\partial t} U(t) = \mathcal{H}_l U(t) \qquad t_l \leq t < t_{l+1} \tag{6-13}$$

as is appropriate, while U' generally fails to satisfy this relation.

It is convenient to introduce the time-ordering operator T, defined so that

$$U(t) \equiv T\{U'(t)\} \tag{6-14}$$

This operator formally reorders the various terms that make up an expansion of $U'(t)$ so that all operator products are taken with the factors in an increasing time-order sequence. The special form of $U'(t)$ permits us to write

$$U(t) = T\left\{\exp\left[-(i/\hbar) \int_0^t \mathcal{H}(t')\, dt'\right]\right\} \tag{6-15}$$

where we have arbitrarily set $t_0 = 0$. In this general form, $U(t)$ represents the evolution operator for a general time-dependent, Hermitian, Hamiltonian operator $\mathcal{H}(t)$ and is the proper substitute for the operator $U(t)$ appearing from Eq. (6-3) onward.

It is perhaps worth remarking that for clarity we have been a bit cavalier in our presentation. Since $\mathcal{H}$ is generally unbounded it cannot be applied to every $|\psi\rangle$ nor can its commutator be formed with every ρ. When $\mathcal{H}$ is time independent, we assume it has the requisite property (mathematically called "self-adjoint") so that $\exp(-it\mathcal{H}/\hbar)$ can be defined and is in fact unitary. Much less is known about the properties required of $\mathcal{H}(t)$ in order that (6-15) be defined as a unitary operator; we treat these cases heuristically. When $U(t)$ is defined, however, every state and every density operator in the Schrödinger picture, or every bounded observable in the Heisenberg picture, will evolve as we have indicated.

6-2 OPERATOR EQUATIONS FOR THE ELECTROMAGNETIC FIELD: PRELIMINARIES

In the presence of external sources j_ν, the electromagnetic field fulfills Maxwell's equations, which in suitable (Heaviside) units and in full relativistic glory read

$$\partial^\mu F_{\mu\nu} = j_\nu \tag{6-16a}$$

$$\partial^\mu F^*_{\mu\nu} = 0 \qquad (F^*_{\mu\nu} \equiv \tfrac{1}{2}\epsilon_{\mu\nu\alpha\beta}F^{\alpha\beta}) \tag{6-16b}$$

where $\epsilon_{\mu\nu\alpha\beta}$ is the completely antisymmetric tensor of Levi-Civita. In the quantum theory the antisymmetric tensor field $F_{\mu\nu}$, and the sources j_ν as well, are Hermitian operator functions, and (6-16) is an equation among operators. In order for any solution to exist it is clear that the current must fulfill the conservation law $\partial_\mu j^\mu = 0$.

If we can determine the operator solutions to (6-16) then we can, with the aid of a time-independent density operator ρ, formulate various expectation values associated with the electromagnetic field. It is the first part of this general program that we treat in this chapter.

A. Philosophy toward Field Equations

It is relevant to discuss the philosophy of our approach toward the quantized radiation field in this chapter. In order that just those equations given in (6-16) represent a well-posed problem for $F_{\mu\nu}$, we must assume that j^μ is a given, prescribed, external operator field not dynamically responsive to the field distribution that it helps to determine. It is no surprise if we confess this is largely a model problem done for mathematical simplicity and for pedagogical purposes. There are, however, physical situations which are well approximated by just such a set of equations. These occur when the source is sufficiently macroscopic that the field is unable to perturb it; or more to the point, that coherent and macroscopic effects of the field sufficient to disturb the source do not build up. This excludes a microscopic treatment of certain phenomena but is consistent with a phenomenological approach toward most problems. This is clear since we may assume that the given j^μ is precisely the operator solution determined from an unspecified *coupled* set of "complete field equations." Thus there is nothing inherently incorrect in the conclusions that could be derived from "half" of the field equations.

Nevertheless we shall make an important simplifying assumption about the reactions that go to make up j_ν. Since we are basically concerned about fields generated by thermal or laser-like sources we can imagine the source being rather localized in space and in time. Specifically, as regards time, we shall adopt the "adiabatic switching" point of view in which, it may be imagined, that in the remote past and far-distant future the field is free and not coupled to its sources. Thus our approach would improperly treat the coupling of the radiation field to the myriad of microscopic virtual processes (e.g., electron pair creation), since such sources are commonly thought to be present throughout all space–time. We, therefore, do not include the couplings to virtual fields in our sources and, instead, concentrate on the "concrete" sources (atoms, etc.) giving rise to the processes we seek to examine. We are led in this way to impose physically appropriate boundary conditions on our solutions in the remote past and far-distant future.

Finally, since we are considering the radiation field in the presence of prescribed external sources, we have already destroyed Lorentz invariance. This simply means that the external sources themselves can be thought of as singling out a preferred Lorentz frame. There is no compelling reason, then, to retain a manifestly relativistic formulation. Instead we can profitably make use of the conventional and alternative nonrelativistic approach from which greater physical insight will ensue.

6-3 OPERATOR EQUATIONS FOR THE ELECTROMAGNETIC FIELD: NONRELATIVISTIC ANALYSIS

A. Configuration Space Formulation

We begin our considerations by re-expressing Maxwell's equations in the form [1]

$$\dot{\mathbf{H}} = -\nabla \times \mathbf{E} \qquad \dot{\mathbf{E}} = \nabla \times \mathbf{H} - \mathbf{j} \tag{6-17}$$

$$\nabla \cdot \mathbf{H} = 0 \qquad \nabla \cdot \mathbf{E} = \rho \tag{6-18}$$

[1] There should be no confusion between the charge density and the density operator which are both conventionally denoted by ρ.

Here $\dot{\mathbf{H}} = \partial\mathbf{H}/\partial t$, etc., and we choose units where $c = 1$. The first two of these equations are honest equations of motion whereas the latter two are constraints, i.e., internal consistency conditions imposed at each time and that must be satisfied in order to have any solution.

Traditionally one "solves" the constraint $\nabla \cdot \mathbf{H} = 0$ by the relation $\mathbf{H} = \nabla \times \mathbf{A}$, but the choice of $\mathbf{A}$ is thereby not unique (because it is undetermined up to an arbitrary gradient). Since we have already given up manifest covariance, we are free to choose a *physically* useful and significant solution to the constraint equation, one for which the ambiguity inherent in $\mathbf{H} = \nabla \times \mathbf{A}$ is eliminated from the very beginning.

As a step in determining the physically relevant solution we note that every well-behaved vector field $\mathbf{V}(\mathbf{x})$ (operator or c-number) can be decomposed into a *transverse* and *longitudinal* part,

$$\mathbf{V} = \mathbf{V}^T + \mathbf{V}^L \tag{6-19}$$

with the characteristic properties that

$$\nabla \cdot \mathbf{V}^T \equiv 0 \qquad \nabla \times \mathbf{V}^L \equiv 0 \tag{6-20}$$

We shall shortly give an explicit prescription for such a decomposition, but for the present let us assume it to be valid. The constraint $\nabla \cdot \mathbf{H} = 0$ is seen then to be a condition on $\mathbf{H}^L$ and to impose no conditions on $\mathbf{H}^T$. Consequently, the unconstrained variables $\mathbf{H}^T$ may be uniquely re-expressed in terms of new variables $\mathbf{A}^T$ according to

$$\mathbf{H}^T = \nabla \times \mathbf{A}^T \tag{6-21}$$

It follows, then, that the first of Maxwell's equations becomes simply $\dot{\mathbf{A}}^T = -\mathbf{E}^T$.

The remaining Maxwell's equations decompose in the form $\dot{\mathbf{E}}^L = -\mathbf{j}^L$, $\nabla \cdot \mathbf{E}^L = \rho$, and $\dot{\mathbf{E}}^T = \nabla \times \mathbf{H}^T - \mathbf{j}^T$. The first two of these are simply restatements of the conservation of charge. There is in reality no dynamics in them since, as we shall more clearly see below, $\mathbf{E}^L$ is determined as a function of space and time directly from ρ. The third of the equations above contains the rest of our dynamics. If we make use of the general operator identity

$$\nabla \times (\nabla \times \mathbf{V}) = \nabla(\nabla \cdot \mathbf{V}) - \nabla^2\mathbf{V}$$

we may summarize our two basic dynamical equations in the form

$$\dot{\mathbf{A}}^T = -\mathbf{E}^T \tag{6-22a}$$
$$\dot{\mathbf{E}}^T = -\nabla^2\mathbf{A}^T - \mathbf{j}^T \tag{6-22b}$$

B. Momentum Space Formulation

It is illuminating to carry out a parallel derivation of (6-22) in momentum space. Let us introduce the momentum-space-dependent field variables

$$\mathcal{H}(\mathbf{k}) \equiv \Omega^{-1/2}\int e^{-i\mathbf{k}\cdot\mathbf{x}}\mathbf{H}(\mathbf{x})\, d^3x \qquad (6\text{-}23a)$$
$$\mathcal{E}(\mathbf{k}) \equiv \Omega^{-1/2}\int e^{-i\mathbf{k}\cdot\mathbf{x}}\mathbf{E}(\mathbf{x})\, d^3x \qquad (6\text{-}23b)$$
$$\mathcal{J}(\mathbf{k}) \equiv \Omega^{-1/2}\int e^{-i\mathbf{k}\cdot\mathbf{x}}\mathbf{j}(\mathbf{x})\, d^3x \qquad (6\text{-}23c)$$
$$\tilde{\rho}(\mathbf{k}) \equiv \Omega^{-1/2}\int e^{-i\mathbf{k}\cdot\mathbf{x}}\rho(\mathbf{x})\, d^3x \qquad (6\text{-}23d)$$

For the moment we regard $\Omega^{-1/2}$ as an unspecified normalization factor. For each point $\mathbf{k}$ in momentum space we introduce a set of three mutually perpendicular unit vectors $\mathbf{e}_j(\mathbf{k})$, $j = 1, 2, 3$, such that $\mathbf{e}_3(\mathbf{k}) \cdot \mathbf{k} = k \equiv |\mathbf{k}|$. That is, for each $\mathbf{k} \neq 0$, $\mathbf{e}_3(\mathbf{k})$ is *parallel* to $\mathbf{k}$, whereas $\mathbf{e}_1(\mathbf{k})$ and $\mathbf{e}_2(\mathbf{k})$ are *orthogonal* to $\mathbf{k}$. Every vector field

$$\mathcal{V}(\mathbf{k}) \equiv \Omega^{-1/2}\int e^{-i\mathbf{k}\cdot\mathbf{x}}\mathbf{V}(\mathbf{x})\, d^3x \qquad (6\text{-}24)$$

admits the decomposition at each $\mathbf{k}$

$$\begin{aligned}\mathcal{V}(\mathbf{k}) &= \sum_j \mathbf{e}_j(\mathbf{k})[\mathbf{e}_j(\mathbf{k}) \cdot \mathcal{V}(\mathbf{k})] \\ &\equiv \mathcal{V}^T(\mathbf{k}) + \mathcal{V}^L(\mathbf{k}) \qquad (6\text{-}25)\end{aligned}$$

where the longitudinal and transverse parts are

$$\mathcal{V}^L(\mathbf{k}) \equiv \mathbf{e}_3(\mathbf{k})[\mathbf{e}_3(\mathbf{k}) \cdot \mathcal{V}(\mathbf{k})] \qquad (6\text{-}26a)$$
$$\begin{aligned}\mathcal{V}^T(\mathbf{k}) \equiv\ &\mathbf{e}_1(\mathbf{k})[\mathbf{e}_1(\mathbf{k}) \cdot \mathcal{V}(\mathbf{k})] \\ &+ \mathbf{e}_2(\mathbf{k})[\mathbf{e}_2(\mathbf{k}) \cdot \mathcal{V}(\mathbf{k})] \qquad (6\text{-}26b)\end{aligned}$$

Clearly we have the two identities

$$\mathbf{k} \cdot \mathcal{V}^T(\mathbf{k}) \equiv 0 \qquad \mathbf{k} \times \mathcal{V}^L(\mathbf{k}) \equiv 0 \qquad (6\text{-}27)$$

which, apart from factors of i, are just the momentum-space form of the identities (6-20). We also note that if we set

$$\mathcal{H}^T(\mathbf{k}) \equiv i\mathbf{k} \times \mathcal{A}^T(\mathbf{k}) \qquad (6\text{-}28)$$

then we can *uniquely* solve for $\mathcal{A}^T$ by means of

$$\mathbf{k} \times \mathcal{H}^T(\mathbf{k}) = i\mathbf{k} \times [\mathbf{k} \times \mathcal{A}^T(\mathbf{k})] = -ik^2\mathcal{A}^T(\mathbf{k})$$

that is,

$$\mathcal{A}^T(\mathbf{k}) = i\mathbf{k} \times \mathcal{H}^T(\mathbf{k})/k^2 \qquad (6\text{-}29)$$

The application of the foregoing to Maxwell's equations is straightforward with the usual replacement $\nabla \rightarrow i\mathbf{k}$ under a Fourier transformation. The transcribed equations read

$$\dot{\mathcal{H}} = -i\mathbf{k} \times \mathcal{E} \qquad \dot{\mathcal{E}} = i\mathbf{k} \times \mathcal{H} - \mathcal{J} \tag{6-30}$$
$$i\mathbf{k} \cdot \mathcal{H} = 0 \qquad i\mathbf{k} \cdot \mathcal{E} = \tilde{\rho} \tag{6-31}$$

The constraint equations simply read

$$i\mathbf{k} \cdot \mathcal{H}^L = 0 \qquad i\mathbf{k} \cdot \mathcal{E}^L = \tilde{\rho} \tag{6-32}$$

which have the immediate solutions

$$\mathcal{H}^L(\mathbf{k}) = 0 \qquad \mathcal{E}^L(\mathbf{k}) = -i\mathbf{k}\tilde{\rho}(\mathbf{k})/k^2 \tag{6-33}$$

These equations hold true for all time and we see that $\rho(\mathbf{x}, t)$ fully determines $\mathbf{E}^L(\mathbf{x}, t)$ as stated earlier. Moreover, from (6-30) and (6-32) it follows that $i\mathbf{k} \cdot \dot{\mathcal{E}}^L = -i\mathbf{k} \cdot \mathcal{J}^L = \dot{\tilde{\rho}}$ which is the momentum-space version of the current conservation law. With the aid of (6-28) and (6-29) the two remaining (dynamical) equations become

$$\dot{\mathcal{A}}^T(\mathbf{k}) = -\mathcal{E}^T(\mathbf{k}) \tag{6-34a}$$
$$\dot{\mathcal{E}}^T(\mathbf{k}) = k^2\mathcal{A}^T(\mathbf{k}) - \mathcal{J}^T(\mathbf{k}) \tag{6-34b}$$

where the two components of $\mathcal{J}^T$ are independent and unconstrained. In this formulation we see displayed the fundamental advantage of the momentum-space formulation: The dynamics of the degree of freedom labeled by $\mathbf{k}$ is independent of that at all other points.

There is, however, an important qualification to this remark. Since $\mathbf{A}^T(\mathbf{x})$, $\mathbf{E}^T(\mathbf{x})$, and $\mathbf{j}^T(\mathbf{x})$ are Hermitian fields it follows from (6-23) that

$$[\mathcal{A}^T(\mathbf{k})]^\dagger = \mathcal{A}^T(-\mathbf{k}) \tag{6-35a}$$
$$[\mathcal{E}^T(\mathbf{k})]^\dagger = \mathcal{E}^T(-\mathbf{k}) \tag{6-35b}$$
$$[\mathcal{J}^T(\mathbf{k})]^\dagger = \mathcal{J}^T(-\mathbf{k}) \tag{6-35c}$$

In consequence, in terms of these variables, the dynamics of the degree of freedom labeled by $-\mathbf{k}$ is completely determined by that at $+\mathbf{k}$, which really means that only *one-half* of all $\mathbf{k}$ space labels dynamically independent variables.

Polarization Vectors. Some remarks are in order about the transverse unit vectors $\mathbf{e}_1$ and $\mathbf{e}_2$. They are not uniquely specified further than the condition $\mathbf{e}_1(\mathbf{k}) \cdot \mathbf{e}_2(\mathbf{k}) = 0$. If another pair are introduced rotated with respect to these by an angle θ in the plane transverse to $\mathbf{k}$, then Eq. (6-26b) still remains unchanged. For real vectors, which we have implicitly been considering, the directions $\mathbf{e}_1$ and $\mathbf{e}_2$ correspond to the directions of linear polarization of the $\mathbf{k}$th mode. Alternatively, we may employ left and right circular polarizations if we use

$$\mathbf{e}_+(\mathbf{k}) = [\mathbf{e}_1(\mathbf{k}) + i\mathbf{e}_2(\mathbf{k})]/\sqrt{2} \tag{6-36a}$$
$$\mathbf{e}_-(\mathbf{k}) = [\mathbf{e}_1(\mathbf{k}) - i\mathbf{e}_2(\mathbf{k})]/\sqrt{2} \tag{6-36b}$$

for any pair of real polarization vectors $\mathbf{e}_1$ and $\mathbf{e}_2$. Corresponding to this complex basis are the two transverse field components

$$\mathcal{V}_\pm(\mathbf{k}) = \mathbf{e}_\pm{}^*(\mathbf{k}) \cdot \boldsymbol{\mathcal{V}}(\mathbf{k}) \tag{6-37}$$

which themselves correspond to left and right circularly polarized components, respectively. If a change of basis is made by rotation of both $\mathbf{e}_1$ and $\mathbf{e}_2$ through an angle θ, the new circularly polarized components are related to the old ones simply by

$$\mathcal{V}'_\pm(\mathbf{k}) = e^{\pm i\theta}\mathcal{V}_\pm(\mathbf{k}) \tag{6-38}$$

In any case, the two transverse directions correspond to some choice of orthogonal polarization directions for the transverse radiation field modes.

Polarization Indices. It is convenient to have an index notation for the two orthogonal polarization directions, and we adopt the convention that Greek subscripts (especially λ) cover the range 1, 2 or $+$, $-$ depending on whether linearly or circularly polarized basis vectors have been chosen. Hence, any transverse vector field $\boldsymbol{\mathcal{V}}^T$ has the components $\mathcal{V}_\lambda{}^T$, where the relevant basis is assumed understood. In particular, in polarization component form our dynamical equations (6-34) read

$$\dot{\mathcal{A}}_\lambda{}^T(\mathbf{k}) = -\mathcal{E}_\lambda{}^T(\mathbf{k}) \tag{6-39a}$$
$$\dot{\mathcal{E}}_\lambda{}^T(\mathbf{k}) = k^2\mathcal{A}_\lambda{}^T(\mathbf{k}) - \mathcal{J}_\lambda{}^T(\mathbf{k}) \tag{6-39b}$$

Thus not only is the dynamics for each $\mathbf{k}$ independent, but that associated with each polarization λ evolves independently.

For simplicity in notation *we hereafter drop the superscript T* on all our transverse fields.

Commutation Relations. Prior to solving the dynamical equations (6-39) we must first establish appropriate *boundary conditions*. In the classical theory, the boundary conditions are simply the initial values of the functions $\mathcal{A}_\lambda$ and $\mathcal{E}_\lambda$. In quantum theory these variables are all operators and we must choose $\mathcal{A}_\lambda$ and $\mathcal{E}_\lambda$ operators in accord with the canonical commutation relations.

For simplicity and clarity we imagine our electromagnetic field confined to a large cubic box of dimension L^3, and we impose periodic boundary conditions on our solutions. Volume integrations such as in (6-23) extend over L^3 and are normalized so that $\Omega \equiv L^3$. To satisfy the periodicity, the only $\mathbf{k}$ values allowed in such Fourier decompositions have the components

$$k_j = (2\pi/L)n_j \tag{6-40}$$

where n_j, $j = 1, 2, 3$, is an arbitrary integer. However, we explicitly assume that any component of the fields vanishes if all $n_j \equiv 0$; that is, we exclude the point $\mathbf{k} = 0$ from our discussion entirely.

Due to the relations (6-35), independent dynamical variables are labeled by only one-half of $\mathbf{k}$ space. What we should like to ensure in such a half-space is the standard nonvanishing commutation relation

$$\tfrac{1}{2}[\mathcal{A}_\lambda(\mathbf{k})e^{i\mathbf{k}\cdot\mathbf{x}} + \mathcal{A}_\lambda{}^\dagger(\mathbf{k})e^{-i\mathbf{k}\cdot\mathbf{x}}, \mathcal{E}_{\lambda'}(\mathbf{k}')e^{i\mathbf{k}'\cdot\mathbf{x}} + \mathcal{E}^\dagger_{\lambda'}(\mathbf{k}')e^{-i\mathbf{k}'\cdot\mathbf{x}}] = -i\hbar\,\delta_{\lambda\lambda'}\,\delta_{\mathbf{k}\mathbf{k}'}$$

between Hermitian canonical variables. If we explicitly display the time dependence, then it is evident that this relation will be fulfilled for all $\mathbf{x}$ only if we set

$$[\mathcal{A}_\lambda(\mathbf{k}, t), \mathcal{E}^\dagger_{\lambda'}(\mathbf{k}', t)] = [\mathcal{A}_\lambda{}^\dagger(\mathbf{k}, t), \mathcal{E}_{\lambda'}(\mathbf{k}', t)] = -i\hbar\,\delta_{\lambda\lambda'}\,\delta_{\mathbf{k}\mathbf{k}'} \tag{6-41}$$

with all other equal-time commutators vanishing. In this last relation $\mathbf{k}$ and $\mathbf{k}'$ are free to roam over *all* $\mathbf{k}$ space. These relations are expected to hold for any time t and, in particular, must hold as an initial condition on the solution.

In addition we shall assume that for all equal times t we also have

$$[\mathcal{A}_\lambda(\mathbf{k}, t), \mathcal{J}_{\lambda'}(\mathbf{k}', t)] = 0 \tag{6-42a}$$

$$[\mathcal{E}_\lambda(\mathbf{k}, t), \mathcal{J}_{\lambda'}(\mathbf{k}', t)] = 0 \tag{6-42b}$$

This relation does not imply that $\mathcal{A}$ (or $\mathcal{E}$) commutes with $\mathcal{J}$ for unequal times. These commutation conditions simply mean that the source $\mathcal{J}$ arises from a system dynamically independent from the radiation field itself, such as a collection of atoms. All physical models are constructed so that these two conditions are fulfilled.

HAMILTONIAN. The relevant quantum Hamiltonian may easily be found from the well-known classical form. We may also deduce the Hamiltonian by working backward from our equations of motion and the commutation relations (6-41) and (6-42). Either route leads to an expression we may write as

$$\mathcal{H} = \tfrac{1}{2}\sum_{\lambda,\mathbf{k}} [\mathcal{E}_\lambda{}^\dagger(\mathbf{k})\mathcal{E}_\lambda(\mathbf{k}) + \omega^2\mathcal{A}_\lambda{}^\dagger(\mathbf{k})\mathcal{A}_\lambda(\mathbf{k}) - \hbar\omega - \mathcal{J}_\lambda{}^\dagger(\mathbf{k})\mathcal{A}_\lambda(\mathbf{k}) - \mathcal{J}_\lambda(\mathbf{k})\mathcal{A}_\lambda{}^\dagger(\mathbf{k})] \tag{6-43}$$

where $\omega^2 \equiv \mathbf{k}^2$ and where we have subtracted off an infinite constant, the zero-point energy, to ensure that $\mathcal{H}$ can be well defined. It is instructive to verify that the dynamical equations (6-39) are, indeed, the operator equations in the Heisenberg picture based on the above Hamiltonian. Since in the general case the external source depends explicitly on t, our Hamiltonian is likewise time dependent, $\mathcal{H} = \mathcal{H}(t)$.

C. Creation and Annihilation Operators

Alternative to working with $\mathcal{E}$ and $\mathcal{A}$, we may introduce suitable creation and annihilation operators and re-express various quantities in terms of them. Let us define

$$a_\lambda(\mathbf{k}) = (2\hbar\omega)^{-1/2}[\omega\mathcal{A}_\lambda(\mathbf{k}) - i\mathcal{E}_\lambda(\mathbf{k})] \tag{6-44a}$$
$$a_\lambda^\dagger(\mathbf{k}) = (2\hbar\omega)^{-1/2}[\omega\mathcal{A}_\lambda^\dagger(\mathbf{k}) + i\mathcal{E}_\lambda^\dagger(\mathbf{k})] \tag{6-44b}$$

If, for clarity, we again introduce the time dependence, then it follows from (6-41) that for all $\mathbf{k}$-space points

$$[a_\lambda(\mathbf{k}, t), a_{\lambda'}^\dagger(\mathbf{k}', t)] = \delta_{\lambda\lambda'}\,\delta_{\mathbf{k}\mathbf{k}'} \tag{6-45a}$$
$$[a_\lambda(\mathbf{k}, t), a_{\lambda'}(\mathbf{k}', t)] = [a_\lambda^\dagger(\mathbf{k}, t), a_{\lambda'}^\dagger(\mathbf{k}', t)] = 0 \tag{6-45b}$$

These are just the equal-time commutation relations for infinitely many creation and destruction operators such as we discussed in the last chapter.

In terms of these variables the transcribed Hamiltonian becomes

$$\mathcal{H} = \sum_{\lambda,\mathbf{k}} \{\hbar\omega N_\lambda(\mathbf{k}) - (\hbar/2\omega)^{1/2}[\mathcal{J}_\lambda^\dagger(\mathbf{k})a_\lambda(\mathbf{k}) + \mathcal{J}_\lambda(\mathbf{k})a_\lambda^\dagger(\mathbf{k})]\} \tag{6-46}$$

where

$$N_\lambda(\mathbf{k}) \equiv a_\lambda^\dagger(\mathbf{k})a_\lambda(\mathbf{k}) \tag{6-47}$$

is the number operator for the $(\lambda, \mathbf{k})$th mode. With (6-46) we have expressed the complete radiation field Hamiltonian in the form of independent driven oscillators, one for *each* distinct point of $\mathbf{k}$ space and polarization λ. The only trace of the half $\mathbf{k}$-space aspects discussed earlier is contained in the restriction $\mathcal{J}_\lambda^\dagger(\mathbf{k}) = \mathcal{J}_\lambda(-\mathbf{k})$.

As we observed in the last chapter, a generally sufficient condition for the free field $\mathcal{H}$ to be a good operator is that the total number operator,

$$N = \sum_{\lambda,\mathbf{k}} N_\lambda(\mathbf{k}) \tag{6-48}$$

itself is a good operator. We assume in the present case that both N and $\mathcal{H}$ are good operators. This ensures that the commutation relations (6-45) are well satisfied at all times.

Consistency of Thermal Distribution. As a postscript to this discussion we verify that the free radiation field (in a box!) actually fulfills condition (5-98), which is necessary and sufficient for the density operator ρ of a thermal distribution to be well defined. Using the relation $\omega^2 = \mathbf{k}^2$, Eq. (6-40), and the inequality [2]

$$|\mathbf{n}| \equiv (n_1^2 + n_2^2 + n_3^2)^{1/2} \geq (|n_1| + |n_2| + |n_3|)/\sqrt{3} \equiv \Sigma(\mathbf{n})$$

we may determine that

$$\sum_{\lambda,\mathbf{k}} e^{-\beta\hbar\omega} = 2\sum_{\mathbf{n}} e^{-2\pi\beta\hbar|\mathbf{n}|/L}$$
$$\leq 2\sum_{\mathbf{n}} e^{-2\pi\beta\hbar\Sigma(\mathbf{n})/L} = 2[\tanh(\pi\beta\hbar/\sqrt{3}\,L)^{-3} - 1] \qquad (6\text{-}49)$$

which is finite as required.

6-4 TEMPORAL PROPAGATION CHARACTERISTICS

An explicit equation for $\mathcal{A}_\lambda(\mathbf{k}, t)$ follows directly from (6-39) if we eliminate $\mathcal{E}_\lambda(\mathbf{k}, t)$ and reads

$$\ddot{\mathcal{A}}_\lambda(\mathbf{k}) = -\omega^2\mathcal{A}_\lambda(\mathbf{k}) + \mathcal{J}_\lambda(\mathbf{k}) \qquad (6\text{-}50)$$

This, of course, is just the basic equation for a driven oscillator. An even simpler equation is one for $a_\lambda(\mathbf{k}, t)$, which likewise follows from (6-39), and reads

$$i\dot{a}_\lambda(\mathbf{k}) = \omega a_\lambda(\mathbf{k}) - (2\hbar\omega)^{-1/2}\mathcal{J}_\lambda(\mathbf{k}) \qquad (6\text{-}51)$$

The equation for $a_\lambda^\dagger(\mathbf{k})$ is just the adjoint equation to this one.

A solution to (6-51) can be immediately given as

$$a_\lambda(\mathbf{k}, t) = e^{-i\omega t}a_\lambda(\mathbf{k}, 0) + i(2\hbar\omega)^{-1/2}e^{-i\omega t}\int_0^t e^{i\omega t'}\mathcal{J}_\lambda(\mathbf{k}, t')\,dt' \qquad (6\text{-}52a)$$

where we have arbitrarily chosen our initial time as $t = 0$. If instead we choose the initial time as $t = -\infty$, then we obtain the important solution given by

$$a_\lambda(\mathbf{k}, t) = a_\lambda^{in}(\mathbf{k}, t) + i(2\hbar\omega)^{-1/2}e^{-i\omega t}\int_{-\infty}^t e^{i\omega t'}\mathcal{J}_\lambda(\mathbf{k}, t')\,dt' \qquad (6\text{-}52b)$$

Here

$$a_\lambda^{in}(\mathbf{k}, t) \equiv e^{-i\omega t}a_\lambda^{in}(\mathbf{k}) \qquad (6\text{-}53)$$

denotes the form of the destruction operator in the remote past when the effect of the source is assumed negligible. In either case, since we are

[2] This inequality is a simple restatement of the fact that

$$\sum_{r,s=1}^{3} (|n_r| - |n_s|)^2 \geq 0$$

here *assuming* that $\mathcal{J}_\lambda(\mathbf{k}, t)$ is given we could equally well assume the time integrated expressions as "given." For example, we may put

$$a_\lambda(\mathbf{k}, t) = a_\lambda^{in}(\mathbf{k}, t) + \mathcal{K}_\lambda(\mathbf{k}, t) \tag{6-54}$$

where the given non-Hermitian operator $\mathcal{K}_\lambda$ is related to the current via

$$\mathcal{K}_\lambda(\mathbf{k}, t) = i(2\hbar\omega)^{-1/2}e^{-i\omega t}\int_{-\infty}^{t} e^{i\omega t'}\mathcal{J}_\lambda(\mathbf{k}, t')\,dt' \tag{6-55}$$

We see that $\mathcal{K}_\lambda$ depends nonlocally in time on the sources $\mathcal{J}_\lambda$.

We have noted the conserved nature of the original current four-vector and the assumed commutation properties (6-42) of the transverse components with the radiation field variables. Another important condition that the external current must fulfill is given by the following consideration. Our solution for $a_\lambda(\mathbf{k}, t)$ must fulfill the equal-time canonical commutation relations (6-45) for all t. Because a_λ^{in} already fulfills these relations, we find that $\mathcal{K}_\lambda$ must satisfy

$$[a_\lambda^{in}(\mathbf{k}, t), \mathcal{K}_{\lambda'}^\dagger(\mathbf{k}', t)] + [\mathcal{K}_\lambda(\mathbf{k}, t), a_{\lambda'}^{in\dagger}(\mathbf{k}', t)] + [\mathcal{K}_\lambda(\mathbf{k}, t), \mathcal{K}_{\lambda'}^\dagger(\mathbf{k}', t)] = 0 \tag{6-56a}$$

and

$$[a_\lambda^{in}(\mathbf{k}, t), \mathcal{K}_{\lambda'}(\mathbf{k}', t)] + [\mathcal{K}_\lambda(\mathbf{k}, t), a_{\lambda'}^{in}(\mathbf{k}', t)] + [\mathcal{K}_\lambda(\mathbf{k}, t), \mathcal{K}_{\lambda'}(\mathbf{k}', t)] = 0 \tag{6-56b}$$

along with its adjoint. These conditions on $\mathcal{K}_\lambda(\mathbf{k}, t)$ place restrictions on the external current $\mathcal{J}_\lambda(\mathbf{k}, t)$ for unequal times in order that a solution actually exists.

In essence, the foregoing equations constitute the formal solution to the dynamical equations we have chosen. However, there are two relatively obvious and important special cases worth noting. If the external current $\mathcal{J}_\lambda$ *vanishes* for all t, then so does $\mathcal{K}_\lambda$ and we simply have the *free-field solution*

$$a_\lambda(\mathbf{k}, t) = e^{-i\omega t}a^{in}(\mathbf{k}) \tag{6-57}$$

The next simplest possibility is when the external current $\mathcal{J}_\lambda$ is proportional to the *unit operator* for all t. As a consequence, $\mathcal{K}_\lambda$ is proportional to the unit operator also. That is, we may put

$$\mathcal{K}_\lambda(\mathbf{k}, t) = c_\lambda(\mathbf{k}, t) \tag{6-58}$$

where c_λ is a given complex c-number function. This gives rise to the usual c-number external source solution

$$a_\lambda(\mathbf{k}, t) = e^{-i\omega t}a_\lambda^{in}(\mathbf{k}) + c_\lambda(\mathbf{k}, t) \tag{6-59}$$

In both of these special cases it is evident that a_λ and $a_\lambda^\dagger$ fulfill the required equal-time commutation relations (6-45). Moreover, it is only these cases [i.e., where $\mathcal{J}_\lambda(\mathbf{k}, t)$ is proportional to the unit operator for all t] for which the field operators $\mathcal{A}_\lambda(\mathbf{k}, t)$ and $\mathcal{E}_{\lambda'}(\mathbf{k}', t)$ for a single time t can constitute an irreducible family of operators. The same remark applies to $a_\lambda(\mathbf{k}, t)$ and $a^\dagger_{\lambda'}(\mathbf{k}', t)$ as well, and hence to these forms in the remote past, a_λ^{in} and $a_{\lambda'}^{in\,\dagger}$. If $\mathcal{J}_\lambda(\mathbf{k}, t)$ deviates from the unit operator at some time t, then Eq. (6-42) shows directly that $\mathcal{A}_\lambda(\mathbf{k}, t)$ and $\mathcal{E}_{\lambda'}(\mathbf{k}', t)$ must be reducible, as may well have been suspected.

Finally, it is straightforward to deduce the evolution of other quantities from (6-54) and (6-55). For example, it follows that

$$\mathcal{A}_\lambda(\mathbf{k}, t) = (\hbar/2\omega)^{1/2}[a_\lambda(\mathbf{k}, t) + a_\lambda^\dagger(-\mathbf{k}, t)] \tag{6-60}$$

is given by

$$\begin{aligned}\mathcal{A}_\lambda(\mathbf{k}, t) &= (\hbar/2\omega)^{1/2}[e^{-i\omega t}a_\lambda^{in}(\mathbf{k}) + e^{i\omega t}a_\lambda^{in\,\dagger}(-\mathbf{k})] \\ &\quad + (\hbar/2\omega)^{1/2}[\mathcal{K}_\lambda(\mathbf{k}, t) + \mathcal{K}_\lambda^\dagger(-\mathbf{k}, t)] \\ &= \cos\omega t\,\mathcal{A}_\lambda^{in}(\mathbf{k}) - \omega^{-1}\sin\omega t\,\mathcal{E}_\lambda^{in}(\mathbf{k}) \\ &\quad + \int_{-\infty}^{t} \omega^{-1}\sin\omega(t - t')\mathcal{J}_\lambda(\mathbf{k}, t')\,dt'\end{aligned} \tag{6-61a}$$

We may alternatively combine the first two terms so as to write

$$\mathcal{A}_\lambda(\mathbf{k}, t) = \mathcal{A}_\lambda^{in}(\mathbf{k}, t) + \int_{-\infty}^{t} \omega^{-1}\sin\omega(t - t')\mathcal{J}_\lambda(\mathbf{k}, t')\,dt' \tag{6-61b}$$

These equations constitute the requisite solution of (6-50). The solution for the electric field $\mathcal{E}_\lambda$ follows [from (6-39a)] through time differentiation and reads

$$\mathcal{E}_\lambda(\mathbf{k}, t) = \cos\omega t\,\mathcal{E}_\lambda^{in}(\mathbf{k}) + \omega\sin\omega t\,\mathcal{A}_\lambda^{in}(\mathbf{k}) - \int_{-\infty}^{t} \cos\omega(t - t')\mathcal{J}_\lambda(\mathbf{k}, t')\,dt' \tag{6-62a}$$

or, on combining the first pair of terms,

$$\mathcal{E}_\lambda(\mathbf{k}, t) = \mathcal{E}_\lambda^{in}(\mathbf{k}, t) - \int_{-\infty}^{t} \cos\omega(t - t')\mathcal{J}_\lambda(\mathbf{k}, t')\,dt' \tag{6-62b}$$

Mean Values and Analytic Signals. Two traditional, troublesome aspects may be most easily clarified at this point. Although we have demanded that our solution fulfill the canonical commutation relations, this does not complete the physical specification of any particular solution. Observed values of the field $\mathcal{E}_\lambda$, for example, are distributed with a mean value

$$\langle\mathcal{E}_\lambda(\mathbf{k}, t)\rangle \equiv \mathrm{Tr}[\rho\mathcal{E}_\lambda(\mathbf{k}, t)] \tag{6-63}$$

determined with the aid of the density operator ρ representing the state of the system. It is especially convenient to work with the field $a_\lambda(\mathbf{k}, t)$

from which the other quantities may be determined in a linear fashion. For this variable we have the basic mean relation

$$\langle a_\lambda(\mathbf{k}, t)\rangle = e^{-i\omega t}\langle a_\lambda^{in}(\mathbf{k})\rangle + i(2\hbar\omega)^{-1/2}e^{-i\omega t}\int_{-\infty}^{t} e^{i\omega t'}\langle \mathcal{J}_\lambda(\mathbf{k}, t')\rangle\, dt' \quad (6\text{-}64a)$$

If, for example, ρ were so chosen that $\langle a_\lambda^{in}(\mathbf{k})\rangle = 0$, then (6-64a) would have the appearance of a classical (i.e., c-number) solution to the wave equation with sources $\langle \mathcal{J}_\lambda\rangle$ such that the entire solution *vanished* in the remote past. The lesson to be learned here is the following: In classical theory we may, by suitable boundary conditions on the fields themselves, pick out the relevant physical solution, such as one that vanishes in the remote past before the sources are switched on. In the quantum theory, the analogous operator solution never vanishes—indeed, it takes a very special form due to the constraint of the canonical commutation relations. Rather, it is the specification of the state ρ that singles out the physically relevant *effect* of the homogeneous term, such as being zero on the average.

Still making the analogy of (6-64a) with a classical c-number solution we may raise our second point. No matter what we choose for $\langle a_\lambda^{in}(\mathbf{k})\rangle$, the contribution of the first term to the full solution is always an analytic signal since $\omega = |\mathbf{k}| > 0$. It is natural, then, to ask what are the conditions on the mean source term in order that (6-64a) represent an analytic signal? The time Fourier transform of (6-64a) may readily be worked out to yield

$$\begin{aligned}\langle \tilde{a}_\lambda(\mathbf{k}, \nu)\rangle = {} & \delta(\nu - \nu_k)\langle a_\lambda^{in}(\mathbf{k})\rangle \\ & + i(2\pi)^{-1}(2\hbar\omega)^{-1/2}[\pi\,\delta(\nu - \nu_k) \\ & + i(\nu - \nu_k)^{-1}]\langle \tilde{\mathcal{J}}_\lambda(\mathbf{k}, \nu)\rangle \end{aligned} \quad (6\text{-}64b)$$

where $\nu_k = \omega/2\pi = |\mathbf{k}|/2\pi$. From the Hermitian nature of $\mathbf{j}(\mathbf{x}, t)$ and for real polarization vectors it follows that

$$\langle \tilde{\mathcal{J}}_\lambda(-\mathbf{k}, -|\nu|)\rangle = \langle \tilde{\mathcal{J}}_\lambda{}^\dagger(-\mathbf{k}, -|\nu|)\rangle^* = \langle \tilde{\mathcal{J}}_\lambda(\mathbf{k}, |\nu|)\rangle^*$$

which implies that

$$\begin{aligned}\langle \tilde{a}_\lambda(-\mathbf{k}, -|\nu|)\rangle &= (2\pi)^{-1}(2\hbar\omega)^{-1/2}(|\nu| + \nu_k)^{-1}\langle \tilde{\mathcal{J}}_\lambda(-\mathbf{k}, -|\nu|)\rangle \\ &= (2\pi)^{-1}(2\hbar\omega)^{-1/2}(|\nu| + \nu_k)^{-1}\langle \tilde{\mathcal{J}}_\lambda(\mathbf{k}, |\nu|)\rangle^* \end{aligned} \quad (6\text{-}65)$$

Thus if the mean current $\langle \tilde{\mathcal{J}}_\lambda(\mathbf{k}, \nu)\rangle$ is nonvanishing for some $\mathbf{k}$ and $\nu > 0$, there will *always* be a mode (e.g., $-\mathbf{k}$) in which negative frequencies appear. Strictly speaking, therefore, the expression in (6-64a) represents an analytic signal only for vanishing mean current. However, in a quasi-monochromatic approximation frequently suitable for quantum optics, the spread Δk of allowed $\mathbf{k}$ values in the mean current is extremely small compared to its central value $\bar{k}$. Hence, the relative amplitude of any negative frequency part of (6-64) is extremely small being down by the order of $\Delta k/\bar{k}$. The neglect of such terms is often called the "rotating wave approximation."

A. *Configuration Space Formulation*

The inversion of our basic operator solutions into configuration space is most elegant if we idealize the quantization volume to be all space in order that we may, for example, put

$$\mathbf{A}(\mathbf{x}, t) = (2\pi)^{-3/2} \int e^{i\mathbf{k}\cdot\mathbf{x}} \mathfrak{A}(\mathbf{k}, t)\, d^3k \tag{6-66}$$

[which corresponds to choosing the normalization $\Omega = (2\pi)^3$ in (6-23)]. In such a case it follows from (6-61a) that

$$\begin{aligned} \mathbf{A}(\mathbf{x}, t) = & -\int [D(\mathbf{x} - \mathbf{y}, t)\dot{\mathbf{A}}^{in}(\mathbf{y}) \\ & + \dot{D}(\mathbf{x} - \mathbf{y}, t)\mathbf{A}^{in}(\mathbf{y})]\, d^3y \\ & + \int D_R(\mathbf{x} - \mathbf{y}, t - t')\mathbf{J}(\mathbf{y}, t')\, d^3y\, dt' \end{aligned} \tag{6-67}$$

where we have introduced

$$\begin{aligned} D(\mathbf{x}, t) &\equiv -(2\pi)^{-3} \int e^{i\mathbf{k}\cdot\mathbf{x}} \frac{\sin kt}{k}\, d^3k \\ &= -(4\pi|\mathbf{x}|)^{-1}[\delta(|\mathbf{x}| - t) - \delta(|\mathbf{x}| + t)] \end{aligned} \tag{6-68}$$

and

$$\begin{aligned} D_R(\mathbf{x}, t) &= (4\pi|\mathbf{x}|)^{-1}\, \delta(|\mathbf{x}| - t) \qquad t > 0 \\ &= 0 \qquad t < 0 \end{aligned} \tag{6-69}$$

The two D functions we have defined are two of the basic Green's functions for the wave equation. An analogous equation holds for the electric field $\mathbf{E}(\mathbf{x}, t)$ as well. We remind the reader that all these equations apply to the *transverse* operator fields; recall that for simplicity we have dropped our superscript T explicitly implying transversality.

Clearly the first two terms in (6-67) define a solution of the homogeneous wave equation (which corresponds to the physical solution if $\mathbf{J}$ vanishes). Thus, we may rewrite (6-67) simply as

$$\mathbf{A}(\mathbf{x}, t) = \mathbf{A}^{in}(\mathbf{x}, t) + \int D_R(\mathbf{x} - \mathbf{y}, t - t')\mathbf{J}(\mathbf{y}, t')\, d^3y\, dt' \tag{6-70}$$

in analogy with (6-61b). As we indicated earlier, if $\mathbf{J}(\mathbf{y}, t)$ is proportional to the unit operator for all $\mathbf{y}$ and t, then we find the solution

$$\mathbf{A}(\mathbf{x}, t) = \mathbf{A}^{in}(\mathbf{x}, t) + \mathbf{C}(\mathbf{x}, t) \tag{6-71}$$

where $\mathbf{C}(\mathbf{x}, t)$ is some transverse, c-number field.

We note that the basic physical significance of the mean field values, such as $\langle \mathbf{A}(\mathbf{x}, t) \rangle$, carry over directly from our momentum space discussion. In particular, although the homogeneous term $\mathbf{A}^{in}(\mathbf{x}, t)$ is required in our operator solution, its expectation value may vanish, in which case the mean field is fully determined by that arising from the source. On the other hand, it should be noted that the homogeneous operator accounts for the physically significant field fluctuations of the vacuum, even in regions unaffected by the sources.

For clarity we have once again been somewhat cavalier in our configuration-space discussion. Strictly speaking $\mathbf{A}(\mathbf{x}, t)$ is not a Hermitian operator; to secure one, it is necessary first to use a smooth test function $f(\mathbf{x})$, which may if desired be highly localized about any point and form $\mathbf{A}_f(t) = \int f(\mathbf{x})\mathbf{A}(\mathbf{x}, t)\, d^3x$ which is then an honest Hermitian operator. With this point understood, we shall continue to suppress the required smoothing operations.

6-5 SPATIAL PROPAGATION CHARACTERISTICS

Of equal importance to the time propagation of the field operators in quantum optics is their space propagation behavior. We have discussed in Chapter 1 several aspects of space propagation for classical phenomena. To treat the quantum case let us again readopt a finite quantization volume ($\Omega = L^3$) and re-express the basic dynamical equation (6-22) in terms of functions of $\mathbf{x}$ and ν such as

$$\tilde{\mathbf{A}}(\mathbf{x}, \nu) = \int_{-\infty}^{\infty} e^{2\pi i\nu t}\mathbf{A}(\mathbf{x}, t)\, dt \tag{6-72}$$

If, as usual, we set $\omega = 2\pi\nu$, then we find (still omitting the transverse superscript T) that

$$-i\omega\tilde{\mathbf{A}} = -\tilde{\mathbf{E}} \tag{6-73a}$$
$$-i\omega\tilde{\mathbf{E}} = -\nabla^2\tilde{\mathbf{A}} - \tilde{\mathbf{j}} \tag{6-73b}$$

On eliminating $\tilde{\mathbf{E}}$ we obtain

$$(\nabla^2 + \omega^2)\tilde{\mathbf{A}} = -\tilde{\mathbf{j}} \tag{6-74}$$

which is, of course, just the inhomogeneous vector Helmholtz equation.

We want to present a spatial propagation solution to this equation under slightly special conditions. Imagine that the source is confined to a fixed region of space (as in a thermal source or in a laser) and that we are interested in the values of the field exterior to the source. More explicitly, we are interested in the field at points of space where $\mathbf{j}(\mathbf{x}, t) \equiv 0$ for all t and, hence, where $\tilde{\mathbf{j}}(\mathbf{x}, \nu) \equiv 0$. We may imagine dividing all space into a suitable region R devoid of sources and a complementary region R' in all or in parts of which the source is present. Clearly, for points $\mathbf{x}$ lying within R, we have

$$\tilde{\mathbf{A}}(\mathbf{x}, \nu) = \int_R \delta(\mathbf{x} - \mathbf{y})\tilde{\mathbf{A}}(\mathbf{y}, \nu)\, d^3y \tag{6-75}$$

where the integration extends just over the region R.

Now let us introduce a Green's function $G(\mathbf{x}, \mathbf{y}, \nu)$ for which

$$(\nabla_x^2 + \omega^2)G(\mathbf{x}, \mathbf{y}, \nu) = (\nabla_y^2 + \omega^2)G(\mathbf{x}, \mathbf{y}, \nu) = -\delta(\mathbf{x} - \mathbf{y}) \tag{6-76}$$

There are innumerable such Green's functions—one of which is, of course, the primitive Green's function G_0 introduced in Chapter 1—and we shall shortly choose among them. By substituting into (6-75) and remembering that the source vanishes within R, we find that

$$\begin{aligned}
\tilde{\mathbf{A}}(\mathbf{x}, \nu) &= \int_R [G(\mathbf{x}, \mathbf{y}, \nu)(\nabla_y^2 + \omega^2)\tilde{\mathbf{A}}(\mathbf{y}, \nu) \\
&\quad - \tilde{\mathbf{A}}(\mathbf{y}, \nu)(\nabla_y^2 + \omega^2)G(\mathbf{x}, \mathbf{y}, \nu)]\, d^3y \\
&= \int_R \frac{\partial}{\partial y_j}\left[G(\mathbf{x}, \mathbf{y}, \nu)\frac{\partial}{\partial y_j}\tilde{\mathbf{A}}(\mathbf{y}, \nu)\right. \\
&\quad \left. - \tilde{\mathbf{A}}(\mathbf{y}, \nu)\frac{\partial}{\partial y_j}G(\mathbf{x}, \mathbf{y}, \nu)\right] d^3y \\
&= \int_S \left[G(\mathbf{x}, \mathbf{y}, \nu)\frac{\partial}{\partial n}\tilde{\mathbf{A}}(\mathbf{y}, \nu)\right. \\
&\quad \left. - \tilde{\mathbf{A}}(\mathbf{y}, \nu)\frac{\partial}{\partial n}G(\mathbf{x}, \mathbf{y}, \nu)\right] dS
\end{aligned} \tag{6-77}$$

In the last expression the integration over $\mathbf{y}$ is confined to the surface S separating R and R'. In the usual situation the source is confined to a finite volume, and so the region R may contain the remote portions of space. In such a case it may be thought that the surface integral in (6-77) has a contribution from the "infinite sphere." But recall that we are imagining our system to be in a large quantization volume L^3 with periodic boundary conditions. Such a space is closed and has no boundaries in exact analogy to a circle or to a torus in one or two dimensions, respectively.

An especially convenient choice for $G(\mathbf{x}, \mathbf{y}, \nu)$ is one which vanishes when the point $\mathbf{y}$ lies on S [as is the case in the last line of (6-77)]. For the simple example discussed in Chapter 1, where S was the plane defined by $z = 0$, we determined the relevant G by the method of images. However, for a more general surface S this technique is inadequate. We shall outline the standard proof that a suitable Green's function G (satisfying homogeneous Dirchlet boundary conditions) exists in very general cases.

Let R—the region outside the sources that constitutes the domain of integration in Eq. (6-77)—be a *connected* region. Roughly, this means that any two points in R can be connected by some path lying wholly within R.

Suppose we now imagine that the region R is a cavity in the sense of electromagnetic radiation theory. We can then ask for the (scalar-wave) standing-wave eigenfunctions for this cavity, which are just the eigensolutions of the equation

$$\nabla^2\psi_n(\mathbf{x}) + \omega_n{}^2\psi_n(\mathbf{x}) = 0 \tag{6-78}$$

subject to the boundary condition that $\psi_n(\mathbf{x})$ vanishes on the boundary S of the region R. Alternatively, we may view (6-78) as the eigenvalue equation for a certain single-particle quantum mechanical problem. The energy eigenvalue equation in the Schrödinger representation (configuration space) reads

$$-\frac{\hbar^2}{2m}\nabla^2\psi_n(\mathbf{x}) + V(\mathbf{x})\psi_n(\mathbf{x}) = E_n\psi_n(\mathbf{x})$$

If we now set $V(\mathbf{x}) = 0$ within R and set $V(\mathbf{x}) = +\infty$ within R', then we are led to the quantum problem of a free particle confined to a "container" (defined by R) subject to the boundary condition that $\psi(\mathbf{x}) = 0$ at the "walls of the container" (defined by S). The relevant equation is just (6-78) where $\omega_n{}^2 = 2mE_n/\hbar^2$. In either analog problem it is known that a complete set of orthonormal eigenfunctions exists, ψ_n, $n = 1, 2, \ldots$, which satisfy

$$\sum_{n=1}^{\infty} \psi_n{}^*(\mathbf{x})\psi_n(\mathbf{y}) = \delta(\mathbf{x} - \mathbf{y}) \tag{6-79}$$

Armed with this information we may immediately write down the sought-for Green's function to our original problem as

$$G(\mathbf{x}, \mathbf{y}, \nu) = \sum_{n=1}^{\infty} \frac{\psi_n{}^*(\mathbf{x})\psi_n(\mathbf{y})}{\omega_n{}^2 - \omega^2} \tag{6-80}$$

which satisfies (6-76) and clearly vanishes if $\mathbf{y}$ (or $\mathbf{x}$) lies on S. It should be noted that all the usual resonant aspects of a lossless cavity are exhibited in the terms making up G; each such term performs its traditional frequency-selecting role in the quantum problem as well!

Now that we are assured that an appropriate Green's function exists, we may freely deduce its most important consequences. In particular, it follows that Eq. (6-77) simplifies to

$$\tilde{\mathbf{A}}(\mathbf{x}, \nu) = -\int_S \frac{\partial G}{\partial n}(\mathbf{x}, \mathbf{y}, \nu)\tilde{\mathbf{A}}(\mathbf{y}, \nu)\, dS \tag{6-81}$$

which states that the transverse potential operator at an arbitrary point $\mathbf{x}$ in a region R devoid of sources is linearly related to the transverse potential operators on the surface S surrounding R. Equation (6-81) goes further and states that the behavior for each frequency is determined independently.

Equally interesting is the form Eq. (6-81) takes when expressed in space–time. If we set

$$K(\mathbf{x}, \mathbf{y}, t) \equiv -\int \frac{\partial G}{\partial n}(\mathbf{x}, \mathbf{y}, \nu)e^{-2\pi i\nu t}\, d\nu \tag{6-82}$$

then it follows that the operator fields satisfy the relation

$$\mathbf{A}(\mathbf{x}, t) = \iint_S K(\mathbf{x}, \mathbf{y}, t - t')\mathbf{A}(\mathbf{y}, t')\, dS\, dt' \tag{6-83}$$

There is, of course, nothing sacred about the transverse vector potential in forming such relations. Any quantity which satisfies the free-field wave equation in the region R satisfies analogous equations. For example, it follows from similar reasoning that the electric field $\mathbf{E}(\mathbf{x}, t)$ for a point $\mathbf{x}$ in R fulfills the relation

$$\mathbf{E}(\mathbf{x}, t) = \iint_S K(\mathbf{x}, \mathbf{y}, t - t')\mathbf{E}(\mathbf{y}, t')\, dS\, dt' \tag{6-84}$$

These fundamental connections between the field in empty space and its values on the surface S apply without change for the classical theory studied in the first two chapters. Consequences of these propagation laws that held in the classical theory have their analogs in the quantum theory. In particular, the van Cittert-Zernike theorem as we have presented it in Chapter 1 has a direct quantum analog.

CHAPTER 7

COHERENT-STATE REPRESENTATION OF THE ELECTROMAGNETIC FIELD

7-1 COHERENT STATES: BACKGROUND PROPERTIES

The coherent states, which will figure so importantly in our quantum statistical treatment of the radiation field, have a long and proud history in quantum theory. The essence of their saga is already contained in the story pertaining to a single degree of freedom. Suppose, as in Chapter 5, we let Q and P be an (irreducible) canonical pair of operators, $[Q, P] = i\hbar$, and (choosing for simplicity unit angular frequency) we set $a = (Q + iP)/\sqrt{2\hbar}$, $a^\dagger = (Q - iP)/\sqrt{2\hbar}$, and $N = a^\dagger a$. The properties of these operators and of the number-operator eigenstates, $|n\rangle$, $n = 0, 1, 2, \ldots$, were examined in Chapter 5 in some detail. Here we shall renew that investigation by studying the *coherent states*, vectors of the form

$$|z\rangle \equiv \exp(-\tfrac{1}{2}|z|^2) \sum_{n=0}^{\infty} \frac{z^n}{(n!)^{1/2}} |n\rangle \tag{7-1}$$

defined for all complex numbers z.

A few remarks are in order on notation. On the right side of (7-1) there appears a linear sum of the number eigenstates $|n\rangle$ with complex coefficients formed with z. The indicated linear sum defines a new vector, which we label simply by the complex number z. However, it must be clearly understood that the state "$|1\rangle$," as an eigenstate of N is very different from a similarly written state, "$|1\rangle$," wherein we have chosen $z = 1$ in (7-1).

There is considerable pedagogical value in having an alternate notation for $|z\rangle$ which focuses on the real and imaginary parts of z. If we put

$$z \equiv (q + ip)/\sqrt{2\hbar} \tag{7-2}$$

where q and p are two arbitrary real c-numbers, then we may define

$$|z\rangle \equiv |p, q\rangle \equiv \exp\left[-\frac{1}{4\hbar}(p^2 + q^2)\right] \sum_{n=0}^{\infty} \frac{(q + ip)^n}{(2\hbar)^{n/2}(n!)^{1/2}} |n\rangle \tag{7-3}$$

The adjoint coherent states are similarly defined via

$$\langle z| = \exp(-\tfrac{1}{2}|z|^2) \sum_{n=0}^{\infty} \frac{z^{*n}}{(n!)^{1/2}} \langle n| \tag{7-4a}$$

$$\langle z| = \langle p, q| = \exp\left[-\frac{1}{4\hbar}(p^2 + q^2)\right] \sum_{n=0}^{\infty} \frac{(q - ip)^n}{(2\hbar)^{n/2}(n!)^{1/2}} \langle n| \tag{7-4b}$$

It should be carefully noted that the adjoint state is still labeled generically by z, although in the series expansion the coefficients are formed essentially from powers of z^*.

A. Displaced and Driven Oscillator Eigenstates

DISPLACED OSCILLATOR. The most important historical connection from our point of view is the relation of the coherent states to the eigensolutions of a displaced (or a driven) harmonic oscillator. Let us focus on the ground-state solution of an oscillator conveniently chosen to have unit mass and angular frequency, and which fulfills the equation

$$\mathcal{H}|0\rangle = \tfrac{1}{2}\{P^2 + Q^2 - \hbar\}|0\rangle = 0 \tag{7-5}$$

This is the Hamiltonian for a system which in the ground state has vanishing mean position and momentum:

$$\langle 0|Q|0\rangle = \langle 0|P|0\rangle = 0 \tag{7-6}$$

Now, one of the most important consequences of the commutation relations is the property that

$$U[p, q]^{-1}(\alpha P + \beta Q)U[p, q] = \alpha(P + p) + \beta(Q + q) \tag{7-7}$$

where α and β are arbitrary parameters, and where the unitary operator

$$U[p, q] \equiv \exp[i(pQ - qP)/\hbar] \tag{7-8}$$

In essence, $U[p, q]$ has the effect of translating both the operators P and Q by the c-numbers p and q, respectively. Clearly, $U[p, q]^{-1} = U[-p, -q]$. Equation (7-7) is proved most simply by noting that, quite generally, for two operators X and Y

$$e^{Y}Xe^{-Y} = X + [Y, X] + \frac{1}{2!}[Y, [Y, X]] + \cdots \tag{7-9}$$

a series which in the present application terminates after the second term.

We now consider the relation

$$\begin{aligned} 0 &= U[p, q]\mathcal{H}|0\rangle = U[p, q]\mathcal{H}U[p, q]^{-1}U[p, q]|0\rangle \\ &= \tfrac{1}{2}\{(P - p)^2 + (Q - q)^2 - \hbar\}U[p, q]|0\rangle \end{aligned} \tag{7-10}$$

which follows from repeated use of (7-7). Evidently the state

$$|p, q\rangle \equiv U[p, q]|0\rangle \tag{7-11}$$

is the ground state of a similar oscillator for which the coordinate is displaced by q and the momentum is displaced by p. In particular, the mean position and momentum no longer vanish as before but instead are given as

$$\begin{aligned} \langle p, q|Q|p, q\rangle &= \langle 0|U[p, q]^{-1}QU[p, q]|0\rangle \\ &= \langle 0|(Q + q)|0\rangle = q \end{aligned} \tag{7-12a}$$

and, via a similar calculation, as

$$\langle p, q|P|p, q\rangle = p \tag{7-12b}$$

We show below in detail that the states $|p, q\rangle$ defined here are just the coherent states given in (7-3). For obvious reasons we refer to the above example as a "displaced oscillator."

Another interesting property follows if we consider the time evolution of the displaced oscillators' ground state $|p, q\rangle$ under the action of the *un*displaced Hamiltonian operator $\mathcal{H} = \frac{1}{2}\{P^2 + Q^2 - \hbar\}$. We shall demonstrate later that

$$e^{-it\mathcal{H}/\hbar}|p, q\rangle = |p_{\mathrm{cl}}(t), q_{\mathrm{cl}}(t)\rangle \tag{7-13}$$

where $p_{\mathrm{cl}}(t)$ and $q_{\mathrm{cl}}(t)$ are the classical oscillator solutions given by

$$q_{\mathrm{cl}}(t) = q \cos t + p \sin t \tag{7-14a}$$
$$p_{\mathrm{cl}}(t) = -q \sin t + p \cos t \tag{7-14b}$$

subject to the boundary conditions that $p_{\mathrm{cl}}(0) = p$ and $q_{\mathrm{cl}}(0) = q$. In other words, the state $|p, q\rangle$ evolves in time into another state of the same general kind specified by time-dependent values of the parameters p and q. Pictorially speaking, the state $|p, q\rangle$ does not change its form in time but only its mean position and momentum, and these change in accord with the classical equations of motion.

The evolution of the states $|p, q\rangle$ according to the classical equations of motion holds for arbitrarily small values of p and of q. Nothing is said, however, that this entails a strictly classical interpretation (non-probabilistic, etc.) of such solutions. There is still a nonvanishing variance to measured momentum and coordinate values so long as $\hbar > 0$.

DRIVEN OSCILLATOR. A slightly different argument to introduce the coherent states runs as follows. Consider the original undisplaced Hamiltonian as in (7-5) but now in the presence of external, c-number driving terms p and q coupled to the operators P and Q, respectively, so that

$$\mathcal{H}' = \tfrac{1}{2}\{P^2 + Q^2 - \hbar\} - pP - qQ \tag{7-15a}$$

This case may be called the "driven oscillator" as opposed to the "displaced oscillator," which we considered above. Nevertheless, the states $|p, q\rangle$ are still eigenvectors of $\mathcal{H}'$. To see this we have only to observe that

$$\mathcal{H}' = \tfrac{1}{2}\{(P - p)^2 + (Q - q)^2 - \hbar\} - \tfrac{1}{2}\{p^2 + q^2\} \tag{7-15b}$$

Consequently, using (7-10) we find that

$$\mathcal{H}'|p, q\rangle = -\tfrac{1}{2}\{p^2 + q^2\}|p, q\rangle \tag{7-16}$$

which shows $|p, q\rangle$ to be an eigenvector of $\mathcal{H}'$ with eigenvalue

$$E = -\tfrac{1}{2}\{p^2 + q^2\} \tag{7-17}$$

Moreover, if the driving terms are time dependent [i.e., if $p = p(t)$ and $q = q(t)$ in (7-15a)], then it follows that the state $|p(t), q(t)\rangle$ is an eigenvector of the time-dependent, driven-oscillator Hamiltonian $\mathcal{H}' = \mathcal{H}'(t)$ for each t with eigenvalue $E = E(t) = -\tfrac{1}{2}\{p^2(t) + q^2(t)\}$.

In summary, we note that the coherent states $|p, q\rangle$ are the physically relevant ground states for displaced or driven oscillators. We shall have frequent occasion to exploit the foregoing properties of the coherent states in our subsequent discussion.

B. Minimum-Uncertainty Wave Packets

A very different context in which the coherent states appear is as solutions to the minimum-uncertainty conditions. This property is in many ways quite incidental to our application to quantum optics. However, so traditional is this aspect of coherent states that we would be remiss if we did not spend some time on it.

For brevity let us once again denote the mean of an operator $\mathcal{O}$ in the normalized state $|\psi\rangle$ by

$$\langle \mathcal{O}\rangle \equiv \langle\psi|\mathcal{O}|\psi\rangle \tag{7-18}$$

and call

$$\Delta P \equiv P - \langle P\rangle \tag{7-19a}$$

$$\Delta Q \equiv Q - \langle Q\rangle \tag{7-19b}$$

Then it follows (first by the triangle inequality and then by the Schwarz inequality) that

$$\begin{aligned} \tfrac{1}{2}\hbar = \tfrac{1}{2}|\langle[Q, P]\rangle| &= \tfrac{1}{2}|\langle[\Delta Q, \Delta P]\rangle| \\ &\leq |\langle \Delta Q\, \Delta P\rangle| \leq \langle \Delta Q^2\rangle^{1/2}\langle \Delta P^2\rangle^{1/2} \end{aligned} \tag{7-20}$$

which is the usual form of the Heisenberg uncertainty principle. The minimum uncertainty occurs when $\Delta Q\,|\psi\rangle = -ir\,\Delta P|\psi\rangle$, to "equalize" the Schwarz inequality; for real r, to equalize the triangle inequality; and for positive r to jibe with $[Q, P] = i\hbar$. For further purposes let us choose [1] $r = 1$, which leads to the condition that

$$(Q + iP)|\psi\rangle = (\langle Q\rangle + i\langle P\rangle)|\psi\rangle \tag{7-21a}$$

or dividing by $\sqrt{2\hbar}$, to

$$a|\psi\rangle = \langle a\rangle|\psi\rangle \tag{7-21b}$$

Namely, the minimum-uncertainty states are eigenvectors of the annihilation operator. These eigenvectors are just the coherent states as we now shall show.

C. *Annihilation Operator Eigenvectors*

The third aspect of the coherent states we want to discuss here is the fact that they are eigenvectors of $a = (Q + iP)/\sqrt{2\hbar}$. This property is partly—but by no means all—the reason for their utility in quantum optics.

We know one eigenvector of a for certain and that is the ground state $|0\rangle$ which has the eigenvalue zero. Thus consider the relation

$$\begin{aligned} 0 &= U[p, q]a|0\rangle = U[p, q]aU[p, q]^{-1}U[p, q]|0\rangle \\ &= [a - (q + ip)/\sqrt{2\hbar}]|p, q\rangle \end{aligned} \tag{7-22}$$

using (7-7) and the definition of a. Therefore in the terminology of (7-2) we can write

$$a|z\rangle \equiv a|p, q\rangle = (q + ip)/\sqrt{2\hbar}\,|p, q\rangle \equiv z|z\rangle \tag{7-23}$$

which establishes that the states $|p, q\rangle = U[p, q]|0\rangle$ are, indeed, annihilation operator eigenvectors as was to be shown.

[1] The cases $r \neq 1$ correspond to oscillators of angular frequency $\omega = r^{-1}$. Here we focus on an example with unit angular frequency.

Last, we clinch the fact that the states $|p, q\rangle$ are just the coherent states given in (7-1) or (7-3). The simplest procedure to show this to employ a form of the Baker-Hausdorff formula which specifically reads

$$e^{X+Y} = e^{-1/2[X,Y]}e^X e^Y \tag{7-24}$$

and is valid whenever the commutator $Z = [X, Y]$ commutes with both X and Y. [*Proof of (7-24):* From (7-9) we learn first that

$$\begin{aligned} e^Y e^X &= (e^Y e^X e^{-Y})e^Y = \exp(e^Y X e^{-Y})e^Y \\ &= \exp(X + [Y, X])e^Y = e^{-Z}e^X e^Y \end{aligned}$$

since $Z \equiv [X, Y]$ commutes with X and Y. By iteration it follows that

$$(e^Y e^X)^n \equiv \exp(-\beta_n Z)e^{nX}e^{nY} = e^Y e^X (e^Y e^X)^{n-1}$$

which leads to the recursion relation $\beta_n = n + \beta_{n-1}$ for β_n. Since $\beta_1 = 1$, it follows that $\beta_n = n(n + 1)/2$. Finally, we observe that

$$\begin{aligned} e^{Y+X} &\equiv \lim_{n\to\infty} (e^{Y/n}e^{X/n})^n \\ &= \lim_{n\to\infty} \exp(-\beta_n Z/n^2)e^X e^Y = e^{-1/2[X, Y]}e^X e^Y \end{aligned}$$

which establishes (7-24).] We express the exponent of $U[p, q]$ in the form

$$\begin{aligned} i[pQ - qP]/\hbar &= i[p(a + a^\dagger) + iq(a - a^\dagger)]/\sqrt{2\hbar} \\ &= (q + ip)a^\dagger/\sqrt{2\hbar} - (q - ip)a/\sqrt{2\hbar} \\ &\equiv za^\dagger - z^*a \end{aligned} \tag{7-25}$$

Applying (7-24), with $X = za^\dagger$ and $Y = -z^*a$, we find that

$$\begin{aligned} U[p, q] &= \exp(za^\dagger - z^*a) \\ &= \exp(-\tfrac{1}{2}|z|^2) \exp(za^\dagger) \exp(-z^*a) \end{aligned} \tag{7-26}$$

Consequently, recalling that $a^p|0\rangle = 0$, $p = 1, 2, \ldots$, we see that

$$\begin{aligned} U[p, q]|0\rangle &= \exp(-\tfrac{1}{2}|z|^2) \exp(za^\dagger) \exp(-z^*a)|0\rangle \\ &= \exp(-\tfrac{1}{2}|z|^2) \exp(za^\dagger)|0\rangle \\ &= \exp(-\tfrac{1}{2}|z|^2) \sum_{n=0}^{\infty} \frac{z^n}{n!} (a^\dagger)^n|0\rangle \\ &= \exp(-\tfrac{1}{2}|z|^2) \sum_{n=0}^{\infty} \frac{z^n}{(n!)^{1/2}} |n\rangle \end{aligned} \tag{7-27}$$

where, in the last equation, we have employed Eq. (5-52) to introduce $|n\rangle$.

With Eq. (7-27) we have established the desired connection of the coherent states (7-1) with the ground states of the driven oscillator, the minimum-uncertainty states, and the annihilation operator eigenstates as was our aim. With these traditional remarks to serve as orientation we must now undertake a more comprehensive study of coherent-state properties so as to lay sufficient groundwork for their use in quantum optics.

7-2 FUNDAMENTAL ASPECTS OF COHERENT STATES FOR A SINGLE DEGREE OF FREEDOM

Many of the coherent-state properties we shall ultimately discuss are simple generalizations of ones most easily seen for a single degree of freedom, and we continue our analysis at this level.

A. Preliminaries

We focus our attention on the complex variable form of the coherent states given by

$$|z\rangle \equiv \exp(-\tfrac{1}{2}|z|^2) \sum_{n=0}^{\infty} \frac{z^n}{(n!)^{1/2}} |n\rangle \tag{7-28a}$$

and on the adjoint states given by

$$\langle z| \equiv \exp(-\tfrac{1}{2}|z|^2) \sum_{n=0}^{\infty} \langle n| \frac{z^{*n}}{(n!)^{1/2}} \tag{7-28b}$$

We have already implicitly established that the coherent vectors $|z\rangle$ are all *normalized*. Namely, since $U[p, q]$ is unitary it follows from (7-3) that

$$\langle z|z\rangle = \langle 0|U[p, q]^{-1}U[p, q]|0\rangle = \langle 0|0\rangle = 1 \tag{7-29}$$

More generally, let us determine the matrix element $\langle z|z'\rangle$ for two coherent states which yields

$$\begin{aligned}\langle z|z'\rangle &= \exp(-\tfrac{1}{2}|z|^2 - \tfrac{1}{2}|z'|^2) \sum_{m,n=0}^{\infty} \frac{z^{*m}z'^n}{(m!n!)^{1/2}} \langle m|n\rangle \\ &= \exp(-\tfrac{1}{2}|z|^2 - \tfrac{1}{2}|z'|^2) \sum_{n=0}^{\infty} \frac{z^{*n}z'^n}{n!} \\ &= \exp(-\tfrac{1}{2}|z|^2 + z^*z' - \tfrac{1}{2}|z'|^2)\end{aligned} \tag{7-30}$$

We may also write this relation in the form

$$\begin{aligned}\langle z|z'\rangle &= \exp\{-\tfrac{1}{2}[|z|^2 - z^*z' - z'^*z + |z'|^2 - (z^*z' - z'^*z)]\} \\ &= \exp\{-\tfrac{1}{2}|z - z'|^2 + \tfrac{1}{2}(z^*z' - z'^*z)\} \\ &= \exp\{-\tfrac{1}{2}|z - z'|^2 + i\,\mathrm{Im}(z^*z')\}\end{aligned} \tag{7-31}$$

From this it immediately follows that

$$|\langle z|z'\rangle| = \exp\{-\tfrac{1}{2}|z - z'|^2\} \tag{7-32}$$

an expression which clearly never vanishes. Thus, the collection of coherent states $|z\rangle$ for all complex z is a family of normalized states, no two of which are orthogonal since for all z and z', $0 < |\langle z|z'\rangle| \leq 1$. Practically speaking, however, we may say that $|\langle z|0\rangle| \approx 0$ whenever $|z| \gg 1$. Physically this means that the energy value $|E| = \frac{1}{2}\{p^2 + q^2\}$ involved in the driven oscillator [cf., Eq. (7-17)] should be much greater than the quantized energy-level spacing, which for an oscillator of unit frequency is just given by $\hbar$.

EIGENPROPERTIES. We have already indicated that the states $|z\rangle$ are eigenstates of the annihilation operator a with eigenvalue z, i.e.,

$$a|z\rangle = z|z\rangle \tag{7-33}$$

It is readily seen that the coherent states are the only eigenstates of a. From (7-33) it clearly follows that

$$\langle z'|a|z\rangle = z\langle z'|z\rangle \tag{7-34a}$$

and thus by complex conjugation that

$$\langle z|a^\dagger|z'\rangle = z^*\langle z|z'\rangle \tag{7-34b}$$

It is convenient to express this relation by the formal statement for adjoint states:

$$\langle z|a^\dagger = z^*\langle z| \tag{7-35}$$

However, it should be noted that (7-35) has just the same content as the more usual relation (7-33).

If $F(a)$ denotes a rather general function of a, then it follows from (7-33) that

$$F(a)|z\rangle = F(z)|z\rangle \tag{7-36a}$$

Likewise, for rather general functions $G(a^\dagger)$, it follows from (7-35) that

$$\langle z|G(a^\dagger) = G(z^*)\langle z| \tag{7-36b}$$

which is essentially the same as (7-36a).

In light of (7-33), it is natural to ask whether there exists any eigenstate—call it $|\lambda;?\rangle$—such that

$$a^\dagger|\lambda;?\rangle = \lambda|\lambda;?\rangle \tag{7-37}$$

We can readily show that *no* such states exist. From the adjoint to (5-53b) we learn that (7-37) leads to

$$\langle n|a^\dagger|\lambda;?\rangle = \sqrt{n}\,\langle n-1|\lambda;?\rangle = \lambda\langle n|\lambda;?\rangle \tag{7-38}$$

for $n = 1, 2, \ldots$; and for $n = 0$, Eq. (7-37) implies that

$$\langle 0|a^\dagger|\lambda;?\rangle = \lambda\langle 0|\lambda;?\rangle = 0 \tag{7-39}$$

If $\lambda = 0$, then (7-38) leads to $\langle n-1|\lambda;?\rangle = 0$, $n = 1, 2, \ldots$, i.e., $|\lambda;?\rangle = 0$. If $\lambda \neq 0$, then $\langle 0|\lambda;?\rangle = 0$, which by repeated use of (7-38) implies that $\langle n|\lambda;?\rangle = 0$ for $n = 1, 2, \ldots$, and hence that $|\lambda;?\rangle = 0$. Consequently no nonzero state satisfying (7-37) exists.

Continuity and Analyticity. Let us now elaborate on some *continuity* properties of the coherent states $|z\rangle$. Since $|z\rangle = |p, q\rangle$ is the ground state of the driven oscillator (7-15a), it is physically reasonable that the states $|z\rangle$ and $|z'\rangle$ should be approximately the same for nearby points in the complex plane, which, thus, correspond intuitively to nearly identical driving forces. We may establish the validity of this argument by using the vector norm [defined in Eq. (5-4)] on which is based the traditional measure of the "distance" between two vectors. Quite generally we have the relation that

$$\|\,|z\rangle - |z'\rangle\|^2 = 2[1 - \operatorname{Re}\langle z|z'\rangle] \leq 2(|z| + |z'|)|z - z'| \tag{7-40}$$

which is proved as follows: If $A \equiv -\ln\langle z|z'\rangle = \frac{1}{2}|z - z'|^2 - i\,\operatorname{Im} z^*z'$, then

$$\begin{aligned}
2 - e^{-A} - e^{-A^*} &= \left(\int_0^A + \int_0^{A^*}\right) e^{-x}\,dx = \int_0^1 (Ae^{-Ax} + A^*\,e^{-A^*x})\,dx \\
&\leq 2\int_0^1 |Ae^{-Ax}|\,dx \leq 2\int_0^1 |A|\,dx = 2|A| \leq 2(|\operatorname{Re} A| \\
&\quad + |\operatorname{Im} A|) = |z - z'|^2 + |z^*z' - z'^*z| \leq 2(|z| + |z'|)|z - z'|
\end{aligned}$$

which establishes (7-40). Consequently we see, indeed, that as z converges to z' in the complex plane, the associated vectors $|z\rangle$ converge to $|z'\rangle$ "in norm" or, as one also says, "strongly."

Next let us consider the continuity of $|z\rangle$ in matrix elements. Suppose that $|\psi\rangle$ denotes an arbitrary Hilbert space vector, and let us consider the function

$$\psi(z) \equiv \langle z|\psi\rangle = \exp(-\tfrac{1}{2}|z|^2) \sum_{n=0}^{\infty} \frac{z^{*n}}{(n!)^{1/2}} \langle n|\psi\rangle \tag{7-41}$$

as z varies over the complex plane. From Schwarz's inequality [cf., Eq. (5-3)] it follows that every such $\psi(z)$ is *bounded*,

$$|\psi(z)| = |\langle z|\psi\rangle| \leq \langle\psi|\psi\rangle^{1/2} = \| \, |\psi\rangle \| < \infty \tag{7-42}$$

and *continuous* in z by virtue of the relation

$$\begin{aligned} |\psi(z) - \psi(z')| &= |(\langle z| - \langle z'|)|\psi\rangle| \\ &\leq \| \, |z\rangle - |z'\rangle \| \cdot \| \, |\psi\rangle \| \\ &\leq \{2(|z| + |z'|)|z - z'|\}^{1/2} \| \, |\psi\rangle \| \end{aligned} \tag{7-43}$$

as follows from (7-40).

However, the functions $\psi(z)$ have even stronger properties than continuity. The sum in (7-41) is absolutely convergent for all complex z. That is, since $|\langle n|\psi\rangle| \leq \| \, |\psi\rangle \|$,

$$\sum_{n=0}^{\infty} \frac{|z^*|^n}{(n!)^{1/2}} |\langle n|\psi\rangle| \leq \| \, |\psi\rangle \| \sum_{n=0}^{\infty} \frac{|z^*|^n}{(n!)^{1/2}} \tag{7-44}$$

which converges for all z since the ratio of the nth term to the $(n-1)$th term falls to zero as $|z^*|/\sqrt{n}$. But an everywhere absolutely convergent series in a complex variable *defines* an *entire function*. That is, the expression

$$\exp(\tfrac{1}{2}|z|^2)\psi(z) \equiv f(z^*) = \sum_{n=0}^{\infty} \frac{z^{*n}}{(n!)^{1/2}} \langle n|\psi\rangle \tag{7-45}$$

defines an entire function of z^* for each $|\psi\rangle$. Otherwise said, we may set

$$\psi(z) = \exp(-\tfrac{1}{2}|z|^2) f(z^*) \tag{7-46}$$

which states that every $\psi(z)$ is—apart from a common factor $\exp(-\frac{1}{2}|z|^2)$—given by an entire analytic function. This makes it evidently clear, for example, that each function $\psi(z)$ is infinitely differentiable as a function of both z and z^* [or as a function of p and q, where $z = (q + ip)/\sqrt{2\hbar}$]. Not every entire function is allowed, however, since each $f(z^*)$

is subject to a growth restriction given by

$$|f(z^*)| = |\psi(z) \exp(\tfrac{1}{2}|z|^2)| \leq \| \, |\psi\rangle \| \exp(\tfrac{1}{2}|z|^2) \tag{7-47}$$

The import of the functions $\psi(z)$ is made clear by even further remarkable properties of the coherent states which we shall now set out in detail.

B. Continuous Representation Based on Coherent States

"RESOLUTION OF UNITY." In the traditional view of quantum mechanics one frequently seeks a complete set of commuting observables and uses as a basis set of vectors their common set of eigenvectors. For example, the "n basis" entails the complete orthonormal set $|n\rangle$, $n = 0, 1, 2, \ldots$, which are the eigenvectors of the number operator N. In turn, as we discussed in Chapter 5, this basis gives rise to a canonical functional representation of Hilbert space by functions of n (sequences) defined by $\psi_n = \langle n|\psi\rangle$. The power of this general approach has its origin in a fundamental theorem of Stone and von Neumann which, crudely speaking, states that every Hermitian operator gives rise to an associated functional representation of Hilbert space.

Much less is known in general about "bases" generated by eigenvectors of non-Hermitian operators, such as the destruction operator a. In fact, there is no *a priori* guarantee that the eigenvectors $|z\rangle$ even span the Hilbert space.

For example, the (right) eigenvectors of $a^\dagger$ span nothing, for as we have shown above, there are no eigenvectors of $a^\dagger$. As another example suppose we were dealing with a Fermi oscillator which we assert can be based on 2×2 operators of the form

$$a_f = \begin{pmatrix} 0 & 1 \\ 0 & 0 \end{pmatrix} \quad a_f{}^\dagger = \begin{pmatrix} 0 & 0 \\ 1 & 0 \end{pmatrix} \quad N_f = a_f{}^\dagger a_f = \begin{pmatrix} 0 & 0 \\ 0 & 1 \end{pmatrix}$$

Although the eigenvectors of N_f would span the two-dimensional Hilbert space, the eigenvectors of a_f [of which there is only one $\begin{pmatrix} 1 \\ 0 \end{pmatrix}$ with eigenvalue zero] would not span the full space.

Fortunately, however, the coherent states $|z\rangle$ for all z do, in fact, span the Hilbert space. The first indication of this fact seems to be given by von Neumann in his quantum theory book [5-4] where he remarks, effectively, that the *subset* of all coherent states $|z\rangle$ for which $z = \sqrt{\pi}\,(l + im)$, l and m being arbitrary integers, already spans the Hilbert space. In a physical sense this means that a complete set of states is given by those vectors $|p, q\rangle$ for which the points p and q lie on a rectangular lattice in phase space with a density of one state per "Planck cell" of volume $h = 2\pi\hbar$.

Now, if a subset of coherent states already spans Hilbert space and is, thus, in our terminology a complete set, then the full set of coherent states may be called overcomplete. That is, there must be certain *linear dependencies* among the coherent states, and we shall detail some of these below. Prior to this demonstration we simply reassert that the eigenvectors $|z\rangle$ of the annihilation operator are not only complete, but they are overcomplete.

The completeness of the coherent states has the following *fundamental consequence:* The vanishing of the function $\psi(z) = \langle z|\psi\rangle$ for all z implies the vanishing of the vector $|\psi\rangle$; the converse is, of course, obvious. Thus the *abstract vectors* $|\psi\rangle$ can be put into one-to-one correspondence with complex, bounded *functions* $\psi(z) = \langle z|\psi\rangle$. The analogy with a similar one-to-one correspondence of Hilbert space vectors $|\psi\rangle$ with sequences $\{\psi_n\}$ (where $\psi_n = \langle n|\psi\rangle$) should be evident, and it suggests that we can *represent* the abstract Hilbert space $\mathfrak{H}$ by means of the linear class of functions (say $\mathfrak{C}$) containing $\psi(z) = \langle z|\psi\rangle$ for each $|\psi\rangle \in \mathfrak{H}$.

In order to clinch our representation we must turn the linear space of functions $\mathfrak{C}$ into a Hilbert space by introducing an appropriate inner product. In the canonical Dirac prescription, as we have outlined in Chapter 5, the key formula in such applications is the resolution of unity into one-dimensional projection operators, such as is given in (5-11). In the present case our formulation of inner products, etc., would be *formally identical* in appearance to those of Chapter 5 if we could prove the basic "resolution of unity" given by

$$I = \frac{1}{\pi}\int d^2z|z\rangle\langle z| \tag{7-48}$$

where

$$d^2z \equiv d(\text{Re } z)\, d(\text{Im } z)$$

and the integration extends over the entire complex plane.[2] Of course, the real meaning of (7-48) is embodied in the formula for matrix elements,

$$\langle\lambda|\psi\rangle = \frac{1}{\pi}\int \langle\lambda|z\rangle\langle z|\psi\rangle\, d^2z \tag{7-49}$$

for arbitrary $|\lambda\rangle$ and $|\psi\rangle$. To make headway in proving (7-48), therefore, we focus on (7-49) in which the integrand is an ordinary function.

[2] The earliest use of the resolution of unity given in (7-48) for purposes of forming a functional representation of Hilbert space was that of Klauder [7-4]. Our heuristic derivation of (7-48) follows the one given there.

The elementary proof of (7-49) is quite straightforward. In terms of the expansion (7-41) we see that our desired result reads

$$\langle\lambda|\psi\rangle = \frac{1}{\pi}\int d^2z \exp(-|z|^2) \sum_{m,n=0}^{\infty} \frac{z^{*m}z^n}{(m!n!)^{1/2}} \langle\lambda|m\rangle\langle n|\psi\rangle \qquad (7\text{-}50)$$

If we interchange summation and integration, and introduce polar coordinates, i.e., $z = re^{i\theta}$, $d^2z = r\,dr\,d\theta$, then evidently

$$\begin{aligned}\frac{1}{\pi}\sum_{m,n=0}^{\infty} \langle\lambda|m\rangle\langle n|\psi\rangle(m!n!)^{-1/2} \int_0^\infty \int_0^{2\pi} r^{m+n}e^{i\theta(n-m)} \exp(-r^2)r\,dr\,d\theta \\ = 2\sum_{n=0}^{\infty} \langle\lambda|n\rangle\langle n|\psi\rangle(n!)^{-1} \int_0^\infty r^{2n+1}\exp(-r^2)\,dr \\ = \sum_{n=0}^{\infty}\langle\lambda|n\rangle\langle n|\psi\rangle = \langle\lambda|\psi\rangle \qquad (7\text{-}51)\end{aligned}$$

as was to be shown.

A rigorous proof of (7-49) proceeds slightly differently so as to most easily justify the interchange of limits. Let us first concentrate on showing that

$$\langle\psi|\psi\rangle = \frac{1}{\pi}\int d^2z|\langle z|\psi\rangle|^2$$

By standard theorems we clearly find, for all finite R, that

$$\begin{aligned}\frac{1}{\pi}\int_0^R\int_0^{2\pi} r\,dr\,d\theta|\langle z|\psi\rangle|^2 = \frac{1}{\pi}\sum_{m,n=0}^{\infty}\int_0^R\int_0^{2\pi} r\,dr\,d\theta e^{i\theta(n-m)} \\ \times \langle\psi|m\rangle\langle n|\psi\rangle(m!n!)^{-1/2}r^{m+n}\exp(-r^2) \\ = \sum_{n=0}^{\infty}|\langle n|\psi\rangle|^2\gamma_n(R)\end{aligned}$$

where

$$\gamma_n(R) \equiv 2(n!)^{-1}\int_0^R r^{2n+1}\exp(-r^2)\,dr$$

Evidently $0 < \gamma_n(R) < 1$ for all n and R whereas $\lim_{R\to\infty}\gamma_n(R) = 1$ for all n. Since $\langle n|\psi\rangle$ is square summable (i.e., $|\psi\rangle$ is normalizable) it can readily be established (a sequential "dominated convergence") that

$$\langle\psi|\psi\rangle = \sum_{n=0}^{\infty} |\langle n|\psi\rangle|^2$$

$$= \sum_{n=0}^{\infty} \lim_{R\to\infty} |\langle n|\psi\rangle|^2\gamma_n(R)$$

$$= \lim_{R\to\infty} \sum_{n=0}^{\infty} |\langle n|\psi\rangle|^2\gamma_n(R)$$

$$= \frac{1}{\pi}\int d^2z|\langle z|\psi\rangle|^2$$

as desired. The appropriate result for $\langle\lambda|\psi\rangle$ follows from linearity. This form of the proof of (7-49) is adapted from Bargmann [7-6].

With Eq. (7-48) validated as a suitable resolution of unity into one-dimensional projection operators, we can automatically list (in the canonical Dirac fashion) a variety of properties that pertain to the associated continuous representation of Hilbert space.

Vector Representatives: $\langle z|\psi\rangle$ for all $|\psi\rangle$

Inner Product

$$\langle\lambda|\psi\rangle = \frac{1}{\pi}\int d^2z\langle\lambda|z\rangle\langle z|\psi\rangle \tag{7-52}$$

Operator Representatives: $\langle z|\mathcal{B}|z'\rangle$ for general $\mathcal{B}$

Vector Transformation

$$\langle z|\mathcal{B}|\psi\rangle = \frac{1}{\pi}\int d^2z'\langle z|\mathcal{B}|z'\rangle\langle z'|\psi\rangle \tag{7-53}$$

Operator Transformation

$$\langle z|\mathcal{B}_1\mathcal{B}_2|z''\rangle = \frac{1}{\pi}\int d^2z'\langle z|\mathcal{B}_1|z'\rangle\langle z'|\mathcal{B}_2|z''\rangle \tag{7-54}$$

In turn an associated canonical family of vector and operator decompositions are given by

Vector Decomposition

$$|\psi\rangle = \frac{1}{\pi}\int d^2z|z\rangle\langle z|\psi\rangle \tag{7-55}$$

Operator Decomposition

$$\mathcal{B} = \frac{1}{\pi^2} \int d^2z_1\, d^2z_2 |z_1\rangle\langle z_1|\mathcal{B}|z_2\rangle\langle z_2| \tag{7-56}$$

Viewed alternatively, these latter relations express the inverse map from the coherent-state functional Hilbert space representation to the abstract one.

Reproducing Kernel. One of the essential features of a functional representation based on an overcomplete family of states is the appearance of reproducing kernels. Suppose we let $\mathcal{B}$ in (7-53) be the identity operator I. Then we find that

$$\langle z|\psi\rangle = \frac{1}{\pi} \int d^2z' \langle z|z'\rangle\langle z'|\psi\rangle \tag{7-57}$$

which states that every vector representative $\langle z|\psi\rangle$ fulfills an integral equation with the reproducing kernel

$$\begin{aligned} \mathcal{K}(z; z') &\equiv \langle z|z'\rangle \\ &= \exp\{-\tfrac{1}{2}|z|^2 + z^*z' - \tfrac{1}{2}|z'|^2\} \end{aligned} \tag{7-58}$$

Furthermore, if $|\psi\rangle = |z''\rangle$ above, then (7-57) becomes

$$\langle z|z''\rangle = \frac{1}{\pi} \int d^2z' \langle z|z'\rangle\langle z'|z''\rangle \tag{7-59}$$

which shows the kernel to be a solution of its own integral equation. Essentially, Eq. (7-59) is an idempotent condition that $\mathcal{K}$ satisfies. That is, $\mathcal{K}$ acts like a projection operator when acting on general square-integrable functions of z (and z^*); only those functions fulfilling (7-57) belong in the Hilbert space representation. [3]

Each operator representative function (more simply, matrix element) $\langle z|\mathcal{B}|z'\rangle$ fulfills similar integral equations. If we separately set $\mathcal{B}_1$ and $\mathcal{B}_2$ equal to I in (7-54), we are led to the relations

$$\begin{aligned} \langle z|\mathcal{B}|z''\rangle &= \frac{1}{\pi} \int d^2z' \langle z|z'\rangle\langle z'|\mathcal{B}|z''\rangle \\ &= \frac{1}{\pi} \int d^2z' \langle z|\mathcal{B}|z'\rangle\langle z'|z''\rangle \end{aligned} \tag{7-60}$$

Like (7-57) itself, the relations in (7-60) are evident consequences of the

[3] An extensive and general theory of Hilbert spaces based on reproducing kernels has been developed by Aronszajn [7-8].

basic resolution (7-48). But, since

$$\langle z|z'\rangle \neq 0 \qquad \text{if } z \neq z' \tag{7-61}$$

these relations constitute actual constraints that the vector and operator representatives must satisfy.

Another consequence of the present kind of representation worth noting here is the following. Suppose we set $\mathcal{B} = I$ in (7-56) and determine that

$$I = \frac{1}{\pi^2} \int d^2z_1\, d^2z_2 |z_1\rangle\langle z_1|z_2\rangle\langle z_2| \tag{7-62}$$

which should be compared with

$$I = \frac{1}{\pi} \int d^2z |z\rangle\langle z|$$

which was our basic starting relation. These are two manifestly different decompositions for the same operator in terms of one set of states; the first form involves a superposition of "unlike outer products" $|z_1\rangle\langle z_2|$, whereas the second form involves a superposition of "like outer products" $|z\rangle\langle z|$, i.e., projection operators. That such a multiplicity of decompositions or representations is possible is a consequence of the overcompleteness of the coherent states which takes concrete form in the property (7-61). We may note here that parts of the next chapter are devoted to studying similar multiplicities in coherent-state representations for a number of other operators.

Linear Dependencies. One of the most characteristic properties of an overcomplete set of vectors are linear dependencies of the basis vectors. One such relation is given by (7-55) if we set $|\psi\rangle = |z'\rangle$, for then

$$|z'\rangle = \frac{1}{\pi} \int d^2z |z\rangle\langle z|z'\rangle \tag{7-63}$$

which expresses $|z'\rangle$ in terms of all the coherent states.

Two other relations are also interesting. Let us express z in polar coordinates so that [as used in (7-51)]

$$|z\rangle = |re^{i\theta}\rangle = \exp(-\tfrac{1}{2}r^2) \sum_{n=0}^{\infty} \frac{r^n e^{in\theta}}{(n!)^{1/2}} |n\rangle \tag{7-64}$$

Evidently, we then find that

$$\int_0^{2\pi} e^{ip\theta} |re^{i\theta}\rangle\, d\theta = 0 \qquad p = 1, 2, \ldots \tag{7-65}$$

On multiplying by $r^p r$ and integrating over all r we conclude that

$$\int z^p|z\rangle\, d^2z = 0 \qquad p = 1, 2, \ldots \tag{7-66}$$

On the other hand, any finite number of distinct coherent states $|z_l\rangle$, $l = 1, 2, \ldots, L$, are linearly independent. That is, the only way that

$$\sum_{l=1}^{L} c_l|z_l\rangle = 0 \tag{7-67}$$

is if all $c_l = 0$. We leave the proof of this property to the reader.

C. Examples and Special Features of Coherent-State Vector and Operator Representatives

EXAMPLES OF VECTOR REPRESENTATIVES. Some specific examples of familiar quantum states may help clarify the use and properties of the coherent-state continuous representation. Among the simplest examples are the eigenstates of the harmonic oscillator each of which has the specific functional representation

$$\langle z|n\rangle = (n!)^{-1/2} z^{*n} \exp(-\tfrac{1}{2}|z|^2) \tag{7-68}$$

as is clear from (7-4a).

It is important that one understand just what these functions correspond to—these functions should be related to the traditional Hermite functions which arise as oscillator eigenfunctions in the Schrödinger representation. In this most basic example of all representations, as we have previously indicated, the vectors $|\psi\rangle$ are (practically speaking) represented by functions $\psi(x)$ of one real variable, the operator Q is represented by multiplication with x, and the operator P is represented by differentiation with $-i\hbar\, \partial/\partial x$. Furthermore, the energy eigenvalue equation for an harmonic oscillator with unit mass and angular frequency reads

$$\frac{1}{2}\left(-\hbar^2 \frac{\partial^2}{\partial x^2} + x^2 - \hbar\right)\psi(x) = E\psi(x) \tag{7-69}$$

It is shown in most quantum mechanics textbooks that this equation has (normalizable) solutions whenever $E = n\hbar$, $n = 0, 1, 2, \ldots$, which are simply related to the Hermite functions defined by

$$h_n(y) \equiv \frac{(-1)^n}{[2^n n!\sqrt{\pi}]^{1/2}} \exp(y^2/2) \frac{d^n}{dy^n} \exp(-y^2) \tag{7-70}$$

In particular, the normalized eigensolutions to (7-69) are given as

$$\varphi_n(x) = \hbar^{-1/4} h_n(\hbar^{-1/2}x) \tag{7-71}$$

where explicitly, for example,

$$\varphi_0(x) = (\pi\hbar)^{-1/4} \exp(-\tfrac{1}{2}x^2/\hbar) \tag{7-72a}$$

$$\varphi_1(x) = (\pi\hbar)^{-1/4} \sqrt{2/\hbar}\, x \exp(-\tfrac{1}{2}x^2/\hbar) \tag{7-72b}$$

In any case, the essential point is that the Hermite functions (modulo $\hbar$) $\varphi_n(x)$ represent the same abstract states for each n as do the functions $\langle z|n\rangle$.

The Schrödinger representation of vectors is so traditional and so physically important that it is useful to have a more general connection between it and the representation by the functions $\langle z|\psi\rangle$. Let us adopt the phase-space formulation and write

$$\begin{aligned}\langle p, q|\psi\rangle &= \langle 0|e^{i(qP-pQ)/\hbar}|\psi\rangle \\ &= \langle 0|e^{1/2iqP/\hbar}e^{-ipQ/\hbar}e^{1/2iqP/\hbar}|\psi\rangle\end{aligned} \tag{7-73}$$

the latter form following from a double application of Eq. (7-24). In the Schrödinger representation, Eq. (7-73) simply becomes

$$\begin{aligned}\langle p, q|\psi\rangle &= \int \varphi_0{}^*(x - q/2)e^{-ipx/\hbar}\psi(x + q/2)\, dx \\ &= (\pi\hbar)^{-1/4} \int \exp\,[-\,(x - q/2)^2/(2\hbar) - ipx/\hbar]\,\psi(x + q/2)\, dx\end{aligned} \tag{7-74}$$

where we have made use of the relation [valid for any $\psi(x)$] that

$$e^{1/2iqP/\hbar}\psi(x) = \exp\,(\tfrac{1}{2}q\, \partial/\partial x)\,\psi(x) = \psi(x + q/2) \tag{7-75}$$

Equation (7-74) allows for the conversion of any Schrödinger representative into the phase-space representative $\langle p, q|\psi\rangle$. Clearly $\psi(y)$ can be recovered from $\langle p, q|\psi\rangle$ through the Fourier transform relation

$$\psi(y) = [2\pi\hbar\varphi_0{}^*(-y)]^{-1}\textstyle\int\langle p, 2y|\psi\rangle\, dp \tag{7-76}$$

Indeed, there are several relations of this type to determine $\psi(y)$.

We can exploit the analyticity properties to find an even simpler prescription for $\langle p, q|\psi\rangle$. Let us consider

$$\begin{aligned}\langle p, 0|\psi\rangle &= (\pi\hbar)^{-1/4}\textstyle\int\exp(-ipx/\hbar - \tfrac{1}{2}x^2/\hbar)\psi(x)\, dx \\ &\equiv \exp(-\tfrac{1}{4}p^2/\hbar)g(p)\end{aligned} \tag{7-77}$$

On comparison with (7-46) it is clear that $g(p) = f(-ip/\sqrt{2\hbar})$, so that in virtue of the analyticity of f we can directly win $\langle p, q|\psi\rangle$. In particular, we have

$$\langle p, q|\psi\rangle = \exp\left[-\frac{1}{4\hbar}(p^2 + q^2)\right]g(p + iq) \tag{7-78a}$$

or

$$\langle z|\psi\rangle = \exp(-\tfrac{1}{2}|z|^2)g(i\sqrt{2\hbar}\,z^*) \tag{7-78b}$$

where

$$g(p) \equiv (\pi\hbar)^{-1/4}\exp(\tfrac{1}{4}p^2/\hbar)\int\exp(-ipx/\hbar - \tfrac{1}{2}x^2/\hbar)\psi(x)\,dx \tag{7-79}$$

As an illustration of these equations let us choose

$$\psi(x) = \varphi_{0,\omega}(x) = (\omega/\pi\hbar)^{1/4}\exp(-\tfrac{1}{2}\omega x^2/\hbar) \tag{7-80}$$

which is just an oscillator ground state for a general angular frequency ω. Then, by an application of the basic Gaussian integral (Re $A > 0$)

$$(2\pi)^{-1/2}\int\exp(-ixB - \tfrac{1}{2}x^2/A)\,dx = \sqrt{A}\exp(-\tfrac{1}{2}AB^2)$$

it follows that

$$g(p) = [\tfrac{1}{2}(\omega^{1/2} + \omega^{-1/2})]^{-1/2}\exp\left[-\frac{1}{4\hbar}\frac{(1-\omega)}{(1+\omega)}p^2\right] \tag{7-81}$$

and thus (with $|\psi\rangle$ denoted by $|0_\omega\rangle$)

$$\langle z|0_\omega\rangle = [\tfrac{1}{2}(\omega^{1/2} + \omega^{-1/2})]^{-1/2}\exp\left\{-\tfrac{1}{2}|z|^2 + \frac{1}{2}\frac{(1-\omega)}{(1+\omega)}(z^*)^2\right\} \tag{7-82a}$$

or

$$\langle p, q|0_\omega\rangle = [\tfrac{1}{2}(\omega^{1/2} + \omega^{-1/2})]^{-1/2}\exp\left\{-\frac{1}{2\hbar(1+\omega)}[p^2 + \omega q^2 + i(1-\omega)pq]\right\} \tag{7-82b}$$

If $\omega = 1$, these equations immediately reduce to expressions given earlier for $|0_1\rangle = |0\rangle$. [*Remark:* We emphasize that (7-82) is *not* the "*natural*" coherent-state continuous representation for the ground state of an oscillator of angular frequency ω; the natural one is based on ground states of a driven oscillator *which itself has natural frequency* ω. Indeed, such natural coherent-state continuous representations are all formally identical when expressed as functions of z (i.e., all the functions $\langle z|\psi\rangle$ are the same) but they differ in their physical content in virtue of the definition $z = (\omega^{1/2}q + i\omega^{-1/2}p)/\sqrt{2\hbar}$ used in forming $\langle p, q|\psi\rangle$. We shall encounter these various cases in more detail later when we deal with several different oscillators simultaneously.]

Probability Interpretation of $|\langle z|\psi\rangle|^2$. This is a good point to enlarge on the physical significance of $|\langle z|\psi\rangle|^2$. Suppose we are dealing with a material particle in a one-dimensional space. Then, as is well known, the Schrödinger wave function $\psi(x)$ is the probability amplitude—more to the point: $\rho(x) = |\psi(x)|^2$ is the probability density—for finding the particle at the point. Clearly such events are *mutually exclusive*, i.e., the particle, if measured, will be found at one and only one x at a time. Consequently, the distribution $\rho(x)$ could, in principle, be almost anything.

On the other hand, note first of all that $|\langle p, q|\psi\rangle|^2$ is not the probability density for finding the particle at position q with momentum p. Rather it is the relative frequency that the particle would, if measured, be found in the ground state of an oscillator whose *mean* position is q and whose *mean* momentum is p. Quantum mechanically these "events" are not mutually exclusive since, in view of (7-61), two such states have a certain degree of resemblance. In essence, therefore, with $\rho(z) = |\langle z|\psi\rangle|^2$ we are dealing with a stochastic description with dependent probabilities.

To see a rough classical analog of such a description, consider yourself as blindfolded and firing bullets at random through sheets of newspaper lying on the floor. Let $p(n)$ denote the relative frequency that page number n will be pierced. If all the sheets lie separated on the floor and are not overlapping, then the events (which sheet is pierced) are mutually exclusive. However, if some sheets overlap one another, then the events are generally not mutually exclusive and, as a consequence, there will be constraints fulfilled by the $p(n)$. For example, if sheets 1 and 2 lie exactly on top of one another then we surely have $p(1) = p(2)$. So long as the appropriate constraints are never violated there is nothing wrong in this kind of dependent form of stochastic description.

If we now return to the distribution $\rho(p, q) = |\langle p, q|\psi\rangle|^2$, we may note, in spite of the dependent probabilities, that for macroscopic phase-space regions $E \gg h = 2\pi\hbar$, the expression $h^{-1}\int_E \rho(p, q)\,dp\,dq$ is a reasonably accurate measure of the probability to find the particle within the cell E. It is this property which gives to $\rho(p, q)$ many of the features of a normal classical phase-space distribution $\rho_{\text{cl}}(p, q)$. [4]

EXAMPLES OF OPERATORS. Let us now turn our attention to some operators and see how they look and act in a coherent-state continuous representation. We first focus our attention on the integral-kernel representation $\langle z|\mathcal{B}|z'\rangle$ for the operator $\mathcal{B}$ which is used in the manner indicated in (7-53) and (7-54). To get our feet wet, let us assume that $\mathcal{B}$ is diagonal in the number representation, i.e., $\langle n|\mathcal{B}|m\rangle = b_n\,\delta_{nm}$. In the form (7-28a) it is then clear that

$$\mathcal{B}|z'\rangle = \exp(-\tfrac{1}{2}|z'|^2) \sum_{n=0}^{\infty} \frac{(z')^n}{(n!)^{1/2}}\, b_n|n\rangle \tag{7-83}$$

[4] In this spirit, $\rho(p, q)$ has been studied by Husimi [7-11], Kano [7-12], Mehta and Sudarshan [7-10], and McKenna and Frisch [7-13].

and thus that

$$\langle z|\mathcal{B}|z'\rangle = \exp(-\tfrac{1}{2}|z|^2 - \tfrac{1}{2}|z'|^2) \sum_{n=0}^{\infty} \frac{b_n(z^*z')^n}{n!} \tag{7-84}$$

which is just the appropriate integral kernel. If $\mathcal{B}$ equals the oscillator evolution operator $\exp(-itN)$, then $b_n = \exp(-int)$, and we find that

$$\begin{aligned}\langle z|e^{-itN}|z'\rangle &= \exp(-\tfrac{1}{2}|z|^2 - \tfrac{1}{2}|z'|^2) \sum_{n=0}^{\infty} \frac{(z^*e^{-it}z')^n}{n!} \\ &= \exp(-\tfrac{1}{2}|z|^2 + z^*e^{-it}z' - \tfrac{1}{2}|z'|^2) \\ &= \langle z|e^{-it}z'\rangle = \langle e^{it}z|z'\rangle \end{aligned} \tag{7-85}$$

Note that the matrix elements of the evolution operator are given by a simple transformation on the arguments of the reproducing kernel $\langle z|z'\rangle$ itself. This has the consequence that under the action of this evolution operator the coherent state $|z\rangle$ becomes a new coherent state given by $|z_{\mathrm{cl}}(t)\rangle \equiv |e^{-it}z\rangle$. It is evident that $z_{\mathrm{cl}}(t) = e^{-it}z$ is just the complex classical oscillator solution, and we leave it to the reader to translate the present argument into our usual phase-space language so as to validate (7-13) and (7-14).

Now let us consider some more general operators and their associated integral kernels. Among the simplest such kernels are those corresponding to *normal ordered operators*. Let the operator $\mathcal{B}$ depend on $a^\dagger$ and a, i.e., $\mathcal{B} = \mathcal{B}(a^\dagger, a)$, in such a way that in each factor all creation operators $a^\dagger$ stand to the left of all annihilation operators a. If we assume that $\mathcal{B}$ has a power series expansion in a and $a^\dagger$, then it is given in the form

$$\mathcal{B}(a^\dagger, a) = \sum_{r,s=0}^{\infty} b_{rs}(a^\dagger)^r a^s \tag{7-86}$$

for suitable complex coefficients b_{rs}. Then it is an immediate consequence of (7-36) that

$$\begin{aligned}\langle z|\mathcal{B}(a^\dagger, a)|z'\rangle &= \mathcal{B}(z^*, z')\langle z|z'\rangle \\ &= \sum_{r,s=0}^{\infty} b_{rs}(z^*)^r(z')^s\langle z|z'\rangle \end{aligned} \tag{7-87}$$

the latter form following from (7-86) when it applies.

So valuable is the concept of normal ordered operators that it is useful to introduce a *normal ordering operation* denoted by a double set of colons whose purpose is to reorder the annihilation and creation operators within a factor (with total disregard for their noncommutativity!) so that all $a^\dagger$

are to the left of all a. In the example considered above, $:\mathcal{B}: = \mathcal{B}$ since by assumption $\mathcal{B}$ was already in normal form. However, ordinarily the operator $:\mathcal{O}: \neq \mathcal{O}$. For example, if $\mathcal{O} = aa^\dagger$, then $:aa^\dagger: \equiv a^\dagger a = aa^\dagger - 1 \neq aa^\dagger$ as follows from the commutation relations.

It is important to appreciate that normal ordering is essentially a relation between symbols and the resultant operator depends on the original symbolic representation for $\mathcal{O}$. For example, although $[a, a^\dagger] = 1$, it follows that $:[a, a^\dagger]: = 0$ which differs from $:1: = 1$. Thus some specific symbolic form for $\mathcal{O}$ must be adopted in order to define $:\mathcal{O}:$. It is simplest and most logical to adopt the symbolic form for $\mathcal{O}$ implicit in some preassigned functional form $\mathcal{O} = \mathcal{O}(a^\dagger, a)$ which has as a consequence the important relation

$$\langle z|:\mathcal{O}(a^\dagger, a):|z'\rangle \equiv \mathcal{O}(z^*, z')\langle z|z'\rangle \tag{7-88}$$

Since an arbitrary operator $\mathcal{W}$ can be represented in the form $\mathcal{W}(a^\dagger, a)$, it is clear that by suitable permutations of the symbols (paying due regard to the relation $aa^\dagger = a^\dagger a + 1$) the operator $\mathcal{W}$ may be brought to normal order. That is, for each operator $\mathcal{W}$ there is an associated operator $\mathcal{W}_n(a^\dagger, a)$ such that $\mathcal{W} = :\mathcal{W}_n:$. This is a useful representation for certain applications, and we shall give a prescription later that is sometimes helpful to determine $\mathcal{W}_n$.

For certain $\mathcal{O}$ we can explicitly give $:\mathcal{O}:$ in terms of more familiar operator expressions. A useful generating formula for such purposes is given by

$$\begin{aligned} :\exp(za^\dagger - z^*a): &= \exp(za^\dagger)\exp(-z^*a) \\ &= \exp(\tfrac{1}{2}|z|^2)\exp(za^\dagger - z^*a) \end{aligned} \tag{7-89}$$

in virtue of (7-26). More specifically, consider the example $\mathcal{O}(a^\dagger, a) = \exp(\tau a^\dagger a)$ for which we have

$$\begin{aligned} \langle z|:\exp(\tau a^\dagger a):|z'\rangle &\equiv \exp(\tau z^* z')\langle z|z'\rangle \\ &= \exp[-\tfrac{1}{2}|z|^2 + (1+\tau)z^* z' - \tfrac{1}{2}|z'|^2] \end{aligned} \tag{7-90}$$

If we compare this expression with (7-85) and set $(1 + \tau) \equiv e^{-it}$, or $-it \equiv \ln(1 + \tau)$, then it follows that

$$:\exp(\tau a^\dagger a): = \exp[\ln(1+\tau)(a^\dagger a)] \tag{7-91a}$$

or equivalently that

$$:\exp[(e^{-it} - 1)a^\dagger a]: = \exp[-it(a^\dagger a)] \tag{7-91b}$$

Evidently, if $\tau \to -1$ (or $it \to +\infty$), then

$$:\exp(-a^\dagger a): = |0\rangle\langle 0| \tag{7-92}$$

Differential Operator Representation. Besides the integral-kernel representation of various operators there is a very important alternative representation that they possess. Consider first the operator $a^\dagger$. It follows from (7-35) that

$$\langle z|a^\dagger|\psi\rangle = z^*\langle z|\psi\rangle$$

which shows that in the representation space of functions $\langle z|\psi\rangle$, *the operator $a^\dagger$ is represented by multiplication with z^*.* (This is roughly analogous to the Schrödinger representation, where Q is represented by multiplication with x.) To find an equally simple representation for a, we note first that

$$\begin{aligned}\langle z|a|z'\rangle &= z'\langle z|z'\rangle \\ &= z' \exp(-\tfrac{1}{2}|z|^2 + z^*z' - \tfrac{1}{2}|z'|^2) \\ &= \left(\frac{z}{2} + \frac{\partial}{\partial z^*}\right) \exp(-\tfrac{1}{2}|z|^2 + z^*z' - \tfrac{1}{2}|z'|^2) \\ &= \left(\frac{z}{2} + \frac{\partial}{\partial z^*}\right) \langle z|z'\rangle \end{aligned} \tag{7-93}$$

in virtue of the specific form for $\langle z|z'\rangle$. But the last form of (7-93) obviously holds for general linear sums $\Sigma c_p|z'_p\rangle$ as well. In turn, this implies that $\langle z|a|\psi\rangle = (z/2 + \partial/\partial z^*)\langle z|\psi\rangle$, which means that in the space of functions $\langle z|\psi\rangle$ *we can represent a by the differential operator* $(z/2 + \partial/\partial z^*)$. (This is roughly analogous to $P = -i\hbar\, \partial/\partial x$ in the Schrödinger representation.) Hence, in this representation,

$$\langle z|[a, a^\dagger]|\psi\rangle = [z/2 + \partial/\partial z^*, z^*]\langle z|\psi\rangle = \langle z|\psi\rangle \tag{7-94}$$

which is the form taken by the basic commutation relation.

More generally, it follows that the action of the operator $\mathcal{W} = \mathcal{W}(a^\dagger, a)$ is represented by means of an associated *partial differential operator*, namely,

$$\langle z|\mathcal{W}(a^\dagger, a)|\psi\rangle = \mathcal{W}\left(z^*, \frac{z}{2} + \frac{\partial}{\partial z^*}\right)\langle z|\psi\rangle \tag{7-95}$$

Further, if we employ the form $\langle z|\psi\rangle = \exp(-\frac{1}{2}|z|^2)f(z^*)$ and the operator identity

$$\exp(\tfrac{1}{2}|z|^2)\frac{\partial}{\partial z^*}\exp(-\tfrac{1}{2}|z|^2) = \frac{\partial}{\partial z^*} - \frac{z}{2} \tag{7-96}$$

then we can simply write

$$\begin{aligned}\langle z|\mathcal{W}(a^\dagger, a)|\psi\rangle &= \exp(-\tfrac{1}{2}|z|^2)\mathcal{W}\left(z^*, \frac{\partial}{\partial z^*}\right)\exp(\tfrac{1}{2}|z|^2)\langle z|\psi\rangle \\ &= \exp(-\tfrac{1}{2}|z|^2)\mathcal{W}\left(z^*, \frac{\partial}{\partial z^*}\right)f(z^*)\end{aligned} \tag{7-97}$$

As an example of these formulas, let us recompute the properties of the evolution operator $\exp(-ita^\dagger a)$. In particular we see, based on the identity in (7-75), that

$$\begin{aligned}\langle z|\exp[-it(a^\dagger a)]|\psi\rangle &= \exp(-\tfrac{1}{2}|z|^2)\exp\left(-itz^*\frac{\partial}{\partial z^*}\right)f(z^*)\\ &= \exp(-\tfrac{1}{2}|z|^2)\exp\left(-it\frac{\partial}{\partial \ln z^*}\right)f(\exp[\ln z^*])\\ &= \exp(-\tfrac{1}{2}|z|^2)f(\exp[\ln z^* - it])\\ &= \exp(-\tfrac{1}{2}|z|^2)f(e^{-it}z^*) = \langle e^{it}z|\psi\rangle \end{aligned}\tag{7-98}$$

which is correct in view of the last form of Eq. (7-85).

Of course, we can use the differential operator formulation (7-95) to win ourselves an expression for the coherent-state matrix elements of $\mathcal{W}$ if we just set $|\psi\rangle = |z'\rangle$. In particular,

$$\langle z|\mathcal{W}(a^\dagger, a)|z'\rangle = \mathcal{W}\left(z^*, \frac{z}{2} + \frac{\partial}{\partial z^*}\right)\langle z|z'\rangle \tag{7-99}$$

The partial derivatives here act on terms to the right which include those z^* in $\langle z|z'\rangle$ and possibly some z^* factors within $\mathcal{W}$ itself. Since we explicitly know $\langle z|z'\rangle$ we can make use of the operator identity

$$(\langle z|z'\rangle)^{-1}\frac{\partial}{\partial z^*}\langle z|z'\rangle = \frac{\partial}{\partial z^*} - \frac{z}{2} + z' \tag{7-100}$$

[analogous to (7-96)], to explicitly carry out some of the derivatives. Namely, it follows that

$$\langle z|\mathcal{W}(a^\dagger, a)|z'\rangle = \langle z|z'\rangle\mathcal{W}\left(z^*, z' + \frac{\partial}{\partial z^*}\right) \tag{7-101}$$

where the only remaining derivatives act just on those z^* within $\mathcal{W}$ itself. Clearly, if $\mathcal{W}$ is in normal order (all a to the right), then all derivatives are to the right of any z^* within $\mathcal{W}$, and thus they yield zero since they have only z^* independent terms to act on. In such a case we just recover the form (7-87) for a normal-ordered operator's matrix elements. However, Eqs. (7-99) and (7-101) hold whether or not $\mathcal{W}$ is in normal order.

Diagonal Matrix Elements. We now note yet another *fundamental consequence* of the coherent states most easily seen from the properties of analyticity. Suppose that the diagonal matrix elements of the operator $\mathcal{W}$ *vanish*,

$$\langle z|\mathcal{W}|z\rangle = 0 \tag{7-102}$$

for all z. What then can we conclude? For reasonable operators $\mathcal{W}$ the general matrix elements read

$$\langle z|\mathcal{W}|z'\rangle = \exp(-\tfrac{1}{2}|z|^2 - \tfrac{1}{2}|z'|^2) \sum_{n,m=0}^{\infty} \frac{(z^*)^n(z')^m}{(n!m!)^{1/2}} \langle n|\mathcal{W}|m\rangle \quad (7\text{-}103)$$

which makes it clear that in order for (7-102) to hold, an entire function of the two complex variables z^* and z' (viz., the double series) must vanish on the subdomain where $z' = z$. However, it is known from the theory of several complex variables that if such a two-variable function vanishes on the subdomain $z' = z$ for all z (or even on special subsets thereof!) it vanishes identically. In other words, if $\langle z|\mathcal{W}|z\rangle = 0$ for all z, then $\langle z|\mathcal{W}|z'\rangle = 0$ for all z and z', which simply means that $\mathcal{W} \equiv 0$. The converse is, of course, obvious.

The important conclusion to note here is that an operator $\mathcal{W}$ is uniquely specified by its diagonal matrix elements $W(z) \equiv \langle z|\mathcal{W}|z\rangle$ or in our phase-space form by $W(p, q) \equiv \langle p, q|\mathcal{W}|p, q\rangle$. We can thus "represent" the operators $\mathcal{W}$ by the associated functions $W(z)$. [It should be clearly understood that when we represent *operators* $\mathcal{W}$ by functions $W(z) = \langle z|\mathcal{W}|z\rangle$ we deal with a strictly different kind of "representation" than is meant when we represent *vectors* $|\psi\rangle$ by the functions $\psi(z) = \langle z|\psi\rangle$.]

Now that we have established the uniqueness of the diagonal matrix elements as operator "representatives" let us indicate some of their properties. Given an operator $\mathcal{W}(a^\dagger, a)$, its diagonal matrix elements follow directly from (7-101), on setting $z' = z$, as

$$\langle z|\mathcal{W}(a^\dagger, a)|z\rangle = \mathcal{W}\left(z^*, z + \frac{\partial}{\partial z^*}\right) \quad (7\text{-}104)$$

Alongside this relation let us put Eq. (7-88) evaluated for $z' = z$, which reads

$$\langle z|:\mathcal{O}(a^\dagger, a):|z\rangle = \mathcal{O}(z^*, z) \quad (7\text{-}105)$$

The content of these two relations may be summed up by the equation

$$\begin{aligned}\langle z|\mathcal{W}(a^\dagger, a)|z\rangle &= \mathcal{W}\left(z^*, z + \frac{\partial}{\partial z^*}\right)\\ &\equiv \mathcal{W}_n(z^*, z) = \langle z|:\mathcal{W}_n(a^\dagger, a):|z\rangle\end{aligned} \quad (7\text{-}106)$$

where $\mathcal{W}_n$ is the associated function of z^* and z that arises after the differentiations $\partial/\partial z^*$ within $\mathcal{W}$ have been carried out [as if a "one" stood to the right in (7-104)]. Equation (7-106) provides a conceptually simple prescription to pass from an operator $\mathcal{W}(a^\dagger, a)$ to the *same operator*, but which is now expressed in normal form, namely,

$$:\mathcal{W}_n(a^\dagger, a): = \mathcal{W}(a^\dagger, a) \tag{7-107}$$

For example, if $\mathcal{W} = aa^\dagger$, then

$$\begin{aligned}\langle z|aa^\dagger|z\rangle &= \left(z + \frac{\partial}{\partial z^*}\right) z^* = zz^* + 1 \equiv \mathcal{W}_n(z^*, z)\\ &= \langle z|:(aa^\dagger + 1):|z\rangle\end{aligned}$$

which implies that $aa^\dagger = a^\dagger a + 1$ as we know.

Relations of the foregoing type to deduce normal ordered forms for operators were essentially first introduced by Anderson [7-14] in the context of quantum field theory. More recently, their use in quantum, coherence theory problems has been studied by Louisell [7-2], by Lax [7-15], and by others. A central feature of the approach of these authors may be exhibited if we look at the operator equation $i\hbar(\partial/\partial t)U(t) = \mathcal{H}U(t)$ [compare (6-13)] suitable for the evolution operator $U(t)$. This operator equation may be expressed as a partial differential equation through the chain

$$\begin{aligned}i\hbar \frac{\partial}{\partial t} U_n(z^*, z, t) &= i\hbar \frac{\partial}{\partial t} \langle z|U(a^\dagger, a, t)|z\rangle\\ &= \langle z|\mathcal{H}(a^\dagger, a)U(a^\dagger, a, t)|z\rangle\\ &= \mathcal{H}\left(z^*, z + \frac{\partial}{\partial z^*}\right) U\left(z^*, z + \frac{\partial}{\partial z^*}, t\right)\\ &= \mathcal{H}\left(z^*, z + \frac{\partial}{\partial z^*}\right) U_n(z^*, z, t)\end{aligned} \tag{7-108}$$

of which the solution, U_n, directly leads to a *normally ordered form* for U given by

$$U(a^\dagger, a, t) = :U_n(a^\dagger, a, t): \tag{7-109}$$

This concludes our discussion of examples and properties of vectors and operators in coherent-state continuous representations. We hasten to add that we have largely treated our operators heuristically, ignoring all questions of domains. Quite clearly, however, *our remarks apply to every bounded operator*, and to sufficiently well-behaved unbounded ones as well, e.g., *all polynomials in a and $a^\dagger$*. One can readily invent operators for which our discussion does not apply; e.g., difficulties arise already with (7-83) and (7-84), for those $\mathcal{B}$ such that $b_n = (n!)^\sigma$ whenever $\sigma \geq \frac{1}{2}$. The reader may do well to ponder the less obvious difficulties that occur when $1 > \sigma \geq \frac{1}{2}$.

D. Connection to Segal-Bargmann Spaces

We have noted above that each $\psi(z)$ is related to an entire analytic function in z^* by a fixed factor, namely, that

$$\langle z|\psi\rangle = \psi(z) = \exp(-\tfrac{1}{2}|z|^2)f(z^*)$$

Evidently $f(z^*)$ uniquely determines $\psi(z)$ and vice versa. Hence we can regard just the analytic function itself $f(z^*)$ as a functional *representative* of the abstract vector $|\psi\rangle$. Every member of this functional representation is an entire analytic function. If $f_j(z^*)$ is the entire function which corresponds to $|\psi_j\rangle$, then clearly a suitable definition of inner product is given through the chain

$$\begin{aligned}\langle\psi_1|\psi_2\rangle &= \frac{1}{\pi}\int d^2z\langle\psi_1|z\rangle\langle z|\psi_2\rangle \\ &= \frac{1}{\pi}\int d^2z[f_1(z^*)]^* \exp(-|z|^2)f_2(z^*) \\ &\equiv \int [f_1(z^*)]^*f_2(z^*)\, d\mu \qquad (7\text{-}110)\end{aligned}$$

where here we set

$$d\mu \equiv (\pi)^{-1} \exp(-|z|^2)\, d(\mathrm{Re}\, z)\, d(\mathrm{Im}\, z) \qquad (7\text{-}111)$$

With (7-110) as the scalar product it is intuitively clear that we have formed a Hilbert space composed out of entire functions $f(z^*)$. Such spaces have been employed by Segal [7-5] and Bargmann [7-6] in various quantum applications, and their properties have been studied thoroughly in a paper by Bargmann [7-6]. [5] The connection between the Segal-Bargmann spaces and the coherent-state continuous representations was noted by Schweber [7-7]. The simple connection between $\langle z|\psi\rangle$ and $f(z^*)$ makes it clear that there are numerous features of the Segal-Bargmann spaces that are shared by the coherent-state continuous representations (and a few that are not!). Of all these features we want only to mention that the analyticity properties—which are evidently in the foreground in the Segal-Bargmann form as well—have been used by Bargmann in a way which sheds light on the overcompleteness of the coherent states $|z\rangle$.

Bargmann calls a characteristic set $\mathfrak{S}^*$ of complex values z^* a set such that if $f(z^*) = 0$ for all $z^* \in \mathfrak{S}^*$, then $f(z^*) = 0$ for all z^*. Accordingly this means that if $\psi(z) = 0$ for all $z \in \mathfrak{S}$, then $|\psi\rangle = 0$.[6] Bargmann gives two examples of characteristic sets: (a) Any infinite sequence of points in the complex plane which converge to a finite limit. This example is a

[5] In these various works what we here call $f(z^*)$ is generally called $f(z)$.

[6] In our physicist's terminology, the set of vectors $\{|z\rangle: z \in \mathfrak{S}\}$ is a complete set.

pure consequence of analyticity and includes as a special case the more familiar examples of a line segment or an open set in the complex plane. (b) Any infinite sequence a_ν, $a_\nu \neq 0$, such that

$$\sigma = \sum_{\nu=1}^{\infty} |a_\nu|^{-2-\eta} = \infty \tag{7-112}$$

for some positive η. This condition is a property of an entire analytic function with the growth condition (7-47) superimposed.

We note that von Neumann's observation of a characteristic (i.e., "complete") set determined by a suitable square lattice of points in the complex plane, which we mentioned earlier, is yet a third example of a characteristic set satisfying neither (a) nor (b) above.

Space does not permit us to elaborate on the interesting uses of coherent states and related quantities as generating functions for various states and operators. These techniques were already used by Fock in the earliest days of quantum theory. In the hands of Schwinger, they have provided an elegant approach to quantum field theory rather like the methods alluded to in Chapter 4.

7-3 COHERENT STATES FOR SEVERAL DEGREES OF FREEDOM

The properties of coherent states for several degrees of freedom are straightforward generalizations of our earlier remarks for a single degree of freedom. We shall content ourselves with some definitions and dimensional questions, leaving the rest to the reader's imagination.

Suppose we deal with K degrees of freedom, their appropriate number operators $N_k = a_k{}^\dagger a_k$, $k = 1, 2, \ldots, K$, and their common set of normalized eigenvectors

$$|n_1, n_2, \ldots, n_K\rangle = |\{n_k\}\rangle$$

which we introduced in (5-70). Then the appropriate coherent states depend on K complex variables and are defined by analogy with (7-1) as

$$\begin{aligned} |z_1, z_2, \ldots, z_K\rangle &= |\{z_k\}\rangle \\ &= \sum_{\{n_k\}=0}^{\infty} \left\{ \prod_{k'=1}^{K} \exp(-\tfrac{1}{2}|z_{k'}|^2) \frac{(z_{k'})^{n_{k'}}}{(n_{k'}!)^{1/2}} \right\} |\{n_k\}\rangle \end{aligned} \tag{7-113}$$

along with an obvious definition for the adjoint vectors $\langle\{z_k\}|$.

These states are, of course, ground states of K independent, driven oscillators with appropriate driving forces. Likewise $|\{z_k\}\rangle$ is a simultaneous eigenvector of $a_{k'}$,

$$a_{k'}|\{z_k\}\rangle = z_{k'}|\{z_k\}\rangle \tag{7-114}$$

for each $k' = 1, 2, \ldots, K$.

The overlap of two coherent states is simply

$$\begin{aligned}\langle\{z_k\}|\{z'_k\}\rangle &= \prod_{k=1}^{K} \exp\{-\tfrac{1}{2}|z_k|^2 + z_k{}^*z'_k - \tfrac{1}{2}|z'_k|^2\} \\ &= \exp\left\{-\sum_{k=1}^{K} [\tfrac{1}{2}|z_k|^2 - z_k{}^*z'_k + \tfrac{1}{2}|z'_k|^2]\right\} \\ &= \exp\left\{-\sum_{k=1}^{K} [\tfrac{1}{2}|z_k - z'_k|^2 - i\,\mathrm{Im}(z_k{}^*z'_k)]\right\}\end{aligned} \tag{7-115}$$

the last form following directly from (7-31). Normalization and continuity of the states $|\{z_k\}\rangle$ and analyticity of the functions $f(\{z_k{}^*\}) \equiv \exp(\frac{1}{2}\Sigma|z_k|^2)\langle\{z_k\}|\psi\rangle$ are all immediate.

The key formula in (7-48) for the resolution of unity generalizes to

$$I = \frac{1}{\pi^K}\int \cdots \int |\{z_k\}\rangle\langle\{z_k\}| \prod_{k=1}^{K} d^2z_k \tag{7-116}$$

where $d^2z_k = d(\mathrm{Re}\, z_k)\, d(\mathrm{Im}\, z_k)$ and the integration extends over the whole $2K$-dimensional space. The proof of this resolution follows that given for the single degree of freedom case. It is convenient to write the π^{-K} and volume element more compactly as

$$\pi^{-K} \prod_{k=1}^{K} d^2z_k = d\mu(\{z_k\}) \tag{7-117}$$

so that (7-116) is simply given by

$$I = \int |\{z_k\}\rangle\langle\{z_k\}|\, d\mu(\{z_k\}) \tag{7-118}$$

The whole apparatus of the continuous representation may be introduced with the aid of (7-118). The formula for inner products reads

$$\langle\lambda|\psi\rangle = \int \langle\lambda|\{z_k\}\rangle\langle\{z_k\}|\psi\rangle\, d\mu(\{z_k\}) \tag{7-119}$$

etc. Operators have both kernel and partial differential operator representations. We note that the normal order operation $:\ \ :$ extends so as to put *all* creation operators $a_k{}^\dagger$ to the left of *all* annihilation operators $a_{k'}$ in each factor.

The aspect we want to stress most here is the role played by the angular frequencies ω_k of a problem dealing with several harmonic oscillators. When we deal with more than one oscillator at a time we cannot, in general, choose units so that they all have unit angular frequency. Hence it is most convenient to display the role of each ω_k explicitly.

The physical "coordinate" and "momentum" operators, Q_k and P_k, are related to the a_k and $a_k^\dagger$ according to Eq. (5-68). In similar fashion we introduce our K degree of freedom phase-space form by the decomposition

$$z_k \equiv (\omega_k/2\hbar)^{1/2}q_k + i(1/2\omega_k\hbar)^{1/2}p_k \tag{7-120}$$

for each k. As usual we shall define $|\{p_k, q_k\}\rangle = |\{z_k\}\rangle$. In terms of these variables the functional representative of the simultaneous oscillator ground state $|0\rangle \equiv |\{0\}\rangle$ is given by

$$\varphi_0(\{p_k, q_k\}) = \langle\{p_k, q_k\}|0\rangle = \exp\left[-\frac{1}{4\hbar}\sum_{k=1}^{K}(\omega_k^{-1}p_k^2 + \omega_k q_k^2)\right] \tag{7-121}$$

If we recast this expression as

$$\exp\left\{-\frac{1}{2}\sum_{k=1}^{K}\left[\frac{\frac{1}{2}(p_k^2 + \omega_k^2 q_k^2)}{\hbar\omega_k}\right]\right\}$$

we see that it has the rather easily remembered form:

$$\text{ground state} = \exp\left\{-\frac{1}{2}\sum_{\text{oscill.}}\left[\frac{(\text{classical oscillator energy})}{(\text{quantum level spacing})}\right]\right\} \tag{7-122}$$

It is worth noting the slight distinction in the resolution of unity (7-118) when it is expressed in phase-space form. In particular,

$$I = \int|\{p_k, q_k\}\rangle\langle\{p_k, q_k\}|\, d\mu(\{p_k, q_k\}) \tag{7-123}$$

where, as follows immediately from (7-117) and (7-120),

$$d\mu(\{p_k, q_k\}) = \prod_{k=1}^{K}\frac{dp_k\, dq_k}{2\pi\hbar} \tag{7-124}$$

and the integration extends over all K-dimensional phase space. It follows, therefore, that the function (7-121) satisfies

$$\begin{aligned} 1 &= \int\langle 0|\{p_k, q_k\}\rangle\langle\{p_k, q_k\}|0\rangle\, d\mu(\{p_k, q_k\}) \\ &= \int|\varphi_0(\{p_k, q_k\})|^2\, d\mu(\{p_k, q_k\}) \end{aligned} \tag{7-125}$$

as is readily verified.

7-4 COHERENT STATES FOR INFINITELY MANY DEGREES OF FREEDOM: APPLICATION TO THE ELECTROMAGNETIC FIELD

A. General Features

We now take up the transition ($K \to \infty$) to an infinite number of degrees of freedom suitable for a description of the electromagnetic field. As in Chapter 5, we carry out this transition on the assumption that

$$N = \sum_{k=1}^{\infty} N_k \tag{7-126}$$

and

$$\mathcal{H} = \sum_{k=1}^{\infty} \hbar\omega_k N_k \tag{7-127}$$

are well-defined operators. As we noted there, to win these properties it suffices that our simultaneous number operator eigenstates

$$|n_1, n_2, \ldots\rangle = |\{n_k\}\rangle \tag{7-128}$$

each fulfill the condition

$$\sum_{k=1}^{\infty} n_k < \infty \tag{7-129}$$

and thus are countable in number.

To define the coherent states for infinitely many degrees of freedom, let us first introduce a preliminary state,

$$|\text{pre}\rangle \equiv \sum_{\{n_k\}=0}^{\infty} \left\{ \prod_{k'=1}^{\infty} \frac{(z_{k'})^{n_{k'}}}{(n_{k'}!)^{1/2}} \right\} |\{n_k\}\rangle \tag{7-130}$$

and see for what z_k values it is a bona fide vector. From the orthogonal character of $|\{n_k\}\rangle$ we find that

$$\begin{aligned}
\langle \text{pre}|\text{pre}\rangle &= \sum_{\{n_k\}=0}^{\infty} \prod_{k'=1}^{\infty} \frac{|z_{k'}|^{2n_{k'}}}{(n_{k'}!)} \\
&= \prod_{k'=1}^{\infty} \sum_{n_{k'}=0}^{\infty} \frac{|z_{k'}|^{2n_{k'}}}{(n_{k'}!)} \\
&= \exp\left\{ \sum_{k'=1}^{\infty} |z_{k'}|^2 \right\}
\end{aligned} \tag{7-131}$$

which to be finite requires that $\{z_k\}$ satisfy

$$\sum_{k'=1}^{\infty} |z_{k'}|^2 < \infty \tag{7-132}$$

Since all vectors must have finite norm we shall henceforth adopt the condition (7-132), which evidently has the following basic consequence: The allowed sequences $\{z_k\}$ *themselves form a Hilbert space* $\mathfrak{Z}$ (different from the quantum mechanical Hilbert space $\mathfrak{H}$) with an inner product

$$(\{z_k\}, \{z'_k\}) \equiv \sum_{k=1}^{\infty} z_k{}^* z'_k \tag{7-133a}$$

and (norm)^2

$$\|\{z_k\}\|^2 = (\{z_k\}, \{z_k\}) = \sum_{k=1}^{\infty} |z_k|^2 \tag{7-133b}$$

In other words, the *argument* $\{z_k\}$ of the Hilbert space vector $|\{z_k\}\rangle \in \mathfrak{H}$ is itself a vector in a different, but still infinite-dimensional Hilbert space, $\{z_k\} \in \mathfrak{Z}$. We shall sometimes have occasion to represent the vector in $\mathfrak{Z}$ corresponding to $\{z_k\}$ by other than the sequence $\{z_k\}$.

Always retaining the restriction (7-132), we can now define

$$\begin{aligned} |z_1, z_2, \ldots\rangle = |\{z_k\}\rangle &= \exp\left(-\frac{1}{2}\sum_{k'=1}^{\infty} |z_{k'}|^2\right)|\text{pre}\rangle \\ &= \sum_{\{n_k\}=0}^{\infty} \left\{\prod_{k'=1}^{\infty} \exp(-\tfrac{1}{2}|z_{k'}|^2)\frac{(z_{k'})^{n_{k'}}}{(n_{k'}!)^{1/2}}\right\} |\{n_k\}\rangle \end{aligned} \tag{7-134}$$

as the requisite coherent states along with their adjoints $\langle\{z_k\}|$.

Besides being driven oscillator ground states, the states $|\{z_k\}\rangle$ are simultaneous eigenvectors of $a_{k'}$,

$$a_{k'}|\{z_k\}\rangle = z_{k'}|\{z_k\}\rangle \tag{7-135}$$

for each $k' = 1, 2, \ldots$. In virtue of (7-132) it follows that

$$\lim_{k'\to\infty} a_{k'}|\{z_k\}\rangle = \lim_{k'\to\infty} z_{k'}|\{z_k\}\rangle = 0 \tag{7-136}$$

This has the implication that, for high enough k values, each coherent state tends to look like an oscillator ground state. On the other hand, for any preassigned value of k' there is a coherent state with an arbitrarily high value for $z_{k'}$.

The overlap of two such coherent states is clearly given by the limit as $K \to \infty$ of (7-115), which yields

$$\langle \{z_k\} | \{z'_k\} \rangle = \prod_{k=1}^{\infty} \exp\{-\tfrac{1}{2}|z_k|^2 + z_k{}^* z'_k - \tfrac{1}{2}|z'_k|^2\}$$
$$= \exp\left\{-\sum_{k=1}^{\infty} [\tfrac{1}{2}|z_k|^2 - z_k{}^* z'_k + \tfrac{1}{2}|z'_k|^2]\right\}$$
$$= \exp\left\{-\sum_{k=1}^{\infty} [\tfrac{1}{2}|z_k - z'_k|^2 - i\,\mathrm{Im}(z_k{}^* z'_k)]\right\} \quad (7\text{-}137)$$

Questions of convergence of the infinite products and sums all hinge, of course, on the fundamental restriction (7-132).

A calculation patterned after that leading to (7-40) shows that

$$\| \, |\{z_k\}\rangle - |\{z'_k\}\rangle \|^2 \leq 2(\|\{z_k\}\| + \|\{z'_k\}\|) \cdot \|\{z_k - z'_k\}\| \quad (7\text{-}138)$$

In consequence, two coherent states are nearby whenever the associated sequences $\{z_k\}$ are nearby as vectors in $\mathfrak{Z}$. This property has an important and physically reasonable consequence. Suppose, for a given vector $|\{z_k\}\rangle$, that $z_k \neq 0$ for all k. On physical grounds we suspect that we could approximate the state $|\{z_k\}\rangle$ by the state $|\{z'_k\}\rangle$ for which $z_k \equiv z'_k$, $k \leq M$, while $z'_k \equiv 0$, $k > M$, if M is large enough. Let us call such a sequence a *truncated sequence* and denote it by $\{z_{k,M}\}$. That is,

$$z_{k,M} \equiv z_k \quad (k \leq M) \qquad z_{k,M} \equiv 0 \quad (k > M) \qquad (7\text{-}139)$$

Then it follows from (7-138) and $\|\{z_{k,M}\}\| \leq \|\{z_k\}\|$ that

$$\| \, |\{z_k\}\rangle - |\{z_{k,M}\}\rangle \|^2 \leq 4\|\{z_k\}\| \left\{ \sum_{k=M+1}^{\infty} |z_k|^2 \right\}^{1/2} \qquad (7\text{-}140)$$

which can, indeed, be made arbitrarily small for large enough M, thus confirming our intuition.

The basic functions in the coherent-state continuous representation are given by

$$\psi(\{z_k\}) = \langle \{z_k\} | \psi \rangle \qquad (7\text{-}141)$$

for each $|\psi\rangle \in \mathfrak{H}$. Since the states $|\{n_k\}\rangle$ are complete, so too are the coherent states. Indeed, as before, the coherent states are overcomplete. We have noted for a single degree of freedom that analyticity arguments may be used to find complete, proper subsets of the coherent states. Obviously such arguments apply to several degrees of freedom, and for finitely many of the infinite number of degrees of freedom under present discussion. We wish instead to emphasize a different sort of complete, proper subset which arises only for infinitely many degrees of freedom.

Suppose it is known that

$$\psi(\{z_{k,M}\}) = 0 \tag{7-142}$$

for all $\{z_k\}$ and for all M, i.e., for all truncated sequences. Then it follows for a general state $|\{z_k\}\rangle$ that

$$\begin{aligned} |\langle\{z_k\}|\psi\rangle| &\leq |\langle\{z_{k,M}\}|\psi\rangle| + |(\langle\{z_k\}| - \langle\{z_{k,M}\}|)|\psi\rangle| \\ &\leq \| \, |\{z_k\}\rangle - |\{z_{k,M}\}\rangle\| \cdot \| \, |\psi\rangle\| \\ &\leq 2\| \, |\psi\rangle\| \cdot \|\{z_k\}\|^{1/2} \cdot \left\{ \sum_{k=M+1}^{\infty} |z_k|^2 \right\}^{1/4} \end{aligned} \tag{7-143}$$

which for large enough M can be made as small as desired. In short, Eq. (7-142) leads to the vanishing of $\psi(\{z_k\})$ for *all* sequences $\{z_k\}$ and, thus, to the vanishing of $|\psi\rangle$. More generally, we can easily see that $|\psi\rangle$ is determined by the values of $\psi(\{z_k\})$ for any collection of $\{z_k\}$ sequences which is dense in $\mathfrak{Z}$.

"Resolution of Unity." Let us now turn to the analog for infinitely many degrees of freedom of our usual coherent-state resolution of unity, and the associated inner product in the functional representation. In line with (7-118) and (7-119) we could reasonably expect something like

$$I = \int |\{z_k\}\rangle\langle\{z_k\}| \, d\mu(\{z_k\}) \tag{7-144}$$

and

$$\langle\lambda|\psi\rangle = \int \langle\lambda|\{z_k\}\rangle\langle\{z_k\}|\psi\rangle \, d\mu(\{z_k\}) \tag{7-145}$$

to hold. However, as they stand these equations are quite undefined since we are asking for an integral over infinitely many variables.

On intuitive grounds we might suspect that the relation

$$\langle\lambda|\psi\rangle = \lim_{M\to\infty} \int \langle\lambda|\{z_{k,M}\}\rangle\langle\{z_{k,M}\}|\psi\rangle \, d\mu(\{z_{k,M}\}) \tag{7-146}$$

would hold true where

$$d\mu(\{z_{k,M}\}) \equiv \pi^{-M} \prod_{k=1}^{M} d^2 z_k \tag{7-147}$$

An intuitive basis behind (7-146) is simply this: Since we are dealing only with continuous functions $\langle\{z_k\}|\psi\rangle$, etc., each function, as we remarked earlier, is completely determined by its values on a dense set. The integral (7-146) is defined simply as the limit of a sequence of integrals whose integrands are evaluated on a dense set as M becomes arbitrarily large.

The essentials for a proof of (7-146) may be given as follows. Let us first introduce a sequence of projection operators P_M, $M = 1, 2, \ldots,$

each defined by the property that

$$\langle\{z_k\}|P_M|\{z_k'\}\rangle = \exp\Big[-\tfrac{1}{2}\sum_{k=1}^{\infty}(|z_k|^2+|z_k'|^2)+\sum_{k=1}^{M}z_k{}^*z_k'\Big] \quad (7\text{-}148)$$

This implies, roughly speaking, that P_M is a projection onto the ground state for all degrees of freedom $k > M$. As such it is reasonably clear that $P_M P_{M'} = P_{M'} P_M = P_M$ for $M \leq M'$, and that

$$\lim_{M\to\infty} P_M = I \quad (7\text{-}149)$$

Now a straightforward computation involving Gaussian integrals shows that

$$\int\langle\{z_k'\}|\{z_{k,M}\}\rangle\langle\{z_{k,M}\}|\{z_k''\}\rangle\, d\mu(\{z_{k,M}\}) = \langle\{z_k'\}|P_M|\{z_k''\}\rangle \quad (7\text{-}150)$$

as defined by (7-148). Standard theorems then imply that

$$P_M = \int|\{z_{k,M}\}\rangle\langle\{z_{k,M}\}|\, d\mu(\{z_{k,M}\}) \quad (7\text{-}151)$$

Consequently, we see that for arbitrary $|\lambda\rangle$ and $|\psi\rangle$,

$$\begin{aligned}\langle\lambda|\psi\rangle &= \lim_{M\to\infty}\langle\lambda|P_M|\psi\rangle \\ &= \lim_{M\to\infty}\int\langle\lambda|\{z_{k,M}\}\rangle\langle\{z_{k,M}\}|\psi\rangle\, d\mu(\{z_{k,M}\})\end{aligned} \quad (7\text{-}152)$$

validating (7-146) which was our aim. Finally, by combining (7-149) and (7-151) we see that

$$I = \lim_{M\to\infty}\int|\{z_{k,M}\}\rangle\langle\{z_{k,M}\}|\, d\mu(\{z_{k,M}\}) \quad (7\text{-}153)$$

which is the form taken by our traditional resolution of unity in the present case. Equations (7-152) and (7-153) constitute the proper generalizations of (7-119) and (7-118) to infinitely many degrees of freedom. As abbreviations for the proper limiting relations, we shall frequently use simply (7-144) and (7-145), which can now be given a meaning through the proper relations (7-153) and (7-152).

Continuous Representation. Now that we are able to give meaning to our usual resolution of unity, the whole apparatus of the coherent-state continuous representation may be taken over from our simpler discussion. In particular, the representation of operators may be given by

$$\langle\{z_k\}|\mathcal{B}|\psi\rangle = \int\langle\{z_k\}|\mathcal{B}|\{z_k'\}\rangle\langle\{z_k'\}|\psi\rangle\, d\mu(\{z_k'\}) \quad (7\text{-}154)$$

with the aid of the integral kernel $\langle\{z_k\}|\mathcal{B}|\{z_k'\}\rangle$. There are differential operator representations as well, which are analogous to (7-95). If

$\mathcal{W}(\{a_k^\dagger\}, \{a_k\})$ depends on the creation and annihilation operators, then

$$\langle\{z_k\}|\mathcal{W}(\{a_k^\dagger\}, \{a_k\})|\psi\rangle = \mathcal{W}(\{z_k^*\}, \{z_k/2 + \partial/\partial z_k^*\})\langle\{z_k\}|\psi\rangle \quad (7\text{-}155)$$

Normal ordered operators fulfill

$$\langle\{z_k\}|{:}\mathcal{O}(\{a_k^\dagger\}, \{a_k\}){:}|\{z_k'\}\rangle = \mathcal{O}(\{z_k^*\}, \{z_k'\})\langle\{z_k\}|\{z_k'\}\rangle \quad (7\text{-}156)$$

and we have the relation [cf. (7-106)]

$$\begin{aligned}\langle\{z_k\}|\mathcal{W}(\{a_k^\dagger\}, \{a_k\})|\{z_k\}\rangle &= \mathcal{W}(\{z_k^*\}, \{z_k + \partial/\partial z_k^*\}) \\ &\equiv \mathcal{W}_n(\{z_k^*\}, \{z_k\}) \\ &= \langle\{z_k\}|{:}\mathcal{W}_n(\{a_k^\dagger\}, \{a_k\}){:}|\{z_k\}\rangle \quad (7\text{-}157)\end{aligned}$$

which connects $\mathcal{W}$ and ${:}\mathcal{W}_n{:} = \mathcal{W}$ through their diagonal elements.

In related fashion we may set

$$|\psi\rangle = \int|\{z_k\}\rangle\langle\{z_k\}|\psi\rangle\, d\mu(\{z_k\}) \quad (7\text{-}158)$$

and

$$\mathcal{B} = \iint|\{z_k\}\rangle\langle\{z_k\}|\mathcal{B}|\{z_k'\}\rangle\langle\{z_k'\}|\, d\mu(\{z_k\})\, d\mu(\{z_k'\}) \quad (7\text{-}159)$$

as representations for the abstract vectors $|\psi\rangle$ and operators $\mathcal{B}$, respectively. The reader may easily transcribe into the present context further remarks made in connection with the single degree of freedom example.

Quite clearly our whole discussion including Eqs. (7-152) and (7-153) has a completely analogous phase-space formulation in which we focus attention on q_k and p_k as defined through

$$z_k = (\omega_k/2\hbar)^{1/2}q_k + i(1/2\omega_k\hbar)^{1/2}p_k \quad (7\text{-}160)$$

for all k. We note that in this formulation allowed phase-space sequences $\{p_k, q_k\}$ must fulfill

$$\frac{1}{2\hbar}\sum_{k=1}^{\infty}(\omega_k^{-1}p_k^2 + \omega_k q_k^2) < \infty \quad (7\text{-}161)$$

in virtue of (7-132). The ground-state representative follows directly from (7-137) as

$$\varphi_0(\{p_k, q_k\}) = \langle\{p_k, q_k\}|0\rangle = \exp\left[-\frac{1}{4\hbar}\sum_{k=1}^{\infty}(\omega_k^{-1}p_k^2 + \omega_k q_k^2)\right] \quad (7\text{-}162)$$

which obviously still has the schematic form of (7-122). Let us postpone a further discussion of phase-space aspects until after we examine the radiation field.

B. Application to the Electromagnetic Field

As we have shown in Chapter 6, the electromagnetic field can be viewed as an assemblage of driven harmonic oscillators. When imagined to be in a large cubic box of volume $\Omega = L^3$, the appropriate, independent, normal modes are conveniently labeled by λ and $\mathbf{k}$, a polarization index and a momentum variable quantized in accordance with (6-40). The value $\mathbf{k} \equiv 0$ is explicitly excluded. The label pair λ, $\mathbf{k}$ corresponds to what was generically called k above.

For the present discussion we limit ourselves to the free-radiation field and to the radiation field in the presence of c-number sources. As we noted in Chapter 6, it is only for these cases that an irreducible quantization is possible so that the number eigenstates or the coherent states actually span the full Hilbert space. For these cases the time-dependent form of the annihilation operator for the $(\lambda, \mathbf{k})$th mode is given by (6-59) as

$$a_\lambda(\mathbf{k}, t) = e^{-i\omega t} a_\lambda^{in}(\mathbf{k}) + c_\lambda(\mathbf{k}, t) \tag{7-163}$$

where the angular frequency for this mode is just $\omega = \omega_{\lambda,\mathbf{k}} = |\mathbf{k}|$. In terms of the c-number current $\mathcal{J}_\lambda(\mathbf{k}, t)$, it follows from (6-55) that

$$c_\lambda(\mathbf{k}, t) = i(2\hbar\omega)^{-1/2} e^{-i\omega t} \int_{-\infty}^{t} e^{i\omega t'} \mathcal{J}_\lambda(\mathbf{k}, t')\, dt' \tag{7-164}$$

We take $|\{n_\lambda(\mathbf{k})\}\rangle$ as the number eigenstates of the operators

$$N_\lambda^{in}(\mathbf{k}) = a_\lambda^{in\dagger}(\mathbf{k}) a_\lambda^{in}(\mathbf{k}) \tag{7-165}$$

It follows that the coherent states $|\{z_\lambda(\mathbf{k})\}\rangle$ defined in the manner of (7-134) satisfy the condition

$$a_\lambda^{in}(\mathbf{k})|\{z_\lambda(\mathbf{k})\}\rangle = z_\lambda(\mathbf{k})|\{z_\lambda(\mathbf{k})\}\rangle \tag{7-166}$$

for all λ and $\mathbf{k}$. In turn, the time-dependent annihilation operators satisfy

$$a_\lambda(\mathbf{k}, t)|\{z_\lambda(\mathbf{k})\}\rangle = [e^{-i\omega t} z_\lambda(\mathbf{k}) + c_\lambda(\mathbf{k}, t)]|\{z_\lambda(\mathbf{k})\}\rangle \tag{7-167}$$

and, thus, the coherent states are eigenstates of $a_\lambda(\mathbf{k}, t)$ as well. Let us introduce the abbreviation

$$z_\lambda(\mathbf{k}, t) \equiv e^{-i\omega t} z_\lambda(\mathbf{k}) + c_\lambda(\mathbf{k}, t) \tag{7-168}$$

which, in fact, is just the complex form of the *classical* solution to Maxwell's equations with sources.

If, in the manner of (6-15), we adopt

$$U(t) = T\left\{\exp\left[-\left(i/\hbar\right)\int_{-\infty}^{t} \mathcal{H}(t')\,dt'\right]\right\} \tag{7-169}$$

as the evolution operator with $\mathcal{H}$ being given by (6-46), then

$$a_\lambda(\mathbf{k}, t) = U(t)^{-1} a_\lambda^{in}(\mathbf{k})\, U(t) \tag{7-170}$$

By multiplying (7-167) by $U(t)$, we see that

$$a_\lambda^{in}(\mathbf{k})\, U(t)|\{z_\lambda(\mathbf{k})\}\rangle = z_\lambda(\mathbf{k}, t)\, U(t)|\{z_\lambda(\mathbf{k})\}\rangle \tag{7-171}$$

which implies that

$$U(t)|\{z_\lambda(\mathbf{k})\}\rangle = e^{i\varphi(t)}|\{z_\lambda(\mathbf{k}, t)\}\rangle \tag{7-172}$$

for some phase function $\varphi(t)$. It may be shown that

$$\varphi(t) = \sum_{\lambda,\mathbf{k}} \int_{-\infty}^{t} \mathcal{J}_\lambda(\mathbf{k}, t')\,(2\hbar\omega)^{-1/2}\, \mathrm{Re}[z_\lambda(\mathbf{k}, t')]\, dt' \tag{7-173}$$

which depends on both the initial state and the driving terms. In summary, we note that in the presence of an external c-number source $\mathcal{J}_\lambda(\mathbf{k}, t)$, a coherent state evolves (up to a phase factor) into another coherent state which is completely determined by the classical solution in the presence of the source.

A common application of this basic result is to exhibit photon emission and absorption by c-number sources. Let us ask what distribution for $\{n_k\}$ would be found at time t due to the presence of the source. Clearly from (7-134) we find

$$\begin{aligned} p(\{n_\lambda(\mathbf{k})\}|t) &= |\langle\{n_\lambda(\mathbf{k})\}|U(t)|\{z_\lambda(\mathbf{k})\}\rangle|^2 \\ &= |\langle\{n_\lambda(\mathbf{k})\}|\{z_\lambda(\mathbf{k}, t)\}\rangle|^2 \\ &= \prod_{\lambda,\mathbf{k}} \frac{|z_\lambda(\mathbf{k}, t)|^{2n_\lambda(\mathbf{k})}}{[n_\lambda(\mathbf{k})]!} \exp[-|z_\lambda(\mathbf{k}, t)|^2] \end{aligned} \tag{7-174}$$

which is just a multiple Poisson distribution for all t with

$$\langle n_\lambda(\mathbf{k})\rangle = |z_\lambda(\mathbf{k}, t)|^2 \tag{7-175}$$

These results are traditionally quoted for emission from the vacuum state [for which $z_\lambda(\mathbf{k}) = 0$], and, thus, where $z_\lambda(\mathbf{k}, t) = c_\lambda(\mathbf{k}, t)$, for all λ, $\mathbf{k}$, as given by (7-164).

Free Field. Let us now specialize to the free radiation field with no external currents. In this case for each mode we simply have

$$a_\lambda(\mathbf{k}, t) = e^{-i\omega t} a_\lambda^{in}(\mathbf{k}) \tag{7-176a}$$

$$z_\lambda(\mathbf{k}, t) = e^{-i\omega t} z_\lambda(\mathbf{k}) \tag{7-176b}$$

It is convenient to introduce a few abbreviations for related dynamical variables. If $\mathbf{e}_\lambda(k)$ denote the transverse polarization vectors [which appear in (6-25) and in following equations], then let us define the transverse vectors

$$\mathbf{a}(\mathbf{k}, t) = \sum_\lambda \mathbf{e}_\lambda(\mathbf{k}) a_\lambda(\mathbf{k}, t) \tag{7-177a}$$

$$\mathbf{z}(\mathbf{k}, t) = \sum_\lambda \mathbf{e}_\lambda(\mathbf{k}) z_\lambda(\mathbf{k}, t) \tag{7-177b}$$

which obviously fulfill (with $|\{z\}\rangle \equiv |\{z_\lambda(\mathbf{k})\}\rangle$)

$$\mathbf{a}(\mathbf{k}, t)|\{z\}\rangle = \mathbf{z}(\mathbf{k}, t)|\{z\}\rangle \tag{7-178}$$

Similarly let us define

$$\mathbf{A}^{(+)}(\mathbf{x}, t) = \frac{1}{L^{3/2}} \sum_\mathbf{k} (\hbar/2\omega)^{1/2} e^{i\mathbf{k}\cdot\mathbf{x}} \mathbf{a}(\mathbf{k}, t) \tag{7-179a}$$

$$\mathbf{V}(\mathbf{x}, t) = \frac{1}{L^{3/2}} \sum_\mathbf{k} (\hbar/2\omega)^{1/2} e^{i\mathbf{k}\cdot\mathbf{x}} \mathbf{z}(\mathbf{k}, t) \tag{7-179b}$$

which are clearly *positive frequency functions*, or *analytic signals* in the sense of Chapter 1. In addition let us set

$$\mathbf{E}^{(+)}(\mathbf{x}, t) = -\dot{\mathbf{A}}^{(+)}(\mathbf{x}, t) = \frac{i}{L^{3/2}} \sum_\mathbf{k} (\hbar\omega/2)^{1/2} e^{i\mathbf{k}\cdot\mathbf{x}} \mathbf{a}(\mathbf{k}, t) \tag{7-180a}$$

$$\boldsymbol{\varepsilon}(\mathbf{x}, t) = -\dot{\mathbf{V}}(\mathbf{x}, t) = \frac{i}{L^{3/2}} \sum_\mathbf{k} (\hbar\omega/2)^{1/2} e^{i\mathbf{k}\cdot\mathbf{x}} \mathbf{z}(\mathbf{k}, t) \tag{7-180b}$$

and

$$\mathbf{H}^{(+)}(\mathbf{x}, t) = \nabla \times \mathbf{A}^{(+)}(\mathbf{x}, t)$$
$$\mathfrak{n}(\mathbf{x}, t) = \nabla \times \mathbf{V}(\mathbf{x}, t)$$

We clearly see that the coherent states are eigenstates for all these positive-frequency operators; viz.,

$$\mathbf{A}^{(+)}(\mathbf{x}, t)|\{z\}\rangle = \mathbf{V}(\mathbf{x}, t)|\{z\}\rangle \tag{7-181a}$$
$$\mathbf{E}^{(+)}(\mathbf{x}, t)|\{z\}\rangle = \boldsymbol{\varepsilon}(\mathbf{x}, t)|\{z\}\rangle \tag{7-181b}$$
$$\mathbf{H}^{(+)}(\mathbf{x}, t)|\{z\}\rangle = \mathfrak{n}(\mathbf{x}, t)|\{z\}\rangle \tag{7-181c}$$

The adjoint operators are negative-frequency operators and are so denoted; viz.,

$$[\mathbf{A}^{(+)}(\mathbf{x}, t)]^\dagger \equiv \mathbf{A}^{(-)}(\mathbf{x}, t) \tag{7-182a}$$
$$[\mathbf{E}^{(+)}(\mathbf{x}, t)]^\dagger \equiv \mathbf{E}^{(-)}(\mathbf{x}, t) \tag{7-182b}$$
$$[\mathbf{H}^{(+)}(\mathbf{x}, t)]^\dagger \equiv \mathbf{H}^{(-)}(\mathbf{x}, t) \tag{7-182c}$$

Evidently from their construction the positive-frequency operators [hence the negative frequency ones as well] all commute among themselves.

As is our custom, let us also indicate an alternative phase-space notation for some of the foregoing expressions, which relates them to more familiar physical quantities. In analogy with (6-44a) and (6-35), let us set

$$\mathbf{z}(\mathbf{k}, t) = (\omega/2\hbar)^{1/2}\tilde{\mathbf{a}}(\mathbf{k}, t) - i(1/2\omega\hbar)^{1/2}\tilde{\mathbf{e}}(\mathbf{k}, t) \tag{7-183}$$

where the division between the first and second terms is based on the condition

$$\tilde{\mathbf{a}}^*(\mathbf{k}, t) = \tilde{\mathbf{a}}(-\mathbf{k}, t) \tag{7-184a}$$
$$\tilde{\mathbf{e}}^*(\mathbf{k}, t) = \tilde{\mathbf{e}}(-\mathbf{k}, t) \tag{7-184b}$$

In virtue of this condition the functions

$$\mathbf{a}(\mathbf{x}, t) \equiv \frac{1}{L^{3/2}} \sum_{\mathbf{k}} e^{i\mathbf{k}\cdot\mathbf{x}}\, \tilde{\mathbf{a}}(\mathbf{k}, t) \tag{7-185a}$$

$$\mathbf{e}(\mathbf{x}, t) \equiv \frac{1}{L^{3/2}} \sum_{\mathbf{k}} e^{i\mathbf{k}\cdot\mathbf{x}}\, \tilde{\mathbf{e}}(\mathbf{k}, t) \tag{7-185b}$$

are real. We shall have occasion to make use of

$$\tilde{\mathbf{h}}(\mathbf{k}, t) = i\mathbf{k} \times \tilde{\mathbf{a}}(\mathbf{k}, t) \tag{7-186}$$

and its real configuration space form

$$\mathbf{h}(\mathbf{x}, t) = \frac{1}{L^{3/2}} \sum_{\mathbf{k}} e^{i\mathbf{k}\cdot\mathbf{x}}\, \tilde{\mathbf{h}}(\mathbf{k}, t) \tag{7-187}$$

Our phase-space formulation is most conveniently expressed in terms of the real transverse vectors $\mathbf{e}(\mathbf{x})$ and $\mathbf{a}(\mathbf{x})$. We can also give it even a more direct physical appearance if we use $\mathbf{e}(\mathbf{x})$ and a "derivative" of $\mathbf{a}(\mathbf{x})$, namely $\mathbf{h}(\mathbf{x})$.

Ground-State Representative. Clearly the functions $\mathbf{e}(\mathbf{x})$ and $\mathbf{a}(\mathbf{x})$ [or $\mathbf{h}(\mathbf{x})$] determine the sequence $\{z_\lambda(\mathbf{k})\}$ and so determine the coherent state. To emphasize this fact let us introduce

$$|\mathbf{e}, \mathbf{a}\rangle \equiv |\mathbf{e}, \mathbf{h}\rangle \equiv |\{z_\lambda(\mathbf{k})\}\rangle \tag{7-188}$$

as alternative notations for the coherent states. Although the independent mode form is most convenient for practical calculations, it is instructive to give an example of the alternative phase-space notations.

As our basic example let us derive the ground-state representative expressed as a functional of $\mathbf{e}$ and $\mathbf{h}$. From (7-177b) and (7-183) it follows that

$$\exp\left(-\frac{1}{2}\sum_{\lambda,\mathbf{k}} |z_\lambda(\mathbf{k})|^2\right) = \exp\left(-\frac{1}{2}\sum_{\mathbf{k}} |\mathbf{z}(\mathbf{k})|^2\right)$$
$$= \exp\left(-\frac{1}{4\hbar}\sum_{\mathbf{k}} [\omega^{-1}|\tilde{\mathbf{e}}(\mathbf{k})|^2 + \omega|\tilde{\mathbf{a}}(\mathbf{k})|^2]\right) \tag{7-189}$$

which, on using

$$|\tilde{\mathbf{h}}(\mathbf{k})|^2 = [\mathbf{k} \times \tilde{\mathbf{a}}(\mathbf{k})^*] \cdot [\mathbf{k} \times \tilde{\mathbf{a}}(\mathbf{k})] = \mathbf{k}^2|\tilde{\mathbf{a}}(\mathbf{k})|^2 \tag{7-190}$$

reads (since $\omega^2 = \mathbf{k}^2$)

$$\exp\left(-\frac{1}{4\hbar}\sum_{\mathbf{k}} \omega^{-1}[|\tilde{\mathbf{e}}(\mathbf{k})|^2 + |\tilde{\mathbf{h}}(\mathbf{k})|^2]\right) \tag{7-191}$$

This latter relation assumes its most elegant form if we express it in configuration space and pass to the limit of infinite volume. When we employ the relations

$$\tilde{\mathbf{e}}(\mathbf{k}) = \frac{1}{L^{3/2}}\int e^{-i\mathbf{k}\cdot\mathbf{x}}\mathbf{e}(\mathbf{x})\, d^3x \tag{7-192a}$$

$$\tilde{\mathbf{h}}(\mathbf{k}) = \frac{1}{L^{3/2}}\int e^{-i\mathbf{k}\cdot\mathbf{x}}\mathbf{h}(\mathbf{x})\, d^3x \tag{7-192b}$$

(and their complex conjugates!), as well as the relation

$$\lim_{L\to\infty}\frac{1}{L^3}\sum_{\mathbf{k}}\frac{e^{i\mathbf{k}\cdot(\mathbf{x}-\mathbf{y})}}{|\mathbf{k}|} = \frac{1}{(2\pi)^3}\int\frac{e^{i\mathbf{k}\cdot(\mathbf{x}-\mathbf{y})}}{|\mathbf{k}|}\,d^3k$$
$$= \frac{1}{2\pi^2}\frac{1}{|\mathbf{x}-\mathbf{y}|^2} \tag{7-193}$$

then we readily deduce that (7-191) becomes

$$\varphi_0(\mathbf{e},\mathbf{h}) = \langle\mathbf{e},\mathbf{h}|0\rangle$$
$$= \exp\left\{-\frac{1}{8\pi^2\hbar}\iint\frac{[\mathbf{e}(\mathbf{x})\cdot\mathbf{e}(\mathbf{y}) + \mathbf{h}(\mathbf{x})\cdot\mathbf{h}(\mathbf{y})]}{|\mathbf{x}-\mathbf{y}|^2}\,d^3x\,d^3y\right\} \tag{7-194}$$

Physically, this is an expression for the probability amplitude of the ground state of the radiation field to be found in a displaced ground state for which

$$\langle\mathbf{E}(\mathbf{x})\rangle = \mathbf{e}(\mathbf{x}) \tag{7-195a}$$
$$\langle\mathbf{H}(\mathbf{x})\rangle = \mathbf{h}(\mathbf{x}) \tag{7-195b}$$

such as would be induced by an external source. From a formal point of view, it is worth remarking that the Hilbert space vector in $\mathfrak{Z}$ represented initially by the sequence $\{z_\lambda(\mathbf{k})\}$ is here represented by the pair of real functions $\mathbf{e}(\mathbf{x})$ and $\mathbf{h}(\mathbf{x})$, with a $(\text{norm})^2$ based on the double integral appearing in (7-194).

Our second example is a simple generalization of this, namely,

$$\langle \mathbf{e}, \mathbf{h} | \mathbf{e}', \mathbf{h}' \rangle = \exp \left\{ - \sum_{\mathbf{k}} [|\mathbf{z}(\mathbf{k}) - \mathbf{z}'(\mathbf{k})|^2 - i \operatorname{Im} \mathbf{z}^*(\mathbf{k}) \cdot \mathbf{z}'(\mathbf{k})] \right\} \tag{7-196}$$

as follows from (7-137). The only new term is

$$\begin{aligned} \Phi \equiv \sum_{\mathbf{k}} \operatorname{Im} \mathbf{z}^*(\mathbf{k}) \cdot \mathbf{z}'(\mathbf{k}) &= \frac{1}{2\hbar} \sum_{\mathbf{k}} [\tilde{\mathbf{e}}^*(\mathbf{k}) \cdot \tilde{\mathbf{a}}'(\mathbf{k}) - \tilde{\mathbf{a}}^*(\mathbf{k}) \cdot \tilde{\mathbf{e}}'(\mathbf{k})] \\ &= \frac{i}{2\hbar} \sum_{\mathbf{k}} \frac{1}{\omega^2} [\tilde{\mathbf{e}}^*(\mathbf{k}) \cdot \mathbf{k} \times \tilde{\mathbf{h}}'(\mathbf{k}) + \mathbf{k} \times \tilde{\mathbf{h}}^*(\mathbf{k}) \cdot \tilde{\mathbf{e}}'(\mathbf{k})] \end{aligned} \tag{7-197}$$

In configuration space, and in the limit of infinite volume, we find

$$\Phi = \frac{1}{2\hbar} \int [\mathbf{e}(\mathbf{x}) \cdot \mathbf{a}'(\mathbf{x}) - \mathbf{a}(\mathbf{x}) \cdot \mathbf{e}'(\mathbf{x})] \, d^3x \tag{7-198}$$

or, on making use of

$$\begin{aligned} \lim_{L \to \infty} \frac{1}{L^3} \sum_{\mathbf{k}} \frac{i\mathbf{k} e^{i\mathbf{k} \cdot (\mathbf{x} - \mathbf{y})}}{\omega^2} &= \frac{1}{(2\pi)^3} \int \frac{i\mathbf{k} e^{i\mathbf{k} \cdot (\mathbf{x} - \mathbf{y})}}{|\mathbf{k}|^2} \, d^3k \\ &= \nabla \frac{1}{4\pi |\mathbf{x} - \mathbf{y}|} \end{aligned} \tag{7-199}$$

we can write

$$\Phi = \frac{1}{8\pi\hbar} \iint \left[\mathbf{e}(\mathbf{x}) \cdot \nabla \frac{1}{|\mathbf{x} - \mathbf{y}|} \times \mathbf{h}'(\mathbf{y}) - \mathbf{h}(\mathbf{x}) \cdot \nabla \frac{1}{|\mathbf{x} - \mathbf{y}|} \times \mathbf{e}'(\mathbf{y}) \right] d^3x \, d^3y \tag{7-200}$$

It is clear that by combining (7-200) and (7-194) suitably, an expression for $\langle \mathbf{e}, \mathbf{h} | \mathbf{e}', \mathbf{h}' \rangle$ may be found explicitly. Of course, all these expressions are manifestly gauge invariant.

Additional properties of the coherent states for the radiation field will be taken up in subsequent chapters.

CHAPTER 8

QUANTUM THEORY OF OPTICAL CORRELATION PHENOMENA

8-1 QUANTUM CORRELATION FUNCTIONS

A. Ideal Detectors and Quantum Counting Rates

We return now to treat the interaction of the radiation field and matter with an eye toward a description of counting devices. A full account of such devices would entail a complicated analysis indeed and, following Glauber [8-1], we shall instead approach the subject somewhat phenomenologically. The devices we have in mind here "detect" photons by the process of photon *absorption*. These include conventional photocounters, photoionization devices, photographic plates, etc. In the detection process, a photon is absorbed from the radiation field and the state of the detecting system changes accordingly. In an idealized sense we may regard the detector as a collection of an enormous number of identical, independent elementary systems (e.g., atoms) each of which is originally in its ground state. After absorption (transition to an excited state) the particular elementary system involved may thenceforth be ignored if, for simplicity, we neglect multiple absorption processes at that level. Since detectors are commonly placed outside the source we can regard the radiation field as propagating freely apart from its interaction with the detector. Again, for simplicity, we treat the interaction with the detector to the lowest relevant order in perturbation theory.

We shall be rather general about our analysis of the interaction term but it is good to have some of the underlying motivation clearly in mind. The interaction Hamiltonian which characterizes the field and an atom is basically $-\frac{1}{2}e[\mathbf{p} \cdot \mathbf{A}(\mathbf{r}) + \mathbf{A}(\mathbf{r}) \cdot \mathbf{p}]$. The field operator $\mathbf{A}$ accounts for a single-photon transition in the field, whereas the momentum operator $\mathbf{p}$ accounts for the associated atomic transition. Selection rules may prevent any atomic transition via $\mathbf{p}$ alone, and then one expands $\mathbf{A}(\mathbf{r})$ in a Taylor series about the atomic site until the first nonvanishing contribution is obtained. For simplicity, we shall assume that the unexpanded interaction form suffices in our analysis.

POINT DETECTORS. As a first example suppose we absorb a photon with polarization vector $\mathbf{e}$ at position $\mathbf{r}$ and at time t. The operator $\mathbf{A}^{(+)}(\mathbf{r}, t)$, defined in Eq. (7-179a), is an annihilation operator which annihilates photons at the point $\mathbf{r}$ and at the time t. For the operator that selects photons of polarization $\mathbf{e}$ we may here simply write

$$A^{(+)}(\mathbf{r}, t) = \mathbf{e} \cdot \mathbf{A}^{(+)}(\mathbf{r}, t)$$

Now standard quantum mechanical rules (i.e., "Golden Rule No. 2" and time-dependent perturbation theory)[1] state that the transition probability per unit time from state $|i\rangle$ to state $|f\rangle$ of the radiation field due to the absorption of the appropriate photon is, to the accuracy involved, proportional to

$$|\langle f|A^{(+)}(\mathbf{r}, t)|i\rangle|^2 \tag{8-1}$$

The proportionality factor—say α—includes the absolute square of the transition matrix element of the detecting system besides various inessential factors. If we now assume that the detector is large enough and has a broad enough distribution of states, then α can be sensibly treated as independent of the initial or final radiation states or of the point and time of detection. Consequently, we can determine the total transition rate (the probability per unit time) out of the state $|i\rangle$ due to the appropriate photon absorption as a sum over a complete set of final radiation field states, which then simply reads

$$\begin{aligned}\sum_f \alpha|\langle f|A^{(+)}(\mathbf{r}, t)|i\rangle|^2 &= \alpha \sum_f \langle i|A^{(-)}(\mathbf{r}, t)|f\rangle\langle f|A^{(+)}(\mathbf{r}, t)|i\rangle \\ &= \alpha\langle i|A^{(-)}(\mathbf{r}, t)A^{(+)}(\mathbf{r}, t)|i\rangle \end{aligned} \tag{8-2}$$

Our discussion should make it roughly clear what the assumptions are that go into deriving (8-2). Although, strictly speaking, no practical detector is as simple as we have made out, our derivation has been idealized to focus on the essentials, which can be reasonably well approximated in practice. As such, our result applies to a model or, more accurately, to an idealized detector. However, we shall not continue to

[1] See, for example, the quantum textbook of Schiff [5-2]. "Golden Rule No. 2" refers to the transition rate calculated in first-order perturbation theory. See also the analysis of Glauber [8-2].

make these distinctions, and hereafter we simply call such a device a detector. Moreover, we shall temporarily ignore α (or assume units are so chosen that $\alpha = 1$).

With such detectors at our disposal, let us attempt to describe more involved counting experiments. For simplicity in notation we presently retain the assumption that we are dealing with photons of a given polarization described by $\mathbf{e}$. Suppose we ask for the transition amplitude per unit (time)^2, that we absorb a photon at the (space-time) point $\mathbf{r}_1, t_1$, *and* that we absorb another photon at the point $\mathbf{r}_2, t_2$. In essence, this is a joint probability density for the occurrence of two events—in short, a correlation experiment such as occurs in the work of Hanbury-Brown and Twiss. The relevant transition matrix element reads

$$\langle f|A^{(+)}(\mathbf{r}_2, t_2)A^{(+)}(\mathbf{r}_1, t_1)|i\rangle \tag{8-3}$$

and similar reasoning as above leads to the expression

$$\langle i|A^{(-)}(\mathbf{r}_1, t_1)A^{(-)}(\mathbf{r}_2, t_2)A^{(+)}(\mathbf{r}_2, t_2)A^{(+)}(\mathbf{r}_1, t_1)|i\rangle \tag{8-4}$$

for the required transition rate.

Since the positive-frequency operators $\mathbf{A}^{(+)}(\mathbf{r}, t)$ all commute with one another [as do their adjoints $\mathbf{A}^{(-)}(\mathbf{r}, t)$], the relative ordering of the two $(+)$ factors [as well as the two $(-)$ factors] is not important. What is important to note is that the operators involved stand in *normal order:* all creation operators to the left of all annihilation operators.

In analogy with the two-photon coincident experiment, we can envisage, at least in principle, an n-photon coincident experiment which measures the joint probability per unit (time)^n that n photons, all with polarization vector $\mathbf{e}$, have been absorbed at the points $\mathbf{r}_k, t_k$, $k = 1, \ldots, n$. With completely similar reasoning as before, the relevant probability density is given by the expression

$$\langle i| \prod_{k=1}^{n} A^{(-)}(\mathbf{r}_k, t_k) \prod_{l=1}^{n} A^{(+)}(\mathbf{r}_l, t_l)|i\rangle \tag{8-5}$$

which again is seen to be the mean value of a normally ordered operator. For emphasis we note that this expression is generally quite different from

$$\langle i| \prod_{k=1}^{n} \{A^{(-)}(\mathbf{r}_k, t_k)A^{(+)}(\mathbf{r}_k, t_k)\}|i\rangle \tag{8-6}$$

due to the noncommutativity of $A^{(+)}$ and $A^{(-)}$.

Let us make two straightforward generalizations of the basic equation (8-5). The first deals with including photons of differing polarizations. If we denote the Cartesian components of the transverse vector potential by the subscript j, then all possible polarization information is contained in the tensorial generalization of (8-5) given by

$$\langle i| \prod_{k=1}^{n} A_{j_k}^{(-)}(\mathbf{r}_k, t_k) \prod_{l=1}^{n} A_{j_l}^{(+)}(\mathbf{r}_l, t_l)|i\rangle \tag{8-7}$$

Now, in fact, the component j_k is as much a "label" as the point $\mathbf{r}_k$, t_k, and we shall find it generally convenient to abbreviate the triplet of labels $(\mathbf{r}_k, t_k, j_k)$ by the single label variable x_k. With this meaning understood (8-7) is more simply written

$$\langle i| \prod_{k=1}^{n} A^{(-)}(x_k) \prod_{l=1}^{n} A^{(+)}(x_l)|i\rangle \tag{8-8}$$

Finally we note that (8-8) is in reality the joint probability density conditional on the initial state of the system being specified by the pure state $|i\rangle$. If we do not know the initial state precisely we must average over our ignorance, which, as we discussed in Chapter 5, always leads to the generalization of (8-8) given by

$$\left\langle \prod_{k=1}^{n} A^{(-)}(x_k) \prod_{l=1}^{n} A^{(+)}(x_l) \right\rangle \equiv \operatorname{Tr}\left\{\rho \prod_{k=1}^{n} A^{(-)}(x_k) \prod_{l=1}^{n} A^{(+)}(x_l)\right\} \tag{8-9}$$

where ρ is the *density operator* appropriate to the initial state.

Distributed Detectors. An important extension of the preceding formulation is to account for idealized counters that are not directly sensitive to the value of the field at $\mathbf{r}$ and t but to the field as averaged over a spatial and temporal interval. As in Chapter 3, we may assume that the kth detector is sensitive to an effective field determined, for example, by

$$\begin{aligned} A_e^{(+)}(x) &\equiv A_j^{(+)\mathrm{eff}}(\mathbf{r}, t) \\ &= \Sigma \int S_{jj'}^*(\mathbf{r} - \mathbf{r}', t - t') A_{j'}^{(+)}(\mathbf{r}', t')\, d^3x'\, dt' \end{aligned} \tag{8-10}$$

Here the function $S_{jj'}^*$ is the generalized admittance tensor of the kth detector which samples the field at various points of space and time in order to determine the "effective field." For such counters, the relevant probability per unit $(\text{time})^n$ for an nth-order counting correlation is still given by an expression such as (8-9). However, each field operator now carries a subscript e which through (8-10) accounts for the properties of the detector. Indeed it may even be envisaged in such a generalization that each detector has a distinct admittance function.

The linear nature of (8-10) shows that the properties for all sorts of counters are contained in the elementary correlations given by

$$G^{(n,n)}(x_1, x_2, \ldots, x_n; x_{n+1}, x_{n+2}, \ldots, x_{2n}) \equiv \left\langle \prod_{k=1}^{n} A^{(-)}(x_k) \prod_{l=n+1}^{2n} A^{(+)}(x_l) \right\rangle = \mathrm{Tr}\left\{ \rho \prod_{k=1}^{n} A^{(-)}(x_k) \prod_{l=n+1}^{2n} A^{(+)}(x_l) \right\} \tag{8-11}$$

in which each field variable has its own argument. With these correlation functions and suitable detector admittance functions, all n-photon counting correlation rates may be derived. Conversely, it may easily be shown that (8-11) may be deduced from the rate information contained in all possible counting arrangements. In brief, we may regard the functions $G^{(n,n)}$ in (8-11) for all arguments $x_1, \ldots, x_{2n}$ and for all n as the information (in the popular sense) about the radiation field that is directly deducible from rates for multiple-photon coincidence experiments. All these expressions are mean values of normally ordered products of operators with each term having an equal number of creation and annihilation operators.

Since each field variable now has its own label x, we may obtain the expressions

$$\left\langle \prod_{k=1}^{n} E^{(-)}(x_k) \prod_{l=n+1}^{2n} E^{(+)}(x_l) \right\rangle \tag{8-12}$$

$$\left\langle \prod_{k=1}^{n} H^{(-)}(x_k) \prod_{l=n+1}^{2n} H^{(+)}(x_l) \right\rangle \tag{8-13}$$

or various mixed forms in A, E, and H, by taking appropriate derivatives and making use of Maxwell's (transverse!) equations: $\mathbf{E} = -\mathbf{A}$ and $\mathbf{H} = \nabla \times \mathbf{A}$. Thus all these mean quantities are closely related. Indeed, in Glauber's treatment he deals with counting rates determined by (8-12) rather than (8-11). In practice there is little to choose between the two definitions. For quasi-monochromatic radiation they are proportional to one another to all intents and purposes. On the other hand, Eq. (8-13) would probably be most appropriate (even in a quasi-monochromatic field) to describe n-photon counting rates for a counter the atoms of which were sensitive to magnetic dipole transitions [which arise from the first term in a Taylor series expansion of $\mathbf{A}(\mathbf{r})$ about the atomic site]. For simplicity we continue to restrict our remarks to the correlation functions based on the transverse vector potential.

Mixed-Order Correlation Functions. Clearly, the functions $G^{(n,n)}$ are a subfamily of a whole hierarchy of correlation functions $G^{(n,m)}$ in which the number of creation and annihilation operators are not necessarily identical. These functions are defined by the obvious generalization of (8-11) as

$$G^{(n,m)}(x_1, \ldots, x_n; x_{n+1}, \ldots, x_{n+m}) \equiv \left\langle \prod_{k=1}^{n} A^{(-)}(x_k) \prod_{l=n+1}^{n+m} A^{(+)}(x_l) \right\rangle = \mathrm{Tr}\left\{\rho \prod_{k=1}^{n} A^{(-)}(x_k) \prod_{l=n+1}^{n+m} A^{(+)}(x_l)\right\} \quad (8\text{-}14)$$

and all of them are mean values of normally ordered operators. For many purposes it is convenient to analyze the whole set of correlation functions so as to obtain information about the special ones pertaining to n-photon counting correlations, $G^{(n,n)}$.

All the functions $G^{(n,m)}$ possess rather obvious symmetry properties. These functions are fully symmetric in the n variables $x_1, x_2, \ldots, x_n$ and, separately, are fully symmetric in the m variables $x_{n+1}, x_{n+2}, \ldots, x_{n+m}$. Furthermore, it is clear that

$$[G^{(n,m)}(x_1, \ldots, x_n; x_{n+1}, \ldots, x_{n+m})]^* = G^{(m,n)}(x_{n+1}, \ldots, x_{n+m}; x_1, \ldots, x_n) \quad (8\text{-}15)$$

which reflects the fact that $[A^{(+)}(x)]^\dagger = A^{(-)}(x)$. When $n = m$, this latter condition relates the dependence of $G^{(n,n)}$ on the first set of variables $x_1, \ldots, x_n$ to its dependence on the second set of variables $x_{n+1}, \ldots, x_{2n}$.

Since we are discussing the free radiation field, each of the functions $G^{(n,m)}$ satisfies the free-field wave equation,

$$\left(\nabla_l^2 - \frac{\partial^2}{\partial t_l^2}\right) G^{(n,m)}(\ldots, \mathbf{r}_l, t_l, \ldots) = 0 \quad (8\text{-}16)$$

for every set of its arguments. The behavior of $G^{(n,m)}$ for all distinct times can be deduced from its values for a single common time, say at $t = 0$. Such propagation characteristics are most transparently displayed if we first introduce a description in terms of normal modes as in Chapter 7.

B. *Modal Description*

We may express the annihilation operators appropriate to the normal modes (which arise for quantization in a "box" of volume L^3) according to the relation

$$a_\lambda(\mathbf{k}, t) = \mathbf{e}_\lambda^*(\mathbf{k}) \cdot \mathbf{a}(\mathbf{k}, t)$$
$$= \frac{1}{L^{3/2}} \left(\frac{2\omega}{\hbar}\right)^{1/2} \int e^{-i\mathbf{k}\cdot\mathbf{x}} \mathbf{e}_\lambda^*(\mathbf{k}) \cdot \mathbf{A}^{(+)}(\mathbf{x}, t)\, d^3x \qquad \text{(8-17a)}$$

as follows from (7-179a). In turn, the adjoint relation yields

$$a_\lambda^\dagger(\mathbf{k}, t) = \mathbf{e}_\lambda(\mathbf{k}) \cdot \mathbf{a}^\dagger(\mathbf{k}, t)$$
$$= \frac{1}{L^{3/2}} \left(\frac{2\omega}{\hbar}\right)^{1/2} \int e^{i\mathbf{k}\cdot\mathbf{x}} \mathbf{e}_\lambda(\mathbf{k}) \cdot \mathbf{A}^{(-)}(\mathbf{x}, t)\, d^3x \qquad \text{(8-17b)}$$

for the corresponding creation operator for the $(\lambda, \mathbf{k})$th mode. For notational simplicity let us simply abbreviate the modal label by the subscript k; that is, we set $a_k(t) = a_\lambda(\mathbf{k}, t)$ and $a_k^\dagger(t) = a_\lambda^\dagger(\mathbf{k}, t)$.

Suppose we now take a multiple Fourier transform of $G^{(n,m)}$ and multiply by the appropriate polarization vectors and normalization factors. It is clear that in this way we are led to the quantity

$$\mathcal{G}^{(n,m)}(k_1, t_1, \ldots, k_n, t_n; k_{n+1}, t_{n+1}, \ldots, k_{n+m}, t_{n+m})$$
$$= \operatorname{Tr}\left\{\rho \prod_{r=1}^{n} a_{k_r}^\dagger(t_r) \prod_{s=n+1}^{m+n} a_{k_s}(t_s)\right\} \qquad \text{(8-18)}$$

In this expression, however, the time dependence is quite elementary. According to (7-176a), we see that

$$a_k(t) = \exp(-i\omega_k t) a_k(0) \equiv \exp(-i\omega_k t) a_k \qquad \text{(8-19)}$$

which implies that

$$\mathcal{G}^{(n,m)}(k_1, t_1, \ldots, k_n, t_n; k_{n+1}, t_{n+1}, \ldots, k_{n+m}, t_{n+m})$$
$$= \prod_{r=1}^{n} \exp(i\omega_{k_r} t_r) \prod_{s=n+1}^{n+m} \exp(-i\omega_{k_s} t_s) \mathcal{G}^{(n,m)}(k_1, 0, \ldots, k_n, 0;$$
$$k_{n+1}, 0, \ldots, k_{n+m}, 0) \qquad \text{(8-20)}$$

This expression vividly shows that the full many-time behavior of $G^{(n,m)}$ is determined by its values when all time arguments are set equal to zero. Consequently, dropping the time arguments altogether, we are justified in studying the expression

$$\mathcal{G}^{(n,m)}(k_1, \ldots, k_n; k_{n+1}, \ldots, k_{n+m}) \equiv \left\langle \prod_{r=1}^{n} a_{k_r}^\dagger \prod_{s=n+1}^{n+m} a_{k_s} \right\rangle$$
$$= \operatorname{Tr}\left\{\rho \prod_{r=1}^{n} a_{k_r}^\dagger \prod_{s=n+1}^{n+m} a_{k_s}\right\} \qquad \text{(8-21)}$$

in order to obtain information about the general (n, m)th correlation function. All relevant quantities may be deduced from the $t = 0$ expressions (8-21). In analogy with $G^{(n,m)}$ the functions $\mathcal{G}^{(n,m)}$ are clearly symmetric in the first n arguments and in the last m arguments, and they fulfill the condition

$$[\mathcal{G}^{(n,m)}(k_1, \ldots, k_n; k_{n+1}, \ldots, k_{n+m})]^* = \mathcal{G}^{(m,n)}(k_{n+1}, \ldots, k_{n+m}; k_1, \ldots, k_n) \quad (8\text{-}22)$$

C. Generating Functions

A very convenient way to summarize the information contained in all the correlations (8-21) is with the aid of the *normal ordered, generating functional*

$$\begin{aligned} C_N(\{u_k\}) &\equiv \left\langle \exp\left(\sum_1^\infty u_k a_k^\dagger\right) \exp\left(-\sum_1^\infty u_k^* a_k\right)\right\rangle \\ &= \mathrm{Tr}\left\{\rho \exp\left(\sum_1^\infty u_k a_k^\dagger\right) \exp\left(-\sum_1^\infty u_k^* a_k\right)\right\} \end{aligned} \quad (8\text{-}23)$$

defined for all complex sequences $\{u_k\}$ which satisfy

$$\sum_{k=1}^\infty |u_k|^2 < \infty \quad (8\text{-}24)$$

It is evident that (8-23) contains all the correlation functions since, by differentiation, we see that

$$\mathcal{G}^{(n,m)}(k_1, \ldots, k_n; k_{n+1}, \ldots, k_{n+m}) = \left\{\prod_{r=1}^{n} \frac{\partial}{\partial u_{k_r}} \prod_{s=n+1}^{n+m} \left(-\frac{\partial}{\partial u_{k_s}^*}\right)\right\} C_N(\{u_k\}) \Big|_{\{u_k\}\equiv 0} \quad (8\text{-}25)$$

Closely related to the normal ordered, generating functional is what we can call the "characteristic functional" $C(\{u_k\})$ for the density operator ρ. By making use of (7-26) this quantity can be defined as

$$\begin{aligned} C(\{u_k\}) &= \exp\left(-\tfrac{1}{2}\sum_1^\infty |u_k|^2\right) C_N(\{u_k\}) \\ &= \left\langle \exp\left[\sum_1^\infty (u_k a_k^\dagger - u_k^* a_k)\right]\right\rangle \\ &= \mathrm{Tr}\left\{\rho \exp\left[\sum_1^\infty (u_k a_k^\dagger - u_k^* a_k)\right]\right\} \end{aligned} \quad (8\text{-}26)$$

It is noteworthy that for every sequence $\{u_k\}$ satisfying (8-24), the function $C(\{u_k\})$ is the mean value of a unitary operator [which is just the infinite degree of freedom analog of $U[p, q]$ in Eq. (7-26)]. Just as characteristic functions (Fourier transforms) completely characterize classical probabilities, the analogous functional $C(\{u_k\})$ completely characterizes the quantum mechanical density operator ρ.

Of course, there is nothing sacred about forming generating functionals based on a modal decomposition. Still restricting ourselves to correlations at $t = 0$ for simplicity, we can equally well consider the normal ordered, generating functional given by (all operators at $t = 0$)

$$C_N\{\mathbf{S}\} = \langle \exp(\mathbf{S} \cdot \mathbf{A}^{(-)}) \exp(-\mathbf{S}^* \cdot \mathbf{A}^{(+)}) \rangle \tag{8-27}$$

where we have abbreviated

$$\mathbf{S}^* \cdot \mathbf{A}^{(+)} \equiv \int \mathbf{S}^*(\mathbf{r}) \cdot \mathbf{A}^{(+)}(\mathbf{r})\, d^3x \equiv [\mathbf{S} \cdot \mathbf{A}^{(-)}]^\dagger \tag{8-28}$$

Alternatively, we may consider the closely related characteristic functional

$$C\{\mathbf{S}\} = \langle \exp(\mathbf{S} \cdot \mathbf{A}^{(-)} - \mathbf{S}^* \cdot \mathbf{A}^{(+)}) \rangle \tag{8-29}$$

We shall have occasion to make use of normal ordered, generating functionals and their associated characteristic functionals in our subsequent analysis. It is important to note again that either of these functionals completely specifies the state of the system. Also it is important to note again that counting rate correlations relate only to the functions $G^{(n,n)}$, and make no use of the functions $G^{(n,m)}$ when $n \neq m$.

8-2 FULL AND PARTIAL COHERENCE

A. Definitions and Full Coherence

We have observed above that the information about rates from general correlation counting measurements is contained within the functions $G^{(n,n)}$ (or $\mathcal{G}^{(n,n)}$) defined for general arguments. On the basis of this information we must decide what states of the system are worthy of being called *fully coherent.*

In the classical case it was already noted in Chapter 1 that not only coherent fields but partially coherent and incoherent ones could be distinguished. The decisive quantity for the properties of coherence which enters all classical interference experiments is the mutual coherence function which for a scalar field (or specific polarization) is

$$\Gamma^{(1,1)}(\mathbf{r}, t; \mathbf{r}', t') \equiv \Gamma(\mathbf{r}, t; \mathbf{r}', t') \equiv \langle V^*(\mathbf{r}', t') V(\mathbf{r}, t) \rangle \tag{8-30}$$

In its normalized form, given by

$$\gamma(\mathbf{r}, t; \mathbf{r}', t') \equiv \frac{\Gamma(\mathbf{r}, t; \mathbf{r}', t')}{[\Gamma(\mathbf{r}, t; \mathbf{r}, t)\Gamma(\mathbf{r}', t'; \mathbf{r}', t')]^{1/2}} \tag{8-31}$$

it is called the complex degree of coherence and fulfills $0 \leq |\gamma| \leq 1$ for all arguments. We demonstrated earlier that if for two spatial points $\mathbf{r}$ and $\mathbf{r}'$, $|\gamma| = 1$ for all t and t', then the observed interference pattern was the same as for a nonrandom beam, and thus the field was deemed coherent. If $|\gamma| = 0$ for all t and t', the field was deemed incoherent, whereas if $0 < |\gamma| < 1$, it was deemed partially coherent.

In the quantum case the role of $\Gamma^{(1,1)}$ is played by the correlation function $G^{(1,1)}$. Since $G^{(1,1)}(\mathbf{r}, t; \mathbf{r}, t)$ is proportional to the number of photons arriving at $\mathbf{r}$ in the time interval t to $t + dt$ it is also proportional to the intensity of darkening on a photographic emulsion for such an exposure. For dissimilar space–time points $G^{(1,1)}(\mathbf{r}, t; \mathbf{r}', t')$ is related to the intensity observed in a two-slit experiment just as is $\Gamma^{(1,1)}(\mathbf{r}, t; \mathbf{r}', t')$. Both of these quantities satisfy the free-field wave equation and both are analytic signals in t and in $-t'$.

To proceed further than this comparison we must come to grips with the rather vague concept of "coherence." Being purposefully general, let us say that a "coherent feature" of a statistical ensemble is an observable aspect held in common by each member of the ensemble. Different ensembles will in general have different coherent features. Also the same ensemble can have different sets of coherent features depending on what collection of quantities is deemed "observable." This suggests that we call a "relative coherent feature" one which fulfills the criteria for a coherent feature for a subset of the observables. That is, the criteria for a relative coherent feature are necessary but not generally sufficient for a coherent feature. Intuitively, the greater number of coherent features there are for a given ensemble, the less are the observable fluctuations that exist between individual members of the ensemble. "Full coherence" can be said to exist if the members of the ensemble are identical in all their observable aspects. [2]

As an example of these ideas suppose we have at our disposal machines each of which puts out a complex number. The ensemble consists of the numbers put out by a collection of M identical machines, and let us denote by z_μ the complex number registered by the μth machine, $\mu = 1, \ldots, M (M \gg 1)$. If we can observe both the amplitude and phase of z_μ, then our ensemble is fully coherent if there is a z such that $z_\mu = z$ for all μ. To test mathematically the coherence, we can, if we choose, proceed as

[2] The proper measure-theoretic generalization of these notions is self-evident. We content ourselves with a more intuitive formulation.

follows. Let a denote a complex random variable which as usual takes on the values allowed by the ensemble. Then the fully coherent machine must satisfy

$$M^{-1}\Sigma_\mu z_\mu^n \equiv \langle a^n \rangle = z^n = \langle a \rangle^n$$

for all $n \geq 1$. If we only know that $\langle a^n \rangle = \langle a \rangle^n$ say for $n = 1, 2,$ and 6, then with this information alone we can only say that the machine is relatively coherent. On the other hand, suppose that in principle we can only observe the *modulus* of z_μ. Then a fully coherent ensemble yields $|z_\mu| = |z|$ for all μ, and it satisfies $\langle a^{*n} a^n \rangle = z^{*n} z^n = \langle a^* a \rangle^n$ for all n. This latter example puts essentially no restriction on the value of $\langle a^{*n} a^m \rangle$ when $n \neq m$.

Although it is admittedly crude, our example should serve to motivate the definition of a *fully coherent state* of the radiation field. In the quantum theory we call a state of the radiation field fully coherent if the correlation functions (8-11) corresponding to the (in principle) observable, counter-correlation rates satisfy the property

$$G^{(n,n)}(x_1, \ldots, x_n; x_{n+1}, \ldots, x_{2n}) = \prod_{k=1}^{n} V^*(x_k) \prod_{l=n+1}^{2n} V(x_l) \quad (8\text{-}32)$$

for all arguments and all n, and for some function $V(x) = V(\mathbf{r}, t, j)$, or written as a vector, simply $\mathbf{V}(\mathbf{r}, t)$. Clearly $\mathbf{V}$ must satisfy the free wave equation and be an analytic signal. The function $\mathbf{V}$ is completely determined by (8-32) apart from a single, overall phase factor. This factorization condition does not explicitly apply to the correlation function $G^{(n,m)}$ for $n \neq m$.

In a sense, of course, it is a matter of definition of what is and what is not observable in principle. It is a cardinal rule in quantum theory that Hermitian variables such as the electric or magnetic field (suitably averaged over a small region of space) are regarded as observables and that by diligent effort experiments to measure the distribution of expected values for $E(x)$ or $H(x)$ are, in principle, possible. It is plausible—we need not spell out the details—that from this information one can deduce the (complex) mean value of $A^{(+)}(x)$, namely, $G^{(0,1)}(x)$. Moreover, one could deduce all $G^{(n,m)}$ from analogous gedanken experiments on suitable Hermitian variables. In such a conceptual situation we would call a state of the radiation "fully coherent" if

$$G^{(n,m)}(x_1, \ldots, x_n; x_{n+1}, \ldots, x_{n+m}) = \prod_{k=1}^{n} V^*(x_k) \prod_{l=n+1}^{n+m} V(x_l) \quad (8\text{-}33)$$

holds for all n and m and for all arguments x. It is not difficult to see that such fully coherent states of the radiation field are precisely the pure coherent states and no others. However, we shall follow current practice and refer to the fully coherent states as those that fulfill only the $G^{(n,n)}$ factorization conditions and which correspond to the "in practice," observable information deducible from counters alone.[3] Quite clearly, coherent states are fully coherent in this sense as well, but there are other states that satisfy (8-32) besides the coherent states.

Another form for the condition of full coherence is worth noting. The functions $\mathcal{G}^{(n,m)}$ given in (8-18) differ from $G^{(n,m)}$ essentially by a spatial Fourier transform on each of their arguments. Whenever $G^{(n,m)}$ factors into a product of terms so too would its Fourier transform. The time dependence of that factorization must conform to the general dependence behavior given in (8-20). Hence we immediately see that an alternative criterion for full coherence is the property that

$$\begin{aligned}\mathcal{G}^{(n,n)}(k_1, \ldots, k_n; k_{n+1}, \ldots, k_{2n}) &= \left\langle \prod_{r=1}^{n} a^\dagger_{k_r} \prod_{s=n+1}^{2n} a_{k_s} \right\rangle \\ &= \prod_{r=1}^{n} z^*_{k_r} \prod_{s=n+1}^{2n} z_{k_s} \end{aligned} \tag{8-34}$$

for some sequence $\{z_k\}$ and for all n. We see from this that full coherence is a property of the state ρ at a fixed time, say at $t = 0$. If the mean values of ρ satisfy these consistency requirements, then the radiation field is fully coherent over all space and for all time.

Finally we note yet another form for the condition of full coherence. If we observe that $G^{(1,1)}(x, x) = V^*(x)V(x)$, then we can immediately deduce the relation

$$|G^{(n,n)}(x_1, x_2, \ldots, x_{2n})|^2 = \prod_{k=1}^{2n} G^{(1,1)}(x_k, x_k) \tag{8-35}$$

which holds for all n. We show below that this condition implies (8-32) and so the two are actually equivalent.

B. *Partial Coherence*

Whenever the conditions (8-32) are not fulfilled, we have one or another kind of partial coherence. To each such case it would be ideal if we could attach a unique "figure of merit" or a "degree of coherence" as was useful in the case of two-slit interference experiments. At the present time, however, no particular definition stands out as being uni-

[3] In the optical regime such information is surely the most practical to obtain for it is hard with available circuitry, even with nanosecond (10^{-9}) resolving times, to learn much about anything other than envelope behavior of signals with oscillations of the order of 10^{15} cps.

versally preferable in this respect. It cannot be hoped to capture the essence of *all* forms of partial coherence as they affect *all* possible experiments in one, or in a few significant parameters.

First-Order Coherence. Nonetheless, it is interesting to focus on the consequences of one especially interesting case where less than full coherence may occur. Earlier, we defined a "relative coherent feature" as one which satisfied some but not necessarily all of the criteria for a coherent feature. Suppose, following Glauber [8-2], we say that a radiation field has "first-order coherence" if we know only that

$$G^{(1,1)}(x, y) = V^*(x)V(y) \tag{8-36}$$

for all x and y and for some function $V(x)$.[4] What then can we deduce, in particular, regarding the higher-order correlation functions $G^{(n,n)}$?

We begin our argument with the relation

$$|G^{(1,1)}(x, y)|^2 = G^{(1,1)}(x, x)G^{(1,1)}(y, y) \tag{8-37}$$

which is a direct consequence of (8-36). For simplicity in notation here let us denote $G^{(1,1)}$ simply by G. We first show that (8-37) actually implies (8-36). If we set

$$G(x, y) = e^{w(x,y)+i\varphi(x,y)} = G^*(y, x) \tag{8-38}$$

where w and φ are real, then we learn that

$$w(x, y) = \tfrac{1}{2}[w(x, x) + w(y, y)]$$

Thus if $B(x) \equiv \exp[\tfrac{1}{2}w(x, x)]$, then

$$G(x, y) = B(x)B(y)e^{i\varphi(x,y)} = \langle A^{(-)}(x)A^{(+)}(y)\rangle \tag{8-39}$$

From its basic definition, $G(x, y)$ satisfies the condition (for all finite sums and complex coefficients c_k) that

$$\begin{aligned}\sum_{j,k} c_j^*c_kG(x_j, x_k) &= \sum_{j,k} c_j^*c_kB(x_j)B(x_k) \exp[i\varphi(x_j, x_k)] \\ &\equiv \sum_{j,k} d_j^*d_k \exp[i\varphi(x_j, x_k)] \geq 0\end{aligned} \tag{8-40}$$

since this is the mean value of a positive operator. For any finite set of points, the matrix M, whose elements are $M_{jk} \equiv \exp[i\varphi(x_j, x_k)]$, is Hermitian and positive, and each element fulfills $|M_{jk}| \equiv 1$. Applied to three

[4] It should be noted that an experimenter equipped only with an interferometer (and not with photocounters) can deduce information *only* about $G^{(1,1)}$. According to our definition, if he finds that relation (8-36) is true, then as far as he is concerned the field has "full coherence."

arbitrary points and the associated three-by-three matrix, it follows that $M_{12}M_{23}M_{31} = 1$, for otherwise $\det(M) = 2\,\mathrm{Re}[M_{12}M_{23}M_{31} - 1] < 0$. But this condition implies for three arbitrary points that

$$\varphi(x, y) + \varphi(y, z) + \varphi(z, x) = 0 \tag{8-41}$$

which, as we now show, severely restricts the functional form of $\varphi(x, y)$. If, for a fixed z, we set $\alpha_z(y) \equiv -\varphi(y, z)$, then

$$\varphi(x, y) = \alpha_z(y) - \alpha_z(x) \tag{8-42}$$

In turn, $\alpha_z(y)$ differs from $\alpha_0(y)$ (i.e., at $z = 0$) by a constant since $\alpha_z(y) - \alpha_o(y) = \alpha_z(0)$, independent of y. In other words, there is a real function $\alpha(y) = \alpha_0(y)$ uniquely determined, up to an additive constant, by (8-41) such that $\varphi(x, y) = \alpha(y) - \alpha(x)$. It follows, therefore, that

$$G(x, y) = B(x)B(y)e^{-i[\alpha(x)-\alpha(y)]} = V^*(x)V(y) \tag{8-43}$$

We note that we cannot *determine* $\alpha(x)$ (even up to a constant) by this argument, but we can determine that one *exists* and thereby deduce that $G(x, y)$ can be represented as the product of two functions. Thus (8-36) and (8-37) are equivalent.

If we recast (8-36) into its equivalent ($t = 0$) modal form [cf. (8-21)], then we learn that

$$\langle a_k^\dagger a_l \rangle = z_k^* z_l \tag{8-44}$$

for all k and l, and some sequence $\{z_k\}$. On the assumption that this sequence does not vanish identically, then the operator

$$b \equiv \Sigma u_l a_l \equiv \frac{\Sigma z_l^*}{(\Sigma z_m^* z_m)^{1/2}} a_l \tag{8-45}$$

satisfies the relations

$$[b, b^\dagger] = \Sigma u_l u_k^* [a_l, a_k^\dagger] = \Sigma u_l u_l^* = 1 \tag{8-46}$$

and

$$\begin{aligned} \langle b^\dagger b \rangle &= \Sigma u_l u_k^* \langle a_k^\dagger a_l \rangle \\ &= \Sigma u_l u_k^* z_k^* z_l = \Sigma z_m^* z_m > 0 \end{aligned} \tag{8-47}$$

Thus b is a conventionally normalized annihilation operator for which $\langle b^\dagger b \rangle \neq 0$.

Suppose we now regard the transition from the a_l to $b \equiv b_1$ as the first of a whole string of transformations that arise from a unitary change of basis as in

$$b_m \equiv \Sigma u_{ml} a_l \tag{8-48}$$

where

$$\Sigma u_{ml} u_{nl}^* = \delta_{mn} \tag{8-49}$$

Clearly, $u_{1l} \equiv u_l \equiv z_l^*/(\Sigma z_k^* z_k)^{1/2}$, and from the orthogonality relation (8-49) we see that

$$\begin{aligned} \langle b_m{}^\dagger b_n \rangle &= \Sigma u_{mk}^* z_k{}^* u_{nl} z_l = \Sigma u_{mk}^* u_{1k} u_{nl} u_{1l}^* (\Sigma z_p{}^* z_p) \\ &= \delta_{m1}\, \delta_{n1} (\Sigma z_p{}^* z_p) \end{aligned} \tag{8-50}$$

In particular, for the number operators $b_m{}^\dagger b_m$,

$$\langle b_m{}^\dagger b_m \rangle = 0 \qquad (m \neq 1) \tag{8-51}$$

Since the number operator has positive expectation value in every state except the ground state, this condition simply means that the modes described by b_m and $b_m{}^\dagger$ must be *completely unoccupied* for all $m \neq 1$. Thus the field is the field of a *single mode* (not necessarily a normal mode!) that satisfies the single restriction (8-47).

If we define

$$|\tilde{n}\rangle \equiv (n!)^{-1/2} (b^\dagger)^n |0\rangle \tag{8-52}$$

as the normalized number eigenstates corresponding to this single mode, then ρ has the general form

$$\rho = \sum_{n,m=0}^{\infty} |\tilde{n}\rangle \rho_{nm} \langle \tilde{m}| \tag{8-53}$$

for a density matrix satisfying

$$\langle b^\dagger b \rangle = \sum_{n=0}^{\infty} n \rho_{nn} = \sum_k z_k{}^* z_k \tag{8-54}$$

The higher-order correlation functions are determined either from (8-21) or from an analogous relation involving the $b_m{}^\dagger$ and b_m. According to (8-51) or (8-53), however, only the b $(= b_1)$ terms can contribute to give a nonzero result. It is convenient to describe the terms $\langle b^{\dagger n} b^m \rangle$ by means of the relative expressions

$$g_{n,m} \equiv \frac{\langle b^{\dagger n} b^m \rangle}{\langle b^\dagger b \rangle^{1/2(n+m)}} \tag{8-55}$$

On the basis of this definition and the relation $a_l = \Sigma u_{ml}^* b_m$, it follows that

$$\begin{aligned} \langle a_{k_1}^\dagger \cdots a_{k_n}^\dagger a_{l_1} \cdots a_{l_m} \rangle &= u_{k_1} \cdots u_{k_n} u_{l_1}^* \cdots u_{l_m}^* \langle b^{\dagger n} b^m \rangle \\ &= z_{k_1}^* \cdots z_{k_n}^* z_{l_1} \cdots z_{l_m} \frac{\langle b^{\dagger n} b^m \rangle}{(\Sigma z_p{}^* z_p)^{1/2(n+m)}} \\ &= g_{n,m} \cdot (z_{k_1}^* \cdots z_{k_n}^* z_{l_1} \cdots z_{l_m}) \end{aligned} \tag{8-56}$$

Finally, after appropriate scaling and a multiple Fourier transform, we learn that

$$G^{(n,m)}(x_1, \ldots, x_n; x_{n+1}, \ldots, x_{n+m}) = g_{n,m} \prod_{k=1}^{n} V^*(x_k) \prod_{l=n+1}^{n+m} V(x_l) \tag{8-57}$$

which is the general form taken by the (n,m)th correlation function for a field having first-order coherence.

For purposes of photon counting correlations, we have previously agreed to limit our attention to the correlation functions $G^{(n,n)}$. For these we evidently find

$$G^{(n,n)}(x_1, \ldots, x_n; x_{n+1}, \ldots, x_{2n}) = g_n \prod_{k=1}^{n} V^*(x_k) \prod_{l=n+1}^{2n} V(x_l) \tag{8-58}$$

where we have set

$$g_n \equiv g_{n,n} \equiv \frac{\langle b^{\dagger n} b^n \rangle}{\langle b^\dagger b \rangle^n} \tag{8-59}$$

which are all real, nonnegative numbers.[5] Clearly the set of numbers $\{g_n\}$ characterize, along with $V(x)$, the properties of the counting rates for a field with first-order coherence. If $g_n = 1$, $n = 1, 2, \ldots, M$, then, following Glauber, the field is said to have Mth-order coherence. This is related to the fact that, if $g_n = 1$ for *all* n, then the field is fully coherent since $G^{(n,n)}$ then has the canonical form (8-32). Evidently the conditions (8-35) for $n \geq 2$, coupled with (8-58), imply $g_n = 1$ for all n; thus the complete set of relations (8-35) imply full coherence of the field as we remarked earlier.

It may be instructive to give some examples of density operators and to see what are the corresponding expressions for g_n. If we set $M \equiv b^\dagger b$, then it follows from (5-47) that

$$g_n = \frac{\langle M \cdot (M-1) \cdot (M-2) \cdots (M - [n-1]) \rangle}{\langle M \rangle^n} \equiv \frac{\langle M!/(M-n)! \rangle}{\langle M \rangle^n} \tag{8-60}$$

Consequently, if $\rho = |\tilde{m}\rangle\langle\tilde{m}|$, a pure number eigenstate, then

$$g_n = \frac{m!}{m^n (m-n)!} \tag{8-61}$$

which vanishes for all $n > m$. If

$$\rho = \exp(-\beta M)/\langle \exp(-\beta M) \rangle \tag{8-62}$$

as for a "thermal" (or chaotic) distribution of the single possible mode,

[5] This result for $G^{(n,n)}$ was first derived by Titulaer and Glauber [8-3].

then

$$g_n = n! \tag{8-63}$$

[*Proof of* (8-63)*:* If we set $\lambda \equiv e^{-\beta}$, then

$$\mathrm{Tr}\{M!/(M-n)!e^{-\beta M}\} = \sum_{m=0}^{\infty} \lambda^m \frac{m!}{(m-n)!} = \lambda^n \frac{d^n}{d\lambda^n} \sum_{m=0}^{\infty} \lambda^m$$

$$= \lambda^n \frac{d^n}{d\lambda^n} \frac{1}{1-\lambda} = \frac{n!\lambda^n}{(1-\lambda)^{n+1}}$$

Hence, for $n = 0$ and 1,

$$\mathrm{Tr}\{e^{-\beta M}\} = (1-\lambda)^{-1} \qquad \mathrm{Tr}\{Me^{-\beta M}\} = \lambda(1-\lambda)^{-2}$$

By combining these facts, we find

$$g_n = [\lambda(1-\lambda)^{-1}]^{-n} n!\lambda^n/(1-\lambda)^n = n!$$

as was to be shown.] Such a field can never have more than first-order coherence. Full coherence requires that $g_n = 1$ and thus that $\langle b^{\dagger n} b^n \rangle = \langle b^\dagger b \rangle^n$ for all n. In consequence, we see that the general relation

$$\sum_{n=0}^{\infty} \frac{\lambda^n}{n!} \langle b^{\dagger n} b^n \rangle = \langle :\exp(\lambda b^\dagger b): \rangle = \langle \exp[\ln(1+\lambda) b^\dagger b] \rangle$$

$$= \sum_{m=0}^{\infty} (1+\lambda)^m \rho_{mm} \tag{8-64}$$

leads to the special case

$$\sum_m (1+\lambda)^m \rho_{mm} = \exp(\lambda \langle b^\dagger b \rangle) \tag{8-65}$$

which implies that

$$\rho_{mm} = \frac{1}{m!} \frac{d^m}{d\lambda^m} \exp(\lambda \langle b^\dagger b \rangle) \bigg|_{\lambda=-1} = \frac{\langle b^\dagger b \rangle^m}{m!} \exp(-\langle b^\dagger b \rangle) \tag{8-66}$$

Thus, in order to have full coherence it is necessary that the diagonal matrix elements ρ_{mm} have a Poisson distribution.

It is worth noting here that the result given in (8-57) has a direct analog in the conventional classical theory for $\Gamma^{(n,m)}$. Our derivation can readily be adapted (or reinterpreted) to show that the first-order coherence condition $|\gamma| \equiv 1$, or

$$|\Gamma^{(1,1)}(x, y)|^2 = \Gamma^{(1,1)}(x, x)\Gamma^{(1,1)}(y, y) \tag{8-67}$$

leads, for some $V(x)$, to the relation

$$\Gamma^{(n,m)}(x_1, \ldots, x_n; x_{n+1}, \ldots, x_{n+m}) = \gamma_{n,m} \prod_{k=1}^{n} V^*(x_k) \prod_{l=n+1}^{n+m} V(x_l) \quad (8\text{-}68)$$

Here

$$\gamma_{n,m} \equiv \frac{\langle v^{*n} v^m \rangle}{\langle v^* v \rangle^{1/2(n+m)}} \quad (8\text{-}69)$$

defined in terms of some classical ensemble for the single complex variable v. By analogy with (8-58) we see that

$$\Gamma^{(n,n)}(x_1, \ldots, x_n; x_{n+1}, \ldots, x_{2n}) = \gamma_n \prod_{k=1}^{n} V^*(x_k) \prod_{l=n+1}^{2n} V(x_l) \quad (8\text{-}70)$$

where

$$\gamma_n \equiv \gamma_{n,n} \equiv \frac{\langle v^{*n} v^n \rangle}{\langle v^* v \rangle^n} \quad (8\text{-}71)$$

are clearly real, positive coefficients. Alternatively if we set $X = v^*v$, and define (for a suitable $\sigma \geq 0$)

$$\langle X^n \rangle \equiv \int_0^\infty X^n \sigma(X)\, dX \quad (8\text{-}72)$$

then $\gamma_n \equiv \langle X^n \rangle / \langle X \rangle^n$. It follows that

$$\begin{aligned}
\gamma_{n+1} - \gamma_n &= \int_0^\infty \left(\frac{X}{\langle X \rangle} - 1 \right) \frac{X^n}{\langle X \rangle^n} \sigma(X)\, dX \\
&\geq \int_0^\infty \left(\frac{X}{\langle X \rangle} - 1 \right) \frac{X^n}{\langle X \rangle^n} \sigma(X)\, dX \\
&\quad - \int_0^\infty \left(\frac{X}{\langle X \rangle} - 1 \right) \left(\frac{X^n}{\langle X \rangle^n} - 1 \right) \sigma(X)\, dX \\
&= \int_0^\infty \left(\frac{X}{\langle X \rangle} - 1 \right) \sigma(X)\, dX = 0
\end{aligned} \quad (8\text{-}73)$$

Namely, that the γ_n form a nondecreasing sequence

$$1 \equiv \gamma_1 \leq \gamma_2 \leq \gamma_3 \leq \cdots \leq \gamma_n \leq \cdots \quad (8\text{-}74)$$

This property makes it evident that the conventional classical description cannot adequately describe counting rates for all first-order coherent fields since, as we saw previously, if there are at most m photons in such a field, then $g_n \equiv 0$ for all $n > m$ in direct conflict with the requirement that all $\gamma_n \geq 1$.

It must be emphasized that the relations (8-58) [or even their classical analogs (8-70)] for the consequences of first-order coherent fields make heavy use of the fact that $G(x, y) \equiv V^*(x)V(y)$ over *all* space or that $\langle a_k^\dagger a_l \rangle \equiv z_k^* z_l$ for *all* modes. If we know these relations only approximately, then the slick form of (8-58) is generally lost. Consider, for example, that in contrast to $\langle b_2^\dagger b_2 \rangle = 0$ [cf. (8-51)] we suspect that possibly

$$\langle b_2^\dagger b_2 \rangle = \epsilon \tag{8-75}$$

where ϵ is arbitrarily small but positive, e.g., $\epsilon = 10^{-137}$. As far as occupancy of the second mode is concerned, the density operator could be given by

$$\rho = \alpha|0\rangle\langle 0| + \beta \sum_{n_2=1}^{\infty} \frac{1}{n_2{}^3} |\tilde{n}_2\rangle\langle\tilde{n}_2| \tag{8-76}$$

Here α and β are chosen so that $\mathrm{Tr}(\rho) = 1$ and $\mathrm{Tr}(\rho b_2^\dagger b_2) = \epsilon$, which implies that β is small ($\sim\epsilon$) but positive. Nevertheless, the expression for $G^{(2,2)}$ [or $\mathcal{G}^{(2,2)}$] involves the term

$$\mathrm{Tr}\{\rho(b_2^\dagger)^2 b_2{}^2\} = -\epsilon + \beta \sum_{n_2=1}^{\infty} \frac{1}{n_2} = \infty \tag{8-77}$$

Hence, the contribution from the second mode, which is imperceptably small in the correlation function $G^{(1,1)}$, is completely dominant in $G^{(2,2)}$ and in *all* higher-order correlation functions $G^{(n,n)}$. This clearly invalidates the general result (8-58). Unless all the analogs of this type of example can be physically ruled out, there seems little substitute for a determination of the higher-order correlation functions than that of direct measurement.

Degrees of Coherence. We conclude this section by mentioning a few definitions that several authors have used to treat questions of partial coherence. Glauber [8-2] has introduced the set of normalized correlation functions

$$g^{(n)}(x_1, \ldots, x_{2n}) = G^{(n,n)}(x_1, \ldots, x_{2n}) \Big/ \prod_{k=1}^{2n} \{G^{(1,1)}(x_k, x_k)\}^{1/2} \tag{8-78}$$

For present purposes we choose to regard the $g^{(n)}$ as quantum extensions and generalizations of the classical, complex degree of coherence γ. If for some x, $G^{(1,1)}(x, x) = 0$, then the numerator vanishes as well and we define $g^{(n)}$ by continuity in such cases if we can. From (8-35) it is evident that the condition

$$|g^{(n)}(x_1, \ldots, x_{2n})| = 1 \tag{8-79}$$

for all arguments and all n ensures that the field has full coherence For a field with first-order coherence, on the other hand, it follows from (8-58) that

$$|g^{(n)}(x_1, \ldots, x_{2n})| = g_n \tag{8-80}$$

independent of all coordinate values. As we have seen in the fundamental example of a chaotic field possessing first-order coherence $g_n = n!$, and so the functions $g^{(n)}$ need not be bounded by unity.

In an alternative prescription, more deliberately aimed at generalizing the classical degree of coherence γ, Mehta [8-5] defines a set of "even-order complex degrees of coherence" according to the rule

$$g^{(n,n)}(x_1, \ldots, x_{2n}) \equiv \frac{G^{(n,n)}(x_1, \ldots, x_{2n})}{\left\{\prod_{k=1}^{2n} G^{(n,n)}(x_k, x_k, \ldots, x_k)\right\}^{1/2n}} \tag{8-81}$$

This quantity is not defined unless there are n photons in the field, and to define the whole sequence $g^{(n,n)}$ requires that there be an infinite number of photons in the field. Even with this kind of normalization the quantity $g^{(n,n)}$ can still become arbitrarily large since there need not be n photons with nonvanishing amplitudes at every point of space as is required for a nonzero divisor in (8-81). Apart from these difficulties, Mehta shows that if

$$|g^{(n,n)}(x_1, \ldots, x_{2n})| = 1 \tag{8-82}$$

for a given $n(= n_0)$ and for all arguments, then this condition holds for *all* $n \geq n_0$ and for all arguments.

We can make this result plausible as follows. For $n = 1$, Mehta's and Glauber's definitions coincide; i.e., $g^{(1)} = g^{(1,1)}$, and so the condition

$$|g^{(1,1)}(x, y)| = 1 \tag{8-83}$$

leads to first-order coherence. It follows, therefore, that $G^{(n,n)}$ is given by (8-58), and, if all $g_n \neq 0$, we see without difficulty that (8-82) is fulfilled for all n. According to Mehta, then, a field having first-order coherence would be deemed to have "complete even-order coherence."

The last prescription we shall consider has been introduced and extensively studied by Sudarshan [8-4]. Its introduction is largely motivated by a desire to use quantities that are more nearly direct generalizations of the classical degree of coherence, and which are useful measures of the purity of excited modes. To distinguish the present definitions from the foregoing examples we may call these degrees "coherence indices."

Specifically, we consider the "coherence index of order n" defined by

$$S^{(n,n)}(x_1, \ldots, x_n; x_{n+1}, \ldots, x_{2n}) \equiv \frac{G^{(n,n)}(x_1, \ldots, x_n; x_{n+1}, \ldots, x_{2n})}{[G^{(n,n)}(x_1, \ldots, x_n; x_n, \ldots, x_1) \times G^{(n,n)}(x_{2n}, \ldots, x_{n+1}; x_{n+1}, \ldots, x_{2n})]^{1/2}} \tag{8-84}$$

If the denominator vanishes for some arguments so too does the numerator, and $S^{(n,n)}$ is defined by continuity wherever possible. In order for $S^{(n,n)}$ to be defined for all n there must be an infinite number of photons in the field. For $n = 1$, $S^{(1,1)}$ coincides with $g^{(1,1)}$ and $g^{(1)}$. Consequently, if $|S^{(1,1)}(x_1; x_2)| = 1$ for all arguments, the field has "first-order coherence." So long as all $g_n \neq 0$ it follows directly from (8-58) that in this case

$$|S^{(n,n)}(x_1, \ldots, x_{2n})| = 1 \tag{8-85}$$

for all n. Moreover, as with (8-81), it is possible to show that the validity of (8-85) for a given $n(= n_0)$ and all arguments implies (8-85) for *all* $n \geq n_0$ and all arguments whenever they are defined. In both cases the radiation field is that of a single mode, as with first-order coherence, plus an admixture of other states each with at most $n_0 - 1$ photons. Since $S^{(n,n)}$ is sensitive only to states with n or more photons, the admixture in question does not affect $S^{(n_0,n_0)}$.

There are two important features of the coherent indices worth noting. First of all, let us show that

$$0 \leq |S^{(n,n)}(x_1, \ldots, x_{2n})| \leq 1 \tag{8-86}$$

for all n and all arguments when the ratio is defined. Let $\mathcal{A}$ and $\mathcal{B}$ be general operators, and let us recall (5-18) for the decomposition of a density operator, and (5-3) for Schwarz's inequality. It then follows that

$$\begin{aligned} |\langle \mathcal{A}^\dagger \mathcal{B} \rangle| &= |\Sigma_n \beta_n \langle \psi_n | \mathcal{A}^\dagger \mathcal{B} | \psi_n \rangle| \\ &\leq \Sigma_n \beta_n |\langle \psi_n | \mathcal{A}^\dagger \mathcal{B} | \psi_n \rangle| \\ &\leq \Sigma_n \{\beta_n \langle \psi_n | \mathcal{A}^\dagger \mathcal{A} | \psi_n \rangle\}^{1/2} \{\beta_n \langle \psi_n | \mathcal{B}^\dagger \mathcal{B} | \psi_n \rangle\}^{1/2} \\ &\leq \{\Sigma_n \beta_n \langle \psi_n | \mathcal{A}^\dagger \mathcal{A} | \psi_n \rangle\}^{1/2} \{\Sigma_m \beta_m \langle \psi_m | \mathcal{B}^\dagger \mathcal{B} | \psi_m \rangle\}^{1/2} \\ &= \langle \mathcal{A}^\dagger \mathcal{A} \rangle^{1/2} \langle \mathcal{B}^\dagger \mathcal{B} \rangle^{1/2} \end{aligned} \tag{8-87}$$

which is a generalized Schwarz inequality. If we choose

$$\begin{aligned} \mathcal{A} &= A(x_n) A(x_{n-1}) \cdots A(x_1) \\ \mathcal{B} &= A(x_{n+1}) A(x_{n+2}) \cdots A(x_{2n}) \end{aligned}$$

then the stated inequality for $S^{(n,n)}$ follows.

The second feature of a coherence index we wish to emphasize relates to its interpretation as a visibility index. Much as $1 \pm |\gamma_{12}(\tau)|$ represents the relative extremes in intensity attainable under suitable two-slit geometries [cf. (1-23)], it is plausible that

$$1 \pm |S^{(n,n)}(x_1, \ldots, x_{2n})|$$

represents the correlated n-fold intensity extremes at the indicated points. Hence we may set

$$\mathcal{V}^{(n,n)} = |S^{(n,n)}(x_1, \ldots, x_{2n})| \tag{8-88}$$

as a generalized "visibility index." From the foregoing remarks if a measurement shows for some n_0 that $\mathcal{V}^{(n_0,n_0)} \equiv 1$, then we are assured that the field is that of a single mode—described by its mode function $V(x)$ and moments $g_{n,m}$ in (8-55)—plus an admixture of states each with at most $n_0 - 1$ photons. In order to measure such a quantity by interferometric methods it is generally necessary to employ nonlinear beam-mixing devices so as to generate wave fields proportional to the product of the wave-field amplitude at several points.

According to (8-11), we may also interpret any of the various normalized correlation functions as normalized forms of the multiple-photon coincidence rates. The measurement of the latter provides one possible way to determine $g^{(n)}$, $g^{(n,n)}$, and $S^{(n,n)}$ in a given case.

8-3 PHOTON COUNTING DISTRIBUTIONS

A. Rates and Counts for a Single Normal Mode

Prior to deriving the counting distribution (for the number of counts observed in a finite time interval) for a general state of the field, it is convenient to carry out a simpler discussion as if only a single normal mode of the radiation field were excited. We want to discuss both counting rates and counting distributions for finite times for such an example.

Let us denote the creation and annihilation operators for our distinguished normal mode simply by

$$a^\dagger(t) = e^{i\omega t}a^\dagger \tag{8-89a}$$
$$a(t) = e^{-i\omega t}a \tag{8-89b}$$

The counting rates appropriate to such a field may be simply expressed as

$$\pi(p) = \alpha_0{}^p\langle a^\dagger(t_1) \cdots a^\dagger(t_p)a(t_p) \cdots a(t_1)\rangle \tag{8-90}$$

The coefficient α_0 is related to the quantum efficiency factor α by the connection between the transverse vector potential and the normal modes. In particular, we see directly from (7-179a) that

$$\alpha_0 = \frac{\alpha\hbar}{2\omega L^3} \tag{8-91}$$

In virtue of (8-89) the rate $\pi(p)$ is actually independent of all time arguments,

$$\pi(p) = \alpha_0{}^p\langle(a^\dagger)^p a^p\rangle \tag{8-92}$$

Hence, in particular, $\pi(p)$ is the rate that p photons would be absorbed simultaneously, say all at $t = 0$.

It is interesting to remark that $\pi(p)$—viewed as the rate for simultaneous absorption of p photons—can be deduced from rather different arguments than used previously. If we view this problem as an "event" in which the field divests itself of p photons, then there are a number of mutually exclusive modes for this event to occur. In particular, we may determine the rate on the assumption that there are p, or $p + 1, \ldots,$ or in general $p + n$ photons present, the probability for which is

$$P(p+n) \equiv \mathrm{Tr}\{\rho|p+n\rangle\langle p+n|\} \tag{8-93}$$

We next note that there are $p!\binom{p+n}{p} = (p+n)!/n!$ ways that p photons can be selected from a supply of $p + n$ photons if each of the orders of selection is viewed as distinct. Ignoring the proportionality factor $\alpha_0{}^p$, we see that the rate for yielding p photons is given by

$$\pi(p) = \sum_{n=0}^{\infty} \frac{(p+n)!}{n!} P(p+n) \tag{8-94}$$

It follows from (5-52) that

$$\frac{\sqrt{(p+n)!}}{\sqrt{n!}}\,|p+n\rangle = \frac{(a^\dagger)^{p+n}}{\sqrt{n!}}\,|0\rangle = (a^\dagger)^p|n\rangle$$

and, thus, we find that

$$\begin{aligned}\pi(p) &= \sum_{n=0}^{\infty} \mathrm{Tr}\{\rho(a^\dagger)^p|n\rangle\langle n|a^p\} \\ &= \mathrm{Tr}\{\rho a^{\dagger p} a^p\} = \langle(a^\dagger)^p a^p\rangle \end{aligned} \tag{8-95}$$

as desired. For clarity we have here simply assumed that only one mode is present, but that is not essential to the basic argument.

Our next task is the derivation of a formula for *counting probabilities* from the counting rates, still assuming only one normal mode is excited.

That is, we want to know the probability that a detector will detect m photons in a time interval T. We shall give two different arguments to derive $P(m, T)$.

MULTIATOM DETECTOR. The first method to find $P(m, T)$ is roughly similar to that used by Glauber [8-2]. Let us imagine that our detector is composed of N atoms, where N is an enormous number and which we eventually let tend to infinity. In turn, let us suppose that $s^p\langle a^{\dagger p}a^p\rangle$ is the rate that p photons are absorbed by p *specific* atoms (all of which are assumed to act as independent, identical agents!). Here s is the sensitivity for a single atomic detector which is regarded as being extremely small, of the order N^{-1}. Since the rate is so small the probability that those p specific atoms will have absorbed p photons in a time T is given by

$$s^p \int_0^T \cdots \int_0^T \langle a^{\dagger p}a^p\rangle \, dt_1 \cdots dt_p = s^p T^p \langle a^{\dagger p}a^p\rangle = \langle :(sTa^\dagger a)^p: \rangle \quad (8\text{-}96)$$

which is valid for times T such that $\langle :(sTa^\dagger a)^p:\rangle \ll 1$. From this expression it follows that the probability that $p - 1$ specific atoms have absorbed and that one specific atom has *not* absorbed is given by

$$\langle :(sTa^\dagger a)^{p-1}: \rangle - \langle :(sTa^\dagger a)^p: \rangle = \langle :(sTa^\dagger a)^{p-1}(1 - sTa^\dagger a): \rangle \quad (8\text{-}97)$$

By induction, the probability that $p - r$ specific atoms have absorbed photons and that r specific atoms have not absorbed after a time T is given by

$$\langle :(sTa^\dagger a)^{p-r}(1 - sTa^\dagger a)^r: \rangle \quad (8\text{-}98)$$

Now, the probability $P(m, T)$ that exactly m photons have been absorbed in a detector with N atoms is given by the number of distinguishable ways this process could take place times the elementary probability for each event, namely by

$$P(m, T) = \frac{N!}{(N - m)!\, m!} \langle :(sTa^\dagger a)^m (1 - sTa^\dagger a)^{N-m}: \rangle \quad (8\text{-}99)$$

In the limit that $N \to \infty$ and $s \to 0$ such that $Ns = \alpha_0$ is finite we find that

$$P(m, T) = \left\langle : \frac{(\alpha_0 Ta^\dagger a)^m}{m!} \exp(-\alpha_0 Ta^\dagger a) : \right\rangle \quad (8\text{-}100)$$

Since we have gone to the limit $s \to 0$, this expression should be valid for all T.

Limitations of the Result. Practically speaking, this conclusion is quite correct, but in a strict sense (8-100) may not hold for all T. To see that this aspect is rather common, it is convenient to deal with the generating function

$$Q(\lambda, T) \equiv \sum_{m=0}^{\infty} (1 - \lambda)^m P(m, T)$$

$$= \langle :\exp(-\lambda\alpha_0 T a^\dagger a): \rangle = \sum_{p=0}^{\infty} \frac{(-\lambda)^p}{p!} \alpha_0{}^p T^p \langle a^{\dagger p} a^p \rangle$$

$$= \langle \exp(\ln[1 - \lambda\alpha_0 T] a^\dagger a) \rangle = \sum_{n=0}^{\infty} (1 - \lambda\alpha_0 T)^n P(n) \qquad (8\text{-}101)$$

Here we have made use of (7-91a), and $P(n)$ is the distribution of photons in our singled-out mode. In order that $P(m, T)$ represent a valid distribution for all T, i.e.,

$$0 \leq P(m, T) \leq 1 \qquad \sum_{m=0}^{\infty} P(m, T) = 1 \qquad (8\text{-}102)$$

it is clearly necessary that $0 \leq Q(\lambda, T) \leq 1$ for all T so long as $0 \leq \lambda \leq 1$. Consider, however, a pure state with an odd number n_0 of photons for which $P(n_0) = 1$ and all other $P(n)$ vanish. When $0 < \lambda \leq 1$ in such a case, we see that $Q(\lambda, T) = (1 - \lambda\alpha_0 T)^{n_0} < 0$ for sufficiently large T, namely, for all $T > (\lambda\alpha_0)^{-1} \geq \alpha_0{}^{-1}$.

It is not difficult to show that this kind of limitation is quite general, and that, for an arbitrary state, $P(m, T)$ is always a valid distribution so long as

$$T \leq \frac{1}{\alpha_0} = \frac{2\omega L^3}{\alpha\hbar} \qquad (8\text{-}103)$$

Moreover, the limiting distribution at $T = \alpha_0{}^{-1}$ is just

$$P(m, \alpha_0{}^{-1}) = P(m) \qquad (8\text{-}104)$$

Namely, in a time $\alpha_0{}^{-1}$ the distribution of the counts received by the detector is just the distribution of the photons in the single normal mode of the field.

The appearance of the quantization volume in the limit (8-103) shows that the upper bound $\alpha_0{}^{-1}$ can be made arbitrarily big and is thus largely academic. Nevertheless, it is instructive to understand the reason behind such a limitation. Suppose as an example we let there be just *one* photon in the normal mode so that

$$P(m, T) = \langle 1 | : \frac{(\alpha_0 T a^\dagger a)^m}{m!} \exp(-\alpha_0 T a^\dagger a) : | 1 \rangle \qquad (8\text{-}105)$$

or specifically that

$$P(0, T) = 1 - \alpha_0 T \tag{8-106a}$$
$$P(1, T) = \alpha_0 T \tag{8-106b}$$

all other terms vanishing. The limitation $\alpha_0 T \leq 1$ is clearly in evidence here, but more important this result is essentially incorrect anyway: The rates we have derived here via perturbation theory and the "Golden Rule" do not properly account for depletion of the initial state as time evolves.

A more suitable result for this single-photon example can be obtained as follows. The initial rates calculated via perturbation theory are still valid, namely,

$$\pi(1) = \alpha_0 \langle a^\dagger a \rangle = \alpha_0 \qquad \pi(p) \equiv 0 \qquad p \geq 2 \tag{8-107}$$

Indeed, α_0 is the correct rate of photon absorption at *any* given time conditional on the fact that *no* photons have been counted previously. Thus $1 - \alpha_0\, dt$ is the probability at any given time that no photon is counted in the interval dt conditional on the fact that no photons have been counted previously. It follows that (in the same spirit as the calculation in Chapter 2)

$$P(0, T) = \text{“}\prod_{t}^{t+T} (1 - \alpha_0\, dt)\text{”} = \exp(-\alpha_0 T) \tag{8-108a}$$

and as a consequence

$$P(1, T) = 1 - P(0, T) = 1 - \exp(-\alpha_0 T) \tag{8-108b}$$

which is physically much more reasonable than (8-106). Clearly, for times such that $\alpha_0 T \ll 1$, the two results agree.

It may be worth remarking that similar limitations apply to the distribution given by (8-100) for any state for which the counting rates $\pi(p)$ all vanish if $p \geq M$ (for some $M \geq 2$). Thus one should be cautioned against too literal an interpretation of (8-100) for all states and all times so long as the "box" size $L < \infty$. Nevertheless, when we shall discuss below all the modes of the field and more physical states of the radiation field, it will become clear that these difficulties have no significance from a practical standpoint.

"DIAGONAL" COHERENT-STATE REPRESENTATION. Our second method to derive the counting distribution $P(m, T)$ is rather different than that used above although the result is the same. The reader may recall that in our derivation of the Poisson counting distribution in Chapter 2 we were greatly aided by the assumption that the events (i.e., counts) occurring in different time intervals were statistically independent. Now it is precisely this question that the counting rates deal with: The joint probability that p photons will be counted at times $t_1, \ldots, t_p$, and in the intervals $dt_1, \ldots, dt_p$ is given by

$$\alpha_0{}^p\langle a^{\dagger p}a^p\rangle\, dt_1 \cdots dt_p \tag{8-109}$$

These events will be statistically independent if the probability factorizes into a multiple of elementary, single-event probabilities, i.e., if for all p

$$\alpha_0{}^p\langle a^{\dagger p}a^p\rangle\, dt_1 \cdots dt_p = \prod_{l=1}^{p} \{\alpha_0\langle a^\dagger a\rangle\, dt_l\} \tag{8-110}$$

Clearly this just requires that

$$\langle a^{\dagger p}a^p\rangle = (\langle a^\dagger a\rangle)^p \tag{8-111}$$

for all p. This condition is not vacuous for it is exactly what occurs for a pure coherent-state density operator $\rho = |z\rangle\langle z|$.

Since the counting events in different time intervals are statistically independent for a coherent state, we may carry over directly the results of the calculation in Chapter 2 for an elementary rate $\pi(1) = dp(t)/dt$ given by

$$\frac{dp(t)}{dt} = \alpha_0\langle a^\dagger a\rangle = \alpha_0\langle z|a^\dagger a|z\rangle = \alpha_0|z|^2 \tag{8-112}$$

In particular, we find that the counting distribution [cf. Eq. (2-2)] reads

$$P(m, T|z) = \frac{(\alpha_0 T|z|^2)^m}{m!} \exp(-\alpha_0 T|z|^2) \tag{8-113}$$

which is a Poisson distribution with mean $\bar{m} = \alpha_0 T|z|^2$, and which is valid for *all* T. We have added the conditional label z to remind ourselves we are dealing with a coherent state.

If we make use of the general relation for diagonal matrix elements of ordered operators given in (7-105), then we can write

$$\begin{aligned} P(m, T|z) &= \langle z|\!:\frac{(\alpha_0 T a^\dagger a)^m}{m!} \exp(-\alpha_0 T a^\dagger a)\!:\!|z\rangle \\ &= \mathrm{Tr}\left\{|z\rangle\langle z|\!:\frac{(\alpha_0 T a^\dagger a)^m}{m!} \exp(-\alpha_0 T a^\dagger a)\!:\right\} \end{aligned} \tag{8-114}$$

For those density operators that we can write in the form of a normalized, linear superposition of coherent-state projection operators,

$$\rho = \frac{1}{\pi}\int \varphi(z)|z\rangle\langle z|\, d^2z \tag{8-115}$$

we can win the counting distribution directly from the formula

$$\begin{aligned} P(m, T) &= \frac{1}{\pi} \int \varphi(z) P(m, T|z)\, d^2z \\ &= \operatorname{Tr} \left\{ \rho \colon \frac{(\alpha_0 T a^\dagger a)^m}{m!} \exp(-\alpha_0 T a^\dagger a) \colon \right\} \\ &= \left\langle \colon \frac{(\alpha_0 T a^\dagger a)^m}{m!} \exp(-\alpha_0 T a^\dagger a) \colon \right\rangle \end{aligned} \tag{8-116}$$

in accord with (8-100). If $\varphi(z)$ is a conventional probability density, then the so defined $P(m, T)$ is necessarily a valid distribution for all T.

We shall show below the remarkable result that (in a distribution sense to be made precise) *every* ρ can be written in the "diagonal" coherent-state representation (8-115). Quite evidently the weighting by φ cannot always be positive since otherwise one could not make any pure-state density operators except the coherent state ones. A negative weighting is also required by the fact that otherwise the counting distributions $P(m, T)$ would, for any state, be a valid distribution for all T, and we have already seen counterexamples to this.

It should be emphasized that such negative weightings need give rise to no difficulties whatsoever so long as no basic rules are violated. A simple example can help clarify the role of negative weightings. Suppose that $P_2(n)$ and $P_3(n)$ are valid probability distributions, then so too is their weighted sum $P_1(n) \equiv \frac{1}{2}P_2(n) + \frac{1}{2}P_3(n)$. Consequently the relation

$$P_3(n) \equiv 2P_1(n) - P_2(n) \equiv \sum_{\alpha=1}^{2} \varphi_\alpha P_\alpha(n) \tag{8-117}$$

certainly defines a valid probability distribution and yet involves a normalized ($\Sigma\varphi_\alpha = 1$) linear weighting with negative terms. All properties of $P_3(n)$ may be deduced from (8-117). In particular, the moments are given by $\langle n^p \rangle_3 = \Sigma\varphi_\alpha \langle n^p \rangle_\alpha$, etc.

It is noteworthy that the "diagonal" representation for ρ in (8-115) leads to an equation for the quantum counting distribution—in the first line of (8-116)—formally identical to that which arises in a conventional classical calculation of this distribution. In this formal connection, the weight $\varphi(z)$ is the analog of the classical distribution. As we shall see this formal analogy can be fruitfully exploited in many applications.

B. Counting Distributions for the Radiation Field

Point Detectors. Guided by the discussion for a single mode it is not too difficult to determine the counting distribution for the radiation field. Suppose we deal first with a counter sensibly localized at the point $\mathbf{r}$ in space which is equally sensitive to all polarizations. Then, according to

(8-9), the counting rates for the joint observation of n photons at $\mathbf{r}$ at times $t_1, t_2, \ldots, t_n$ is given by

$$\alpha^n \sum_{\text{polariz.}} \left\langle \prod_{k=1}^{n} A^{(-)}(t_k) \prod_{l=1}^{n} A^{(+)}(t_l) \right\rangle \tag{8-118}$$

Here we have suppressed a common variable $\mathbf{r}$ and have not written out the vector indices for A explicitly. Suppose this rate *factorizes* in the form

$$\prod_{k=1}^{n} \left\{ \alpha \sum_{\text{polariz.}} \langle A^{(-)}(t_k) A^{(+)}(t_k) \rangle \right\} = \prod_{k=1}^{n} \{ \alpha \langle \mathbf{A}^{(-)}(t_k) \cdot \mathbf{A}^{(+)}(t_k) \rangle \} \tag{8-119}$$

for all n and for all time arguments. This, in fact, is just the property for a coherent state of the radiation field for which $\rho = |\{z_\lambda(\mathbf{k})\}\rangle\langle\{z_\lambda(\mathbf{k})\}|$. In such a state the counts in separate time intervals are statistically independent, and, moreover, in the notation of (7-181a), the elementary counting rate reads

$$\begin{aligned} \alpha\langle \mathbf{A}^{(-)}(t) \cdot \mathbf{A}^{(+)}(t) \rangle &= \alpha \langle \{z_\lambda(\mathbf{k})\} | \mathbf{A}^{(-)}(t) \cdot \mathbf{A}^{(+)}(t) | \{z_\lambda(\mathbf{k})\} \rangle \\ &= \alpha \mathbf{V}^*(t) \cdot \mathbf{V}(t) = \alpha |\mathbf{V}(t)|^2 \end{aligned} \tag{8-120}$$

Consequently, the argument used to derive the Poisson statistics in Chapter 2 applies again, and we find for a coherent state that

$$P(m, T + t, t | \{z_\lambda(\mathbf{k})\}) = \frac{\left(\alpha \int_t^{T+t} |\mathbf{V}(t')|^2 \, dt' \right)^m}{m!} \exp \left[-\alpha \int_t^{T+t} |\mathbf{V}(t')|^2 \, dt' \right] \tag{8-121}$$

which, of course, need not be stationary (independent of t).

For those density operators that we can write as linear superpositions of the form

$$\rho = \int \varphi(\{z_\lambda(\mathbf{k})\}) |\{z_\lambda(\mathbf{k})\}\rangle\langle\{z_\lambda(\mathbf{k})\}| \, d\mu(\{z_\lambda(\mathbf{k})\}) \tag{8-122}$$

which we shall make precise below in roughly the manner of (7-153), it follows that

$$\begin{aligned} P(m, T + t, t) &= \int \varphi(\{z_\lambda(\mathbf{k})\}) P(m, T + t, t | \{z_\lambda(\mathbf{k})\}) \, d\mu(\{z_\lambda(\mathbf{k})\}) \\ &= \left\langle : \frac{\left(\alpha \int_t^{T+t} \mathbf{A}^{(-)}(t') \cdot \mathbf{A}^{(+)}(t') \, dt' \right)^m}{m!} \right. \\ &\qquad \left. \times \exp \left[-\alpha \int_t^{T+t} \mathbf{A}^{(-)}(t') \cdot \mathbf{A}^{(+)}(t') \, dt' \right] : \right\rangle \end{aligned} \tag{8-123}$$

which represents our desired solution. As in the single mode case we can, in fact, represent *every* ρ in the fashion of (8-122) in a distribution sense that we spell out below. Consequently, (8-123) represents the appropriate counting distribution for a point counter and a general state ρ. In turn, the generating function reads

$$Q(\lambda, T+t, t) \equiv \sum_{m=0}^{\infty} (1-\lambda)^m P(m, T+t, t)$$
$$= \left\langle :\exp\left[-\lambda\alpha \int_t^{T+t} \mathbf{A}^{(-)}(t') \cdot \mathbf{A}^{(+)}(t')\, dt'\right]:\right\rangle \quad (8\text{-}124)$$

DISTRIBUTED DETECTORS. Now consider a distributed counter, one which is sensitive over a region of space and time. We may imagine initially that we can deal with a simple admittance tensor $\mathsf{S}^*(\mathbf{r}, t)$ which determines the relative amplitude and phase with which the field contributes. Initially, this simply means that the effective field that enters the n-photon counting rates is expressed by

$$\mathbf{A}_e^{(+)}(t') = \int \mathsf{S}^*(\mathbf{r}, t'-t_1) \cdot \mathbf{A}_e^{(+)}(\mathbf{r}, t_1)\, d^3r\, dt_1 \quad (8\text{-}125)$$

In addition, we may next imagine that specific properties of S^* are not under our control precisely and we must sum over the various possible admittance tensors. In the single-photon counting rate this has the consequence that we replace $\alpha\langle \mathbf{A}^{(-)}(\mathbf{r}, t') \cdot \mathbf{A}^{(+)}(\mathbf{r}, t')\rangle$ by the general quantity

$$\sum_{\substack{\text{relevant} \\ S^*}} \alpha\langle \mathbf{A}_e^{(-)}(\mathbf{r}, t') \cdot \mathbf{A}_e^{(+)}(\mathbf{r}, t')\rangle \equiv \alpha\langle \mathbf{A}^{(-)} \cdot \mathsf{Y} \cdot \mathbf{A}^{(+)}\rangle \quad (8\text{-}126)$$

where we have introduced the abbreviation

$$\mathbf{A}^{(-)} \cdot \mathsf{Y} \cdot \mathbf{A}^{(+)} \equiv \int \mathbf{A}^{(-)}(r_1, t_1) \cdot \mathsf{Y}(\mathbf{r}_1, t'-t_1; \mathbf{r}_2, t'-t_2) \cdot \mathbf{A}^{(+)}(\mathbf{r}_2, t_2)\, d^3r_1\, d^3r_2\, dt_1\, dt_2 \quad (8\text{-}127)$$

Here the tensor Y represents the spatial and temporal spectral properties of the detector. The most important idealization in practice is for the case where

$$\mathsf{Y} = \sigma(\mathbf{r}_1)\,\delta(\mathbf{r}_1 - \mathbf{r}_2)\,\delta(t'-t_1)\,\delta(t'-t_2) \quad (8\text{-}128)$$

where $\sigma(\mathbf{r})$ is the relative density of detector atoms and which vanishes outside the detector. In this case we simply have

$$\mathbf{A}^{(-)} \cdot \mathsf{Y} \cdot \mathbf{A}^{(+)} = \int \mathbf{A}^{(-)}(\mathbf{r}, t') \cdot \mathbf{A}^{(+)}(\mathbf{r}, t')\sigma(\mathbf{r})\, d^3r \quad (8\text{-}129)$$

For a coherent state the n-photon counting rates still factorize into a product of elementary rates given by

$$\alpha\langle \mathbf{A}^{(-)} \cdot \mathsf{Y} \cdot \mathbf{A}^{(+)}\rangle = \alpha\mathbf{V}^* \cdot \mathsf{Y} \cdot \mathbf{V}$$
$$\equiv \alpha \int \mathbf{V}^*(\mathbf{r}_1, t_1) \cdot \mathsf{Y}(\mathbf{r}_1, t'-t_1; \mathbf{r}_2, t'-t_2) \cdot \mathbf{V}(\mathbf{r}_2, t_2)\, d^3r_1\, d^3r_2\, dt_1\, dt_2 \quad (8\text{-}130)$$

From this fact it follows that the counting distribution for this "Y-detector" in a coherent state is given by

$$P_Y(m, T+t, t|\{z_\lambda(\mathbf{k})\}) = \frac{\left\{\alpha \int_t^{T+t} (\mathbf{V}^* \cdot \mathsf{Y} \cdot \mathbf{V})\, dt'\right\}^m}{m!} \exp\left\{-\alpha \int_t^{T+t} (\mathbf{V}^* \cdot \mathsf{Y} \cdot \mathbf{V})\, dt'\right\} \quad (8\text{-}131)$$

rather than by (8-121). Nevertheless, we can still represent a general ρ in the form (8-122), and thus determine for the Y-detector and the state ρ that

$$P_Y(m, T+t, t) = \int \varphi(\{z_\lambda(\mathbf{k})\}) P_Y(m, T+t, t|\{z_\lambda(\mathbf{k})\})\, d\mu(\{z_\lambda(\mathbf{k})\})$$
$$= \left\langle : \frac{\left\{\alpha \int_t^{T+t} \mathbf{A}^{(-)} \cdot \mathsf{Y} \cdot \mathbf{A}^{(+)}\, dt'\right\}^m}{m!} \exp\left\{-\alpha \int_t^{T+t} \mathbf{A}^{(-)} \cdot \mathsf{Y} \cdot \mathbf{A}^{(+)}\, dt'\right\} : \right\rangle \quad (8\text{-}132)$$

Evidently the modified generating function reads

$$Q_Y(\lambda, T+t, t) = \sum_{m=0}^{\infty} (1-\lambda)^m P_Y(\lambda, T+t, t)$$
$$= \left\langle :\exp\left\{-\lambda\alpha \int_t^{T+t} [\mathbf{A}^{(-)} \cdot \mathsf{Y} \cdot \mathbf{A}^{(+)}]\, dt'\right\}: \right\rangle \quad (8\text{-}133)$$

In summary, it is clear that no matter what form the spectral properties of the detector take, the counting distributions are basically weighted Poisson distributions with the weighting $\varphi(\{z_\lambda(\mathbf{k})\})$ describing the state ρ being completely independent of the details of the counter.

MULTIPLE DETECTORS. Next, we indicate the generalization of these results appropriate to a number of counters distributed at various locations. To win this result we note again that in a coherent state the counting events are statistically independent for various points of space as well as for various times. In such a state, the joint probability that the qth counter, $q = 1, 2, \ldots, Q$, will detect m_q counts in a time interval from t_q to $\tau_q \equiv t_q + T_q$ is given by

$$P(\mathbf{m}, \boldsymbol{\tau}, \mathbf{t}|\{z_\lambda(\mathbf{k})\}) \equiv P(m_1, \ldots, m_Q; \tau_1, \ldots, \tau_Q; t_1, \ldots, t_Q|\{z_\lambda(\mathbf{k})\})$$
$$= \prod_{q=1}^{Q} P_{Y_q}(m_q, \tau_q, t_q|\{z_\lambda(\mathbf{k})\}) \quad (8\text{-}134)$$

where the latter expressions are defined in (8-131). In consequence, the joint counting distribution in a general state is given by

$$P(\mathbf{m}, \boldsymbol{\tau}, \mathbf{t}) = \int \varphi(\{z_\lambda(\mathbf{k})\}) P(\mathbf{m}, \boldsymbol{\tau}, \mathbf{t}|\{z_\lambda(\mathbf{k})\})\, d\mu(\{z_\lambda(\mathbf{k})\}) \quad (8\text{-}135)$$

There are obvious expressions for $P(\mathbf{m}, \boldsymbol{\tau}, \mathbf{t})$ and an associated generating function $Q(\boldsymbol{\lambda}, \boldsymbol{\tau}, \mathbf{t})$ as means of normal ordered operator expressions which we do not bother to write down. We shall have occasion to discuss the joint counting distributions in the last chapter for several experimentally interesting cases.

Properties for Infinite Quantization Volume. There is one final topic to clarify regarding all of the counting distributions we have discussed. The results quoted above still depend implicitly on the size of the quantization volume through their dependence on the parameter L. We have previously seen how certain distributions (for a single normal mode) were only meaningful for times less than $2\omega L^3/(\alpha\hbar)$. These technical difficulties disappear if we now take the limit $L \rightarrow \infty$. We can imagine that the limiting operation $L \rightarrow \infty$ is appended to Eqs. (8-132) and (8-133) in order to finally define the general counting distribution and its generating function for a Y-detector.

The basic property which makes the counting distributions asymptotically independent of L and, thus, well behaved in the limit $L \rightarrow \infty$ is simply the wave-packet nature of radiation fields with finite total energy. It follows that a wave-packet signal can be in the vicinity of a realistic (finite-sized!) detector for only a finite time interval. As a consequence, for example, the single-detector distribution $P(m, T + t, t)$ attains a limiting form as $T \rightarrow \infty$ governed by the temporal duration of the wave packet at the detector site; it does not indefinitely grow in magnitude, as we found was possible for a single normal mode in a finite quantization volume.

8-4 OPTICAL EQUIVALENCE THEOREM

In our previous discussion we asserted that every density operator could be represented in a certain sense in the "diagonal" form (8-115) or (8-122). The utility of such a representation has already been demonstrated in the rapid derivation of the counting distribution that it permitted. Indeed, we shall find it extremely useful as a computation tool in several applications. In order to gain insight into the diagonal representation as well as to make its meaning precise it is especially convenient to start with the consideration of a single degree of freedom.

A. "Diagonal" Representation for Single Degree of Freedom

Heuristic Remarks. The general problem we seek to study can be phrased as representing an operator T in the diagonal form

$$T = \int \varphi(z) |z\rangle\langle z| \, d\mu \tag{8-136}$$

Here we set $d\mu = \pi^{-1} d^2z$ to save writing π^{-1}, and we have generalized (8-115) somewhat to consider more general operators than just density operators. The basic question is: What operators T can we represent in this fashion and what are the associated weights $\varphi(z)$?

Quite clearly, if $z = x + iy$, then

$$\varphi(z) = \pi\, \delta(z - z_0) \equiv \pi\, \delta(x - x_0)\delta(y - y_0) \tag{8-137}$$

leads to $T = |z_0\rangle\langle z_0|$, a projection operator on a coherent state. If $\varphi(z) \equiv 1$, we recover the basic resolution of unity given in (7-48).

For more general operators it is useful to begin as follows. Suppose we consider the diagonal coherent-state matrix elements

$$\begin{aligned} T(z') \equiv \langle z'|T|z'\rangle &= \int \varphi(z)\langle z'|z\rangle\langle z|z'\rangle\, d\mu \\ &= \int \varphi(z) \exp(-|z' - z|^2)\, d\mu \end{aligned} \tag{8-138}$$

We have already seen in Chapter 7 that T is fully determined by these diagonal matrix elements. Consequently, if the weight $\varphi(z)$ fulfills (8-138), it automatically fulfills the more general statement (8-136). The form of (8-138) is that of a convolution integral, and it suggests that we Fourier transform everything in sight. For this purpose, let us choose our phase-space formulation so as to bring into focus the real and imaginary parts of z. That is, we consider

$$\begin{aligned} T(p', q') &\equiv \langle p', q'|T|p', q'\rangle \\ &= \int \varphi(p, q) \exp\left\{-\frac{1}{2\hbar}[(p' - p)^2 + (q' - q)^2]\right\} d\mu \end{aligned} \tag{8-139}$$

where now $d\mu = dp\, dq/(2\pi\hbar)$. If we define

$$\tilde{T}(x, k) \equiv \int e^{i(xp-kq)/\hbar}\, T(p, q)\, d\mu \tag{8-140a}$$

$$\tilde{\varphi}(x, k) \equiv \int e^{i(xp-kq)/\hbar}\, \varphi(p, q)\, d\mu \tag{8-140b}$$

and note that

$$\exp\left[-\frac{1}{2\hbar}(x^2 + k^2)\right] = \int e^{i(xp-kq)/\hbar} \exp\left[-\frac{1}{2\hbar}(p^2 + q^2)\right] d\mu \tag{8-141}$$

it follows by the convolution theorem that

$$\tilde{T}(x, k) = \tilde{\varphi}(x, k) \exp\left[-\frac{1}{2\hbar}(x^2 + k^2)\right]$$

Consequently, we see that

$$\tilde{\varphi}(x, k) = \tilde{T}(x, k) \exp\left[\frac{1}{2\hbar}(x^2 + k^2)\right] \tag{8-142}$$

which, on the face of it, claims that every operator T has a diagonal representation[6] with a weight $\varphi(z)$ *defined* as the Fourier transform of $\tilde{T}(x, k) \exp[(1/2\hbar)(x^2 + k^2)]$.

To make sense of (8-136), therefore, we need to understand the Fourier transform of (8-142). Quite clearly if (8-142) defines an absolutely integrable function, then the Fourier transform is well defined, but this need not always be the case. To gain further insight into the diagonal representation, we need to examine the quantity $\tilde{T}(x, k)$ in closer detail. For this purpose it is convenient to recall a few properties of distribution theory, which is the mathematical theory that makes precise and generalizes concepts such as Dirac's δ function.

DISTRIBUTIONS—KNOWN BY THE COMPANY THEY KEEP. Although most readers will intuitively think of the δ function as a highly peaked singular function, it is more properly regarded as a functional or as a kind of operator. Namely, given a certain class of functions, it maps those functions into complex numbers defined as the function evaluated at a specific argument. In symbols, we generally write (as, indeed, we have frequently done!)

$$f(x_0) = \int \delta(x - x_0) f(x)\, dx \tag{8-143}$$

although the right-hand side is, strictly speaking, a notational abuse since there is no quantity that can serve as an integrand in the classic Lebesgue definition of an integral. Two prescriptions serve to make $\delta(x - x_0)$ a precise concept. The first form abandons the integral and simply says that $\delta_{x_0}\{f\} \equiv f(x_0)$, i.e., δ_{x_0} is viewed as a functional which maps the function into the value it assumes at x_0. The second form, known more popularly as generalized functions, defines the action of δ_{x_0} by

$$f(x_0) = \lim_{M\to\infty} \int \delta_M(x - x_0) f(x)\, dx \tag{8-144}$$

where $\delta_M(x)$ is some sequence of well-behaved functions [e.g., $\delta_M(x) = (M/\pi)^{1/2} \exp(-Mx^2)$] for each of which the integral makes sense. Obviously, there are many sequences which can serve to define a given distribution. In any case, it is evidently convenient to *define* the symbolic right-hand side of (8-143) by either of the two proper forms of definitions, which, of course, is always implicitly assumed.

No matter what is the ultimate mode of definition, δ is not defined on all functions $f(x)$, as may happen if x_0 is a point of discontinuity. This gives rise to the notion of *test functions* (just our smooth functions of

[6] The first argument suggesting the exceptional generality of the diagonal representation of operators is due to Sudarshan [8-7].

Chapter 3!), a class of functions on which a given distribution can be defined. For δ, for example, the allowed test functions must be continuous. In many cases, however, it is convenient to take as test functions less than *all* the functions for which a *given* distribution is defined so that we may simultaneously consider several distributions and linear combinations thereof. The classical example here is the set of complex test functions $f(x)$ of the real variable x all of which are infinitely differentiable and fall off at infinity faster than any inverse power (often abbreviated as "rapid decrease"). Each such function is defined for distributions that involve any finite number of derivatives of δ functions or for those which grow like some polynomial at infinity. Such distributions, generically of the indicated form, are called "tempered distributions,"[7] and the space of test functions is called the tempered distribution test function space and is denoted by $\mathcal{S}$. Stated otherwise, the tempered distributions are linear functionals[8] on the space $\mathcal{S}$—they map each element of $\mathcal{S}$ into a complex number. This does not imply that any *given* distribution (say δ) cannot be defined on a wider class of functions, but rather that it is convenient to limit attention to certain useful spaces (such as $\mathcal{S}$) whose properties can be carefully studied.

Another classic test function space called $\mathfrak{D}$ is composed of complex functions $f(x)$ for real x, each of which is infinitely differentiable and vanishes outside of a finite region. An example of such a function is given by $f(x) = \exp[-(1 - x^2)^{-2}]$, $|x| \leq 1$, and $f(x) \equiv 0$ otherwise. Since this class of test functions is smaller than $\mathcal{S}$ the class of allowed distributions is correspondingly larger. In particular, the function $\varphi(x) = \exp(x^2)$ is a distribution on $\mathfrak{D}$ [since $\int \varphi(x)f(x)\,dx \equiv \varphi\{f\}$ defines a linear functional on $\mathfrak{D}$] but it is not a tempered distribution.

Fourier transforms of distributions are defined via associated Fourier transforms of their test function spaces. For example, for every test function $f(x)$ in $\mathcal{S}$, let us introduce the function

$$\tilde{f}(y) = (2\pi)^{-1/2}\int e^{-iyx}f(x)\,dx \tag{8-145}$$

It is not too difficult to see that this transformation maps $\mathcal{S}$ onto itself since the Fourier transform of an infinitely differentiable function with rapid decrease has the very same properties. In consequence, the distribution $\tilde{\varphi}$ defined by analogy with Parseval's formula so that $\tilde{\varphi}\{\tilde{f}^*\} \equiv \varphi\{f^*\}$ for all $f(x)$ in $\mathcal{S}$ (where φ is a tempered distribution) is itself a tem-

[7] "Polynomial growth" must be carefully interpreted. Although e^x is not a tempered distribution, $e^x \exp(ie^x)$ is tempered since it is the derivative of a bounded function, $-i \exp(ie^x)$.

[8] Strictly speaking, tempered distributions are continuous linear functionals but we shall ignore this sophistication because the topologies needed to define continuity in test functions are unduly complicated for our purposes.

pered distribution. For example, if $\varphi = \delta(x - x_0)$, then $\tilde{\varphi} = (2\pi)^{1/2} \exp(-iyx_0)$, which is clearly well defined on all of $\mathcal{S}$.

Although it is evidently convenient when the Fourier transformation leaves a given class of test functions (and, hence, their associated distributions) invariant, there is no requirement that this be so. We can also consider the Fourier transformation of test functions in $\mathfrak{D}$ each of which vanishes outside a finite interval. The associated Fourier-transformed test functions defined as in (8-145) cannot similarly vanish outside a finite interval (since they are boundary values of entire functions). Hence the space—called $\mathcal{Z}$—which they form has no function in common with $\mathfrak{D}$ except the zero function, $f(x) = \tilde{f}(y) \equiv 0$! However, it should be noted that since $\mathfrak{D}$ is a subspace of $\mathcal{S}$, the Fourier transform space $\mathcal{Z}$ is likewise a subspace of $\mathcal{S}$. A distribution [e.g., $\exp(-\frac{1}{2}x^2)$] on $\mathfrak{D}$ may be a distribution on $\mathcal{Z}$ as well, but since the spaces are distinct this need not always be the case. Nevertheless, every distribution $\tilde{\varphi}$ on $\mathcal{Z}$ is obtained through the Fourier transformation of a distribution φ on $\mathfrak{D}$ by the identification $\tilde{\varphi}\{\tilde{f}^*\} \equiv \varphi\{f\}$ for all $f(x)$ in $\mathfrak{D}$. By this process new distributions may, in fact, be introduced, but they are fully defined by their values on their *own* space of test functions $\mathcal{Z}$ (even though they may not be defined on $\mathfrak{D}$). In truth, a distribution is known by the company it keeps!

As we have noted, distributions are not generally defined via their functional values (and an associated integral) but rather, say, by means of a sequence of functions. Sometimes, it is even difficult to "picture" the distribution as a function. For example, even though $\delta''(x)$ vanishes if $x \neq 0$, it is impossible to give it a *value* at $x = 0$. Even worse to visualize is the distribution on $\mathcal{Z}$ which is the Fourier transform of $\exp(x^2)$. These examples show the special utility of defining distributions via sequences of visualizable, tangible, and integrable functions. All our distributions can be defined in such sequential fashion, and this will be the prescription we shall follow to make various distributions precise.

Application to "Diagonal" Representations. The nature of the function $T(p, q)$ in (8-139) depends on the particular operator T. If T is a bounded operator, then $T(p, q)$ is a bounded, continuous, infinitely differentiable function. We are especially interested in the cases where T is a trace-class operator (thus including density operators) each of which has the canonical form given by (5-18). In particular, for these operators

$$\begin{aligned} T(p, q) &= \langle p, q|T|p, q\rangle \\ &= \sum_{j=1}^{\infty} \beta_j \langle p, q|\lambda_j\rangle\langle\psi_j|p, q\rangle \end{aligned} \tag{8-146}$$

for some absolutely summable sequence β_j and orthonormal bases $|\lambda_j\rangle$ and $|\psi_j\rangle$. It follows for such operators that

$$\int |T(p, q)|\, d\mu \leq \sum_{j=1}^{\infty} |\beta_j| \int |\langle p, q|\lambda_j\rangle\langle\psi_j|p, q\rangle|\, d\mu$$

$$\leq \sum_{j=1}^{\infty} |\beta_j| \equiv \|T\|_1 < \infty \tag{8-147}$$

which is based on Schwarz's inequality in the continuous representation. Consequently, the Fourier transform $\tilde{T}(x, k)$ is a continuous, bounded (by $\|T\|_1$) *function* for every trace-class operator. In turn, therefore,

$$\tilde{\varphi}(x, k) \equiv \tilde{T}(x, k) \exp\left[\frac{1}{2\hbar}(x^2 + k^2)\right] \tag{8-148}$$

is a *continuous function* for every trace-class operator with the bound

$$|\tilde{\varphi}(x, k)| \leq \|T\|_1 e^{1/2\hbar(x^2+k^2)} \tag{8-149a}$$

Indeed as we shall show below

$$|\tilde{\varphi}(x, k)| \leq \|T\|_1 e^{1/4\hbar(x^2+k^2)} \tag{8-149b}$$

It is clear that all such functions $\tilde{\varphi}(x, k)$ determine distributions on $\mathfrak{D}_2$, the space of two-variable functions $f(x, k)$ which are infinitely differentiable and which vanish outside some finite region of x, k space. [9] This is evident for

$$\int \tilde{\varphi}(x, k) f(x, k)\, d\mu \tag{8-150}$$

where $d\mu = dx\, dk/(2\pi\hbar)$ is well defined for all such $f(x, k)$. It is the Fourier transform of such functions that interest us for the diagonal representation of trace-class operators. In general, such a Fourier transform is a distribution and not a function.

To make sense of such a Fourier transform in the general case, let us use a sequence prescription. In particular, let us introduce functions $\tilde{\varphi}_M(x, k)$ which as $M \to \infty$ approach $\tilde{\varphi}(x, k)$ (in some sense) and yet for each of which a well-behaved function $\varphi_M(p, q)$ exists as a Fourier transform. In other words, we define a sequence of operators

$$T_M = \int \varphi_M(p, q) |p, q\rangle\langle p, q|\, d\mu \tag{8-151}$$

by means of the weight functions $\varphi_M(p, q)$, which tend to the given operator T. If we were content to ask only for general matrix elements

[9] Although we make no use of the result it may be noted that if T is any bounded operator or polynomial in $a\dagger$ and a, then $\tilde{\varphi}(x, k)$ is always a distribution on $\mathfrak{D}_2$, though it is not necessarily given by a function.

$\langle\lambda|T|\psi\rangle$, then it would be adequate to cook up a sequence T_M such that for all $|\lambda\rangle$ and $|\psi\rangle$

$$\lim_{M\to\infty} \langle\lambda|T_M|\psi\rangle = \langle\lambda|T|\psi\rangle \tag{8-152}$$

However, we are actually interested in a much more stringent requirement since we want to take traces of various expressions involving the density operators.

The operators of interest for which we need the mean values in order to find the counting distributions are actually bounded operators. Mean values of bounded operators are defined for *every* state of the system, and they constitute a maximal, common class of observables from a general quantum mechanical point of view. Indeed, such a class contains the unitary operator which determines the characteristic function $C_{\mathcal{O}}(s) \equiv \mathrm{Tr}(\rho e^{is\mathcal{O}})$ for the distribution of every observable imaginable. If we seek to represent density operators by a sequence, this sequence, to be practical, should permit the direct computation of the mean value of every bounded operator. In symbols, we want to ensure for every bounded operator B that

$$\mathrm{Tr}(TB) = \lim_{M\to\infty} \mathrm{Tr}(T_M B) \tag{8-153}$$

which is considerably more stringent than (8-152).

To put this requirement into practical terms, consider the sequence of trace-class operators defined by

$$Y_M \equiv T - T_M \equiv \sum_{j=1}^{\infty} \gamma_j^{(M)} |\lambda_j^{(M)}\rangle\langle\psi_j^{(M)}| \tag{8-154}$$

the last relation being a consequence of the canonical form (5-18). Then, clearly, we have for any bounded operator B

$$\begin{aligned} |\mathrm{Tr}(Y_M B)| &\le \sum_{j=1}^{\infty} |\gamma_j^{(M)}| \cdot |\langle\psi_j^{(M)}|B|\lambda_j^{(M)}\rangle| \\ &\le \|B\| \sum_{j=1}^{\infty} |\gamma_j^{(M)}| \equiv \|B\| \cdot \|Y_M\|_1 \end{aligned} \tag{8-155}$$

Hence, if the operators T_M converge to T in the so-called "trace-class norm," namely, such that

$$\|T - T_M\|_1 \to 0 \tag{8-156}$$

as $M \to \infty$, then the desired mean-value formula (8-153) is secured for every bounded operator.

To invent sequences of operators T_M that superficially converge to T is not difficult: One need only replace $\tilde{\varphi}(x, k)$ by a series of functions

$\tilde{\varphi}_M(x, k)$ which tend to $\tilde{\varphi}(x, k)$. The heart of the problem lies in finding a sequence such that (8-156) is fulfilled. Two proofs that such sequences exist are available in the literature,[10] and we shall not duplicate either proof in full. Since it sheds light on interesting side topics, we shall outline the method of Rocca [8-10].

For this purpose we need a few additional properties, which we shall make plausible but state mainly without proof. We note from (8-140a) that

$$\begin{aligned}\langle p, q|T|p, q\rangle &= \int \tilde{T}(x, k)e^{i(kq-xp)/\hbar}\, d\mu \\ &= \int \tilde{T}(x, k)\langle p, q| {:}U[k, x]{:} |p, q\rangle\, d\mu \end{aligned} \tag{8-157}$$

as follows from (7-8) and (7-88). In view of the uniqueness of the diagonal elements in specifying T, we see, in fact, that

$$T = \int \tilde{T}(x, k){:}U[k, x]{:}\, d\mu \equiv \int t(x, k)U[k, x]\, d\mu \tag{8-158}$$

where

$$t(x, k) \equiv \frac{\tilde{T}(x, k)}{\langle 0|U[k, x]|0\rangle} = \tilde{T}(x, k) \exp\left[\frac{1}{4\hbar}(x^2 + k^2)\right] \tag{8-159}$$

It should be noted that $t(x, k)$ represents the "Weyl weight function" in the well-known Weyl representation of operators. If we multiply together two operators represented in this fashion, then

$$\begin{aligned} AB &= \int a(x, k)b(x', k')U[k, x]U[k', x']\, d\mu\, d\mu' \\ &= \int a(x, k)b(x', k') \exp[i\tfrac{1}{2}(kx' - xk')/\hbar]U[k + k', x + x']\, d\mu\, d\mu' \\ &\equiv \int (a \star b)(x, k)U[k, x]\, d\mu \end{aligned} \tag{8-160}$$

as follows from the commutation rules, where

$$(a \star b)(x, k) \equiv \int a(x - x', k - k')b(x', k') \exp[i\tfrac{1}{2}(kx' - xk')/\hbar]\, d\mu' \tag{8-161}$$

is called the "twisted convolution product."

In classical analysis recall that every L^1 function $\tau(x)$ is given by the product of two L^2 functions $\alpha(x)$ and $\beta(x)$ such that $\tau(x) = \alpha(x)\beta(x)$. Moreover, Schwarz's inequality implies that

$$\int |\tau(x)|\, dx = \int |\alpha(x)\beta(x)|\, dx \leq \{\int |\alpha(x)|^2\, dx \int |\beta(x)|^2\, dx\}^{1/2} \tag{8-162}$$

There are rather analogous relations that hold among certain operators that act in Hilbert space: Specifically, every trace-class operator T is the product of two so-called Hilbert-Schmidt operators A and B such that $T = AB$. Moreover, a close analog of (8-162) reads

$$\|T\|_1 = \|AB\|_1 \leq \|A\|_2 \cdot \|B\|_2 \tag{8-163}$$

[10] The principal result quoted below was arrived at independently by Klauder [8-9] and by Rocca [8-10].

where

$$\|A\|_2 \equiv \{\mathrm{Tr}(A^\dagger A)\}^{1/2} \tag{8-164}$$

is called the "Hilbert-Schmidt norm" (which differs in general from $\|A\|$ and $\|A\|_1$). Any operator for which (8-164) is finite belongs to the class of Hilbert-Schmidt operators. This class is closed under operator addition and multiplication by c-numbers, and can be turned into a Hilbert space (composed of operators!) by adopting the inner product $(A, B) \equiv \mathrm{Tr}(A^\dagger B)$.

Suppose we approximate $T = AB$ by the sequence $T_M = A_M B_M$, where A_M and B_M are each Hilbert-Schmidt operators. Then, it follows that

$$\begin{aligned}\|T_M - T\|_1 &= \|A_M B_M - A_M B + A_M B - AB\|_1 \\ &\leq \|A_M(B_M - B)\|_1 + \|(A_M - A)B\|_1 \\ &\leq \|B_M - B\|_2 \cdot \|A_M\|_2 + \|A_M - A\|_2 \cdot \|B\|_2\end{aligned} \tag{8-165}$$

Hence to secure convergence of T_M in trace-class norm, it suffices that both A_M and B_M converge in Hilbert-Schmidt norm; this is the key observation in Rocca's argument.

This characterization of the required convergence is especially convenient as we now show. In view of (8-157) and (8-147) it follows that

$$\mathrm{Tr}(T) = \int \langle p, q|T|p, q\rangle \, d\mu = \tilde{T}(0, 0) = t(0, 0) \tag{8-166}$$

For an Hilbert-Schmidt operator B we find

$$\|B\|_2{}^2 = \mathrm{Tr}(B^\dagger B) = (b^\dagger \bigstar b)(0, 0) \equiv \int |b(x, k)|^2 \, d\mu \tag{8-167}$$

where $b^\dagger(x, k) \equiv b^*(-x, -k)$. This relation neatly shows that the class of Hilbert-Schmidt operators B is associated with the space of L^2 functions $b(x, k)$, where the Weyl representation (8-158) links the individual elements. Hence we see that if the Weyl weight functions $a_M(x, k) \to a(x, k)$ and $b_M(x, k) \to b(x, k)$ in the ordinary L^2 sense, then the operators $T_M = A_M B_M \to T = AB$ in trace-class norm. It is intuitively clear (as well as being a classic result) that we can approach (in L^2 norm) $a(x, k)$ [or $b(x, k)$] by a sequence of test functions $a_M(x, k) \epsilon \mathfrak{D}_2$ [or $b_M(x, k) \epsilon \mathfrak{D}_2$], each of which is infinitely differentiable and vanishes outside a finite region. The "twisted convolution" of two such functions,

$$t_M(x, k) \equiv \int a_M(x - x', k - k') b_M(x', k') \exp[i\tfrac{1}{2}(kx' - xk')/\hbar] \, d\mu' \tag{8-168}$$

is likewise infinitely differentiable and vanishes outside a finite region. In consequence, the function

$$\tilde{\varphi}_M(x, k) \equiv t_M(x, k) \exp\left[\frac{1}{4\hbar}(x^2 + k^2)\right] \left\{ \equiv \tilde{T}_M(x, k) \exp\left[\frac{1}{2\hbar}(x^2 + k^2)\right]\right\} \tag{8-169}$$

is infinitely differentiable and falls off at infinity faster than any inverse power of $(x^2 + k^2)$ (since, in fact, it vanishes outside a finite region!). As we noted earlier, the Fourier transform $\varphi_M(p, q)$ of any such function is likewise blessed with infinite differentiability and rapid decrease at infinity. Since $\varphi_M(p, q)$ is the weight function in the diagonal representation, we have fully secured our goal. To summarize:

Every trace-class operator T can be represented by a sequence of trace-class operators

$$T_M \equiv \int \varphi_M(p, q)|p, q\rangle\langle p, q|\, d\mu \tag{8-170a}$$

where the functions $\varphi_M(p, q)$ are infinitely differentiable and fall off at infinity faster than any inverse power, and where

$$\|T - T_M\|_1 \rightarrow 0 \tag{8-170b}$$

A specific example of a sequence φ_M is indicated below.

We can extend slightly Rocca's argument to yield a physically desirable result for density operators. Since every density operator is positive it can be represented as $\rho = B^\dagger B$, where B is an Hilbert-Schmidt operator. Consequently we can take the approximating sequence $A_M = B_M{}^\dagger$ [i.e., $a_M(x, k) = b_M{}^*(-x, -k)$] such that $\rho_M \equiv B_M{}^\dagger B_M$ is a positive operator for each M. With this choice, $\tilde{\varphi}_M{}^*(x, k) = \tilde{\varphi}_M(-x, -k)$ which implies that $\varphi_M(p, q)$ is real. Since normalization is trivial to ensure, each ρ_M can be taken as a true density operator. Thus we may assert:

Every density operator ρ can be represented by a sequence of density operators

$$\rho_M \equiv \int \varphi_M(p, q)|p, q\rangle\langle p, q|\, d\mu \tag{8-171a}$$

where the real functions $\varphi_M(p, q)$ are infinitely differentiable and fall off at infinity faster than any inverse power, and where

$$\|\rho - \rho_M\|_1 \rightarrow 0 \tag{8-171b}$$

Our further discussion is directed to the physically relevant density operator examples although much of it applies to arbitrary trace-class operators.

As was implicit in our original motivation, we note again the property that for *every* bounded operator B, we have

$$\begin{aligned}\langle B\rangle &= \mathrm{Tr}(\rho B) = \lim_{M\rightarrow\infty} \mathrm{Tr}(\rho_M B) \\ &= \lim_{M\rightarrow\infty} \mathrm{Tr} \int \varphi_M(p, q)|p, q\rangle\langle p, q|B\, d\mu \\ &= \lim_{M\rightarrow\infty} \int \varphi_M(p, q)\langle p, q|B|p, q\rangle\, d\mu \\ &\equiv \int \varphi(p, q)\langle p, q|B|p, q\rangle\, d\mu \\ &\equiv \int \varphi(z)\langle z|B|z\rangle\, d\mu \end{aligned} \tag{8-172}$$

In obtaining the third line, use was made of the fact that

$$\int |\varphi_M(p, q)| \, d\mu < \infty$$

while the last steps define a distribution $\varphi(p, q)$—or in complex form $\varphi(z)$—by the well-defined limiting operation. Of course, not every distribution $\varphi(z)$ defined in this way is a "bad actor"; many lead to well-behaved functions for which the last expression may be interpreted as a meaningful and well-defined integral.

It is important to note in the basic result (8-172) the seemingly inessential role played by the uniqueness property of the diagonal elements $\langle z|B|z\rangle$ in specifying B. Clearly, if these diagonal elements all vanished for some $B \neq 0$, then (8-172) would imply nonsense for many density operators.

An alternative statement of our principal result (8-171) shows the practical nature of the approximation. Suppose we restrict ourselves to those bounded operators for which $\|B\| \leq 1$. This subset of bounded operators includes all unitary or projection operators. It also includes the physically interesting operators the mean values of which lead to the counting distributions.

From the property that

$$|\mathrm{Tr}(\rho B) - \mathrm{Tr}(\rho_M B)| \leq \|\rho - \rho_M\|_1 \cdot \|B\| \leq \|\rho - \rho_M\|_1 \quad (8\text{-}173)$$

for all $\|B\| \leq 1$, we see that we can *uniformly* approximate the mean value of all such operators.

> In other words, for *any* density operator ρ describing a system, we can represent the mean $\langle B\rangle \equiv \mathrm{Tr}(\rho B)$ of *every* bounded operator with $\|B\| \leq 1$ *uniformly* (i.e., independent of which B) to an *arbitrary* accuracy by the honest integral
>
> $$\int \varphi(p, q)\langle p, q|B|p, q\rangle \, d\mu \quad (8\text{-}174)$$
>
> where here $\varphi(p, q)$ is an infinitely differentiable, real function of rapid decrease.

Specific Sequential Representations. We have indicated that we can represent $\varphi(z)$ by a sequence of well-behaved weight functions $\varphi_M(z)$. In order to fix on a suitable sequence in actual cases we may appeal to the previous construction. For example, suppose that the state is given by $\rho = B^\dagger B$. Without loss of generality we can fix on a unique B by the requirement that $B = B^\dagger \geq 0$, namely, that $B = \rho^{1/2}$.

We note from (8-140a) that

$$\begin{aligned} \tilde{T}(x, k) &= \int e^{-i(kq - xp)/\hbar}\langle p, q|T|p, q\rangle \, d\mu \\ &= \int \exp[-(uz^* - u^*z)]\langle p, q|T|p, q\rangle \, d\mu \end{aligned} \quad (8\text{-}175)$$

where

$$u \equiv \frac{(x + ik)}{(2\hbar)^{1/2}} \qquad z \equiv \frac{(q + ip)}{(2\hbar)^{1/2}} \tag{8-176}$$

Hence we see from the eigenproperties of the coherent states and Eq. (7-26) that

$$\begin{aligned} \tilde{T}(x, k) &= \int \langle p, q | \exp(-ua^\dagger) T \exp(u^* a) | p, q \rangle \, d\mu \\ &= \mathrm{Tr}\{\exp(-ua^\dagger) T \exp(u^* a)\} \\ &= \mathrm{Tr}\{T \exp(u^* a) \exp(-ua^\dagger)\} \\ &= \mathrm{Tr}\{T \exp(u^* a - ua^\dagger)\} \exp(\tfrac{1}{2}|u|^2) \end{aligned} \tag{8-177}$$

By making use of (8-159), we see that

$$\begin{aligned} t(x, k) &= \mathrm{Tr}\{T U^\dagger[k, x]\} \\ &= \sum_{j=1}^{\infty} \beta_j \langle \psi_j | U^\dagger[k, x] | \psi_j \rangle \end{aligned} \tag{8-178}$$

which is an absolutely convergent series defining a bounded, continuous function. Evidently $|t(x, k)| \leq \Sigma |\beta_j| = \|T\|_1$, which incidently, on combination with (8-159) and (8-148), establishes Eq. (8-149b). In turn, the Weyl weight for $B = \rho^{1/2}$ reads

$$b(x, k) = \sum_{j=1}^{\infty} \beta_j^{1/2} \langle \psi_j | U^\dagger[k, x] | \psi_j \rangle \tag{8-179}$$

the convergence here generally being in the sense of convergence in the L^2 mean. Given the L^2 element $b(x, k)$ it is, in principle, straightforward to approximate it by test functions in $\mathfrak{D}_2$ to determine a suitable sequence via Eq. (8-168).

Alternatively one can approximate $t(x, k)$ directly, rather than going through the $b(x, k)$. In this procedure one establishes the existence of a subsequence

$$t_M(x, k) \equiv t^{J[M]}_{N[M], L, [M]}(x, k) \tag{8-180}$$

in a three-index sequence which gives rise to the desired properties for $\varphi_M(p, q)$ and for T_M, namely, $\|T_M - T\|_1 \to 0$. The basic three-index sequence is given generically by

$$\begin{aligned} t^J_{N,L}(x, k) &\equiv \exp[-W_L(x, k)] t_N{}^J(x, k) \\ &\equiv \exp[-W_L(x, k)] \sum_{j=1}^{J} \beta_j \langle \psi_j; N | U^\dagger[k, x] | \psi_j; N \rangle \end{aligned} \tag{8-181}$$

where we have set

$$|\psi_j; N\rangle \equiv \sum_{n=0}^{N} |n\rangle\langle n|\psi_j\rangle \tag{8-182}$$

where $|n\rangle$ are the usual oscillator eigenstates, and we have introduced (in units where $\hbar = 1$)

$$W_L(x, k) \equiv f(x - L) + f(-x - L) + f(k - L) + f(-k - L) \quad (8\text{-}183)$$

with

$$\begin{aligned} f(y) &\equiv y^4 \exp(-1/y^2) \qquad (y \geq 0) \\ &\equiv 0 \qquad (y < 0) \end{aligned} \quad (8\text{-}184)$$

Such a sequence, cumbersome as it would be in practice, nevertheless fulfills the desired trace-class convergence criterion. The truncation of the series and the approximation of the states as in (8-182) is designed to make $t_N{}^J(x, k)$ a test function in $\mathcal{S}_2$ (infinitely differentiable with rapid decrease); the factor $\exp(-W_L)$ is designed to make

$$\tilde{\varphi}^J_{N,L}(x, k) \equiv t^J_{N,L}(x, k) \exp\left[\frac{1}{4\hbar}(x^2 + k^2)\right] \quad (8\text{-}185)$$

still have rapid decrease (and maintain infinite differentiability).

We note that if $t(x, k)$ happens *already* to be a test function in $\mathcal{S}_2$, then it is adequate to simply consider

$$t_M(x, k) \equiv \exp\,[-W_M(x, k)]t(x, k) \quad (8\text{-}186)$$

or, in other words,

$$\tilde{\varphi}_M(x, k) \equiv \exp[-W_M(x, k)]\tilde{\varphi}(x, k) \quad (8\text{-}187)$$

in this case $\varphi_M(p, q)$ is a test function in $\mathcal{S}_2$ and $\|T_M - T\|_1 \to 0$ as desired.

We hasten to add that the particular sequences given here are not unique, and in some applications it could be useful to have other sequences with which to work.

Significance and Some Examples. Whatever the state ρ of the system the mean of *every* bounded operator is given by (8-172). Especially simple are the operators in normal ordered form, $B = :\mathcal{O}(a^\dagger, a):$, for which

$$\begin{aligned} \langle :\mathcal{O}(a^\dagger, a): \rangle &= \frac{1}{\pi} \int \varphi(z) \langle z| :\mathcal{O}(a^\dagger, a): |z\rangle \, d^2z \\ &= \frac{1}{\pi} \int \varphi(z) \mathcal{O}(z^*, z) \, d^2z \end{aligned} \quad (8\text{-}188)$$

The normal order generating function [cf. (8-23)] is given as

$$\langle \exp(ua^\dagger) \exp(-u^*a) \rangle = \frac{1}{\pi} \int \varphi(z) \exp(uz^* - u^*z) \, d^2z \quad (8\text{-}189)$$

which can be recognized as being related to the Fourier transform of φ. In particular if

$$u \equiv (x + ik)/\sqrt{2\hbar}$$

then

$$\langle \exp(ua^\dagger) \exp(-u^*a) \rangle = \tilde{\varphi}(-x, -k) \tag{8-190a}$$

Premultiplying by $\exp(-\frac{1}{2}|u|^2)$ yields

$$\begin{aligned} \langle \exp(ua^\dagger - u^*a) \rangle &= \langle U[k, x] \rangle \\ &= \tilde{\varphi}(-x, -k) \exp\left[-\frac{1}{4\hbar}(x^2 + k^2) \right] \end{aligned} \tag{8-190b}$$

for the general relation for the characteristic function of the state ρ.

As another example let us reconsider (8-101) for $0 \leq \lambda\alpha_0 T < 1$, which states that the counting distribution generating function is the mean of

$$\mathfrak{Q}_\lambda \equiv \exp(\ln[1 - \lambda\alpha_0 T]a^\dagger a)(= :\exp(-\lambda\alpha_0 T a^\dagger a):) \tag{8-191}$$

which, since $\ln[1 - \lambda\alpha_0 T] \leq 0$, fulfills $\|\mathfrak{Q}_\lambda\| = 1$. Since $\mathfrak{Q}_\lambda$ is bounded we are assured that

$$\begin{aligned} Q(\lambda, T) &\equiv \langle \mathfrak{Q}_\lambda \rangle = \langle :\exp(-\lambda\alpha_0 T a^\dagger a): \rangle \\ &= \frac{1}{\pi} \int \varphi(z) \exp(-\lambda\alpha_0 T|z|^2)\, d^2z \end{aligned} \tag{8-192}$$

The counting distribution is given through the relation

$$Q(\lambda, T) = \sum_{m=0}^{\infty} (1 - \lambda)^m P(m, T) \tag{8-193a}$$

or in operator form we may write

$$\mathfrak{Q}_\lambda = \sum_{m=0}^{\infty} (1 - \lambda)^m \mathcal{P}_m \tag{8-193b}$$

where

$$\mathcal{P}_m \equiv :\frac{(\alpha_0 T a^\dagger a)^m}{m!} \exp(-\alpha_0 T a^\dagger a): \tag{8-194}$$

which is nonnegative for $\alpha_0 T \leq 1$ as follows from remarks made in connection with (8-103). For $\lambda = 0$, $\mathfrak{Q}_0 = I = \sum_{m=0}^{\infty} \mathcal{P}_m$, so that $\|\mathcal{P}_m\| \leq 1$

for all m. Being bounded we are assured that

$$P(m, T) = \langle \mathcal{P}_m \rangle = \left\langle : \frac{(\alpha_0 T a^\dagger a)^m}{m!} \exp(-\alpha_0 T a^\dagger a) : \right\rangle$$
$$= \frac{1}{\pi} \int \varphi(z) \frac{(\alpha_0 T |z|^2)^m}{m!} \exp(-\alpha_0 T |z|^2)\, d^2 z \qquad (8\text{-}195)$$

But, in fact, we can assert even more if we invoke the result stated in connection with Eq. (8-174). It follows for any state ρ of our single normal mode that for all m and all $T \leq \alpha_0^{-1}$ we can calculate $P(m, T)$ to an arbitrary accuracy (e.g., correct to $\pm 10^{-137}$) by Eq. (8-195), where $\varphi(z)$ is an infinitely differentiable function of rapid decrease. This property is far more than can be generally said regarding the counting rates $\alpha_0{}^m \langle a^{\dagger m} a^m \rangle$. Not only can these rates not be uniformly approximated in the general situation, but there are many states for which all or many of these rates do not even exist!

Equations (8-188) and (8-195) make it abundantly clear that the diagonal representation permits us to calculate normal ordered, quantum mechanical expressions by relations which are *formally similar* to the classical calculations when they are formulated in terms of analytic signals. This similarity in form is not only important as a mnemonic device and as a guide toward constructing expressions of interest, but also as a comparatively simple and powerful tool for studying various quantities in quantum coherence theory. This similarity in form does not carry any connotation that the quantum theory is *physically* equivalent to the classical theory, but only that it can be set up to have a *formal* equivalence. It is in this sense that the "optical equivalence theorem" has been formulated and should be interpreted in the general case.

For most of the physical, day-to-day examples encountered in thermal or laser problems, the weight $\varphi(z)$ is, in fact, a positive real function so it can be interpreted as a normal probability density. Examples of these very classical-like cases will be dealt with in special models in the next chapter. Here we should like to examine closer a specific density operator example that gives rise to a weight $\varphi(z)$ which is a true distribution of the type and variety discussed above.

Let us choose as our example the density operator $\rho_\omega = |0_\omega\rangle\langle 0_\omega|$, a pure state based on an oscillator ground state with a frequency $\omega \neq 1$. To determine the weight $\varphi(p, q)$ in phase-space form for such a state we note first (with $\rho_\omega \equiv T_\omega$) that

$$\langle p, q | T_\omega | p, q \rangle = |\langle p, q | 0_\omega \rangle|^2$$
$$= \frac{1}{2} (\omega^{1/2} + \omega^{-1/2}) \exp\left\{ - \frac{1}{\hbar(1 + \omega)} [p^2 + \omega q^2] \right\} \qquad (8\text{-}196)$$

according to the previous evaluation in (7-82b). In turn, we see that

$$\tilde{T}_\omega(x, k) = \exp\left\{-\frac{1}{4\hbar}[(1+\omega)x^2 + (1+\omega^{-1})k^2]\right\} \tag{8-197}$$

the normalization being readily determined from the condition $\tilde{T}_\omega(0, 0) = \mathrm{Tr}(\rho_\omega) = 1$. Finally, the Fourier transform of the proposed weight is given through (8-148) by

$$\tilde{\varphi}_\omega(x, k) = \exp\left\{-\frac{1}{4\hbar}[(\omega-1)x^2 + (\omega^{-1}-1)k^2]\right\} \tag{8-198}$$

which for $\omega < 1$ (or $\omega > 1$) grows as the exponential of a quadratic in x (or k). Thus the need for distributions $\tilde{\varphi}(x, k)$ defined for test functions in $\mathfrak{D}_2$ (infinitely differentiable and vanishing outside a finite region) is by no means academic.

To make sense out of this specific example as a distribution in the diagonal representation, there are two possible approaches. The pragmatic approach simply begins with the general mean values (8-190). In particular, we find that

$$\begin{aligned}\langle U[k, x]\rangle &= \langle 0_\omega | U[k, x] | 0_\omega\rangle \\ &= \tilde{\varphi}_\omega(-x, -k) \exp\left[-\frac{1}{4\hbar}(x^2 + k^2)\right] \\ &= \exp\left\{-\frac{1}{4\hbar}[\omega^{-1}k^2 + \omega x^2]\right\}\end{aligned} \tag{8-199}$$

which incidently coincides with the expression in (7-121) for $K = 1$ for an oscillator whose angular frequency $\omega \neq 1$. The mean value of operators other than the Weyl operators $U[k, x]$ can then be deduced by linearity from the partial information in (8-199). In many ways this pragmatic approach treats the distribution $\varphi(z)$ as a functional and specifies the values it has for a generating set of bounded operators (linear sums of which yield all bounded operators) through the normal order, generating function or through the characteristic function.

On the other hand, the systematic approach would seek to describe the distribution directly, say through a sequence of weight functions $\varphi_M(z)$. Since $t(x, k) = \langle U[-k, -x]\rangle$ as given through (8-199) is clearly infinitely differentiable and has rapid decrease, it is adequate to consider the weight functions given by the Fourier transform of

$$\tilde{\varphi}_M(x, k) = \exp\left\{-W_M(x, k) - \frac{1}{4\hbar}[(\omega-1)x^2 + (\omega^{-1}-1)k^2]\right\} \tag{8-200}$$

where W_M (for $M = L$) is defined in (8-183). Needless to say it is not easy to display the functions $\varphi_M(p, q)$ explicitly although we are assured of their existence and their relevant properties.

Convolution Combinations. Sometimes in discussing a random variable z it is convenient to divide it into two (or even more!) terms, $z = \alpha + \beta$, which are themselves subject to individual fluctuations described by their own distributions. In the present application we may regard

$$\rho_2 = \int \varphi_2(\beta)|\alpha + \beta\rangle\langle\alpha + \beta| \, d\mu(\beta) \tag{8-201a}$$

as the density operator obtained due to fluctuations in the β part of z alone. Likewise we may regard

$$\rho_1 = \int \varphi_1(\alpha)|\alpha + \beta\rangle\langle\alpha + \beta| \, d\mu(\alpha) \tag{8-201b}$$

as the density operator due to fluctuations in the α part of z alone. The combined fluctuations in α and β lead to the density operator

$$\begin{aligned} \rho &= \int \varphi_1(\alpha)\varphi_2(\beta)|\alpha + \beta\rangle\langle\alpha + \beta| \, d\mu(\alpha) \, d\mu(\beta) \\ &\equiv \int \varphi_1(\alpha) * \varphi_2(\alpha)|\alpha\rangle\langle\alpha| \, d\mu(\alpha) \end{aligned} \tag{8-202}$$

where

$$\varphi(\alpha) \equiv \varphi_1(\alpha) * \varphi_2(\alpha) \equiv \int \varphi_1(\alpha - \beta)\varphi_2(\beta) \, d\mu(\beta) \tag{8-203a}$$

This expression is reminiscent of the usual convolution combination of probability densities in classical probability theory.

In a phase-space form we have

$$\varphi(p, q) \equiv \int \varphi_1(p - p', q - q')\varphi_2(p', q') \, d\mu' \tag{8-203b}$$

which after Fourier transformation reads

$$\tilde{\varphi}(x, k) \equiv \tilde{\varphi}_1(x, k)\tilde{\varphi}_2(x, k) \tag{8-204}$$

In the general case where $\varphi(z)$ is a distribution, we may begin our analysis with the relation (8-204). If the distributions φ_1, φ_2, and φ are such that ρ_1, ρ_2, and ρ are true density operators, then (8-204) must hold true where $\tilde{\varphi}_1$, $\tilde{\varphi}_2$, and $\tilde{\varphi}$ are all continuous functions of the type we have analyzed. However, even when $\tilde{\varphi}_1$ and $\tilde{\varphi}_2$ describe density operators, the function $\tilde{\varphi}(x, k)$ defined by (8-204) need not lead to a density operator. An example is given by $\tilde{\varphi}_1 = \tilde{\varphi}_2 = \tilde{\varphi}_\omega(x, k)$ given in (8-198) when $\omega < \frac{1}{2}$ or $\omega > 2$ since $\tilde{\varphi}$ would then violate (8-149b). On the other hand, it is important to note when $\tilde{\varphi}_1$ and $\tilde{\varphi}_2$ describe density operators that the modified convolution product implicit in the definition

$$\tilde{\varphi}(x, k) \equiv \tilde{\varphi}_1(s_1x, s_1k)\tilde{\varphi}_2(s_2x, s_2k) \qquad s_1{}^2 + s_2{}^2 = 1 \tag{8-205}$$

always leads to a diagonal weight $\varphi(\alpha)$ describing a density operator.[11]

Double-Integral Formulation. This section has been devoted to making precise the diagonal representation

$$\rho = \frac{1}{\pi} \int \varphi(z)|z\rangle\langle z|\, d^2z \tag{8-206}$$

which represents ρ as a superposition of "like outer products," or projection operators onto coherent states. There is always another representation given by the general rule (7-56) as

$$\rho = \frac{1}{\pi^2} \iint |z_1\rangle\langle z_1|\rho|z_2\rangle\langle z_2|\, d^2z_1\, d^2z_2 \tag{8-207}$$

which is a superposition of "*un*like outer products" $|z_1\rangle\langle z_2|$. It must be clearly understood that these are generally two completely different decompositions of the same operator as was already the case for the unit operator discussed in (7-62). Evidently the weight function $\langle z_1|\rho|z_2\rangle$ is generally a much better-behaved animal than the distribution $\varphi(z)$. For this reason it has been advocated by Glauber that the double-integral representation is preferable to the diagonal representation when $\varphi(z)$ becomes singular. We choose, however, to "pay the price" of the distributions for $\varphi(z)$—which we have been very careful above to spell out precisely and properly—because of the significant simplification and intuitive value gained by use of the diagonal representation. It may be argued that the use of sequences to define the distributions introduces an extra limiting operation into the formulation and that such a sequence need not be unique. Although these criticisms are, of course, correct they apply equally well to the double-integral form (8-207) when it is recalled that the extra integral itself is defined by a limit and that due to the overcompleteness of the coherent states the integrand (hence the sequence associated with defining the integral) is not unique.

B. "Diagonal" Representation for the Radiation Field

Based on the arguments presented above we wish to investigate the diagonal representation for operators for infinitely many degrees of freedom symbolically written

$$T = \int \varphi(\{z_k\})|\{z_k\}\rangle\langle\{z_k\}|\, d\mu(\{z_k\}) \tag{8-208}$$

Here we have adopted the abbreviation k for the mode label λ, $\mathbf{k}$, and we have written z_k for $z_\lambda(\mathbf{k})$. Since our principal application lies with

[11] This remark is most easily demonstrated by "contraction" techniques discussed by Klauder and McKenna [7-20], but an analysis of this approach would take us too far afield.

diagonal representations for the density operator, we shall restrict our attention to trace-class operators T at the outset.

As was our procedure for the single degree of freedom case, we seek to characterize T by a sequence of trace-class operators T_M for which $\|T - T_M\|_1 \to 0$ in order that the relation

$$\mathrm{Tr}(TB) = \lim_{M\to\infty} \mathrm{Tr}(T_M B) \tag{8-209}$$

hold for all bounded operators B. It should be noted that these requirements, when they are stated abstractly, are just the same as we required for a single degree of freedom. The only change, roughly speaking, is the representation of the annihilation and creation operators involved. In the former case, it is assumed that a single a and $a^\dagger$ form an irreducible set, whereas in the latter case the whole collection of operators $\{a_k\}$ and $\{a_k{}^\dagger\}$ is required to form an irreducible set.

There is, of course, the intermediate case where a finite number of degrees of freedom are the whole story, i.e., where the states $|z_1, \ldots, z_k\rangle$ span the whole Hilbert space. The formulation of diagonal representations for these cases is quite analogous to the single degree of freedom case discussed previously, except for an obvious increase in the number of variables involved. We shall not spell out the full formulation again for finitely many degrees of freedom since the reader may easily make the necessary modifications in the previous arguments. However, we shall actually require some of these generalizations in our treatment of the field case, and we shall state them below without explicit proof.

Our initial procedure, much as it was in proving the basic resolution of unity in Eq. (7-153), is to define the infinite-order integration by a sequence each term of which involves, in an essential fashion, only a finite number of the infinitely many variables. Let us recall the projection operators P_N [introduced in (7-148)] which are defined by

$$\langle\{z_k\}|P_N|\{z_k'\}\rangle \equiv \exp\left\{-\frac{1}{2}\sum_{k=1}^{\infty}(|z_k|^2 + |z_k'|^2) + \sum_{k=1}^{N} z_k{}^* z_k'\right\} \tag{8-210}$$

In effect, the operator P_N projects onto the ground state for all degrees of freedom $k > N$. Armed with these projections, let us define a sequence of trace-class operators that are given by

$$T^N \equiv P_N T P_N \tag{8-211}$$

for all N. We want to show first that the operators T^N converge to T in trace-class norm as $N \to \infty$.

If we make use of the relation $\|BT\|_1 \leq \|T\|_1\|B\|$, valid for an arbitrary trace-class operator T and bounded operator B, respectively, we see that

$$\begin{aligned}\|T^N - T\|_1 &= \|P_N T P_N - T\|_1 \\ &\leq \|P_N(TP_N - T)\|_1 + \|(P_N - I)T\|_1 \\ &\leq \|T(P_N - I)\|_1 + \|(P_N - I)T\|_1 \end{aligned} \tag{8-212}$$

since $\|P_N\| \leq 1$. Let us study the second term in (8-212) further; the first term is completely analogous. If $T \equiv AC$, where both A and C are Hilbert-Schmidt operators, then it follows from (8-163) that

$$\|(P_N - I)AC\|_1 \leq \|(P_N - I)A\|_2 \cdot \|C\|_2 \tag{8-213}$$

In terms of the generic form for A given by

$$A = \sum_{j=1}^{\infty} \alpha_j |\mu_j\rangle\langle\varphi_j| \tag{8-214}$$

where $|\mu_j\rangle$ and $|\varphi_j\rangle$ are vectors in two complete orthonormal bases, and where [cf. (8-164)]

$$\|A\|_2{}^2 \equiv \sum_{j=1}^{\infty} |\alpha_j|^2 < \infty \tag{8-215}$$

it follows that

$$\|(P_N - I)A\|_2{}^2 = \sum_{j=1}^{\infty} |\alpha_j|^2 \langle\mu_j|(I - P_N)|\mu_j\rangle \tag{8-216}$$

Combining this result, and condition (8-215), with the convergence of a general matrix element, $\langle\lambda|P_N|\psi\rangle \to \langle\lambda|\psi\rangle$ [cf. (7-152)], it is evident that for large enough N we can make (8-216) arbitrarily small. Since a similar argument applies to the first term in (8-212) we deduce that

$$\|T^N - T\|_1 = \|P_N T P_N - T\|_1 \to 0 \tag{8-217}$$

Namely, the sequence T^N converges to T in trace-class norm as desired.

Next we show that T^N is an operator that involves only the first N degrees of freedom in an essential way. For this purpose we note that the relation

$$P_N T^N P_N = P_N(P_N T P_N)P_N = P_N T P_N = T^N \tag{8-218}$$

expressed in the continuous representation reads

$$\begin{aligned}\langle\{z_k\}|T^N|\{z_k'\}\rangle = \iint &\langle\{z_k\}|P_N|\{z_k''\}\rangle\langle\{z_k''\}|T^N|\{z_k'''\}\rangle \\ &\times \langle\{z_k'''\}|P_N|\{z_k'\}\rangle \, d\mu(\{z_k''\}) \, d\mu(\{z_k'''\})\end{aligned} \tag{8-219}$$

where these integrals are each defined in the sense of (7-152). We need not explicitly compute such an integral in order to see that (8-210) implies the relation

$$\langle\{z_k\}|T^N|\{z'_k\}\rangle = \exp\left[-\frac{1}{2}\sum_{k=N+1}^{\infty}(|z_k|^2+|z'_k|^2)\right] \times F_N(z_1, \ldots, z_N; z'_1, \ldots, z'_N)$$
$$= \exp\left[-\frac{1}{2}\sum_{k=N+1}^{\infty}(|z_k|^2+|z'_k|^2)\right] \times \langle\{z_{k,N}\}|T^N|\{z'_{k,N}\}\rangle \quad (8\text{-}220)$$

where $\{z_{k,N}\}$ denotes a *truncated sequence* ($z_{k,N} \equiv 0$, $k > N$), which is discussed more fully in connection with Eq. (7-139). Thus, as is entirely plausible, T^N involves only the first N degrees of freedom in an essential way.

In a diagonal representation, it is clear that T^N would have the characteristic form given by

$$T^N = \int \varphi^N(\{z_{k,N}\})|\{z_{k,N}\}\rangle\langle\{z_{k,N}\}|\, d\mu(\{z_{k,N}\}) \quad (8\text{-}221)$$

which involves an integral over only finitely many ($2N$) variables. Quite clearly, this expression fulfills the condition $P_N T^N = T^N P_N = T^N$ necessary to secure (8-220). With this ansatz for T^N it follows that the diagonal, truncated-sequence, coherent-state matrix elements fulfill

$$\langle\{z'_{k,N}\}|T^N|\{z'_{k,N}\}\rangle = T^N(\{z'_{k,N}\})$$
$$= \int \varphi^N(\{z_{k,N}\})|\langle\{z'_{k,N}\}|\{z_{k,N}\}\rangle|^2\, d\mu(\{z_{k,N}\}) \quad (8\text{-}222)$$

which is just the N degree of freedom analog of the basic convolution equation (8-138) with which the analysis of diagonal representations for N degrees of freedom would begin. A calculation patterned after our previous analysis would imply that the continuous function $\tilde{\varphi}^N(x_1, \ldots, x_N; k_1, \ldots, k_N)$, given by the Fourier transform of $\varphi^N(\{z_{k,N}\})$, is a distribution on test functions in $\mathfrak{D}_{2N}$. In analogy to the arguments leading to (8-169), we are assured that we can represent each of the required distributions by a sequence of test functions $\tilde{\varphi}_L{}^N(x_1, \ldots, x_N; k_1, \ldots, k_N)$ in $\mathcal{S}_{2N}$ (i.e., infinitely differentiable with rapid decrease), and that the operators

$$T_L{}^N \equiv \int \varphi_L{}^N(\{z_{k,N}\})|\{z_{k,N}\}\rangle\langle\{z_{k,N}\}|\, d\mu(\{z_{k,N}\}) \quad (8\text{-}223)$$

are defined in terms of functions $\varphi_L{}^N(\{z_{k,N}\})$ each of which is in $\mathcal{S}_{2N}$. Moreover we are assured for each N that

$$\|T^N - T_L{}^N\|_1 \rightarrow 0 \quad (8\text{-}224)$$

as $L \to \infty$. It follows, therefore, that the double sequence of operators $T_L{}^N$ given by (8-223) fulfills

$$\lim_{N\to\infty} \lim_{L\to\infty} \|T - T_L{}^N\|_1 = 0 \tag{8-225}$$

in virtue of the inequality

$$\|T - T_L{}^N\|_1 \leq \|T - T^N\|_1 + \|T^N - T_L{}^N\|_1 \tag{8-226}$$

To finalize the argument we may always choose a single-index subsequence out of the double-index sequence to achieve the same goal. For example, for each fixed N, let us choose $L = L[N]$ as the least integer such that

$$\|T^N - T_L{}^N\|_1 \leq \|T - T^N\|_1 + \frac{1}{N} \tag{8-227}$$

With this choice it is clear that the sequence defined by

$$T_N \equiv T^N_{L[N]} \tag{8-228}$$

fulfills the desired convergence since

$$\|T - T_N\|_1 = \|T - T^N_{L[N]}\|_1 \leq 2\|T - T^N\|_1 + \frac{1}{N} \to 0$$

Consequently, if we introduce

$$\varphi_N(\{z_{k,N}\}) \equiv \varphi^N_{L[N]}(\{z_{k,N}\}) \tag{8-229}$$

then we can state the following basic result:

Every trace-class operator T can be represented by a sequence of operators T_N each of which has a diagonal representation

$$T_N = \int \varphi_N(\{z_{k,N}\}) |\{z_{k,N}\}\rangle\langle\{z_{k,N}\}| \, d\mu(\{z_{k,N}\}) \tag{8-230a}$$

where $\varphi_N(\{z_{k,N}\})$ is an infinitely differentiable function of rapid decrease, and for which

$$\|T - T_N\|_1 \to 0 \tag{8-230b}$$

If $T = \rho$ is a density operator, then $\rho^N \equiv P_N \rho P_N$ is Hermitian and nonnegative. We can always omit from our sequence any initial terms (at most a finite number) for which $\rho^N \equiv 0$; henceforth we shall ignore these. As we did for a single degree of freedom, we can choose each term in the double sequence $\rho_L{}^N$ to be Hermitian and nonnegative. Moreover, in the single-index subsequence $\rho_N \equiv \rho^N_{L[N]}$, defined, for example, in the sense of

(8-227), we can normalize the real function $\varphi_N \equiv \varphi^N_{L[N]}$ so that $\mathrm{Tr}(\rho_N) = 1$. Hence we can assert the following:

Every density operator ρ can be represented by a sequence of density operators ρ_N each of which has the diagonal representation

$$\rho_N = \int \varphi_N(\{z_{k,N}\})|\{z_{k,N}\}\rangle\langle\{z_{k,N}\}|\,d\mu(\{z_{k,N}\}) \qquad \text{(8-231a)}$$

where $\varphi_N(\{z_{k,N}\})$ is an infinitely differentiable, real function of rapid decrease, and for which

$$\|\rho - \rho_N\|_1 \to 0 \qquad \text{(8-231b)}$$

We concentrate on the density operators in the sequel.

The convergence condition (8-231b) and the integrability of φ_N allow us to assert for an *arbitrary* bounded operator B that

$$\begin{aligned} \langle B\rangle &= \mathrm{Tr}(\rho B) = \lim_{N\to\infty} \mathrm{Tr}(\rho_N B) \\ &= \lim_{N\to\infty} \int \varphi_N(\{z_{k,N}\})\langle\{z_{k,N}\}|B|\{z_{k,N}\}\rangle\,d\mu(\{z_{k,N}\}) \\ &\equiv \int \varphi(\{z_k\})\langle\{z_k\}|B|\{z_k\}\rangle\,d\mu(\{z_k\}) \end{aligned} \qquad \text{(8-232)}$$

where the last line defines a distribution (on the functions $\langle\{z_k\}|B|\{z_k\}\rangle$ of infinitely many variables) by means of the preceding line. Moreover we can now define the right-hand side of the relation

$$\rho = \int \varphi(\{z_k\})|\{z_k\}\rangle\langle\{z_k\}|\,d\mu(\{z_k\}) \qquad \text{(8-233)}$$

by means of the limit as $N \to \infty$ of (8-231a) or, equally well, through the mean value formula (8-232) for an arbitrary bounded operator. It is in this sense that the diagonal representation should be understood in our derivation of the counting distributions in the previous section.

An analog of the result stated in connection with (8-174) exists as well. Namely, if we restrict attention to bounded operators for which $\|B\| \leq 1$, then the mean value of all such operators can be approximated uniformly and to an arbitrary accuracy by a formula of the type

$$\int \varphi_N(\{z_{k,N}\})\langle\{z_{k,N}\}|B|\{z_{k,N}\}\rangle\,d\mu(\{z_{k,N}\}) \qquad \text{(8-234)}$$

where N is finite and φ_N is a test function in $\mathcal{S}_{2N}$.

The mean value formula is, as usual, especially simple for normally ordered operators $B = :\mathcal{O}(\{a_k^\dagger\}, \{a_k\}):$. In this case

$$\langle:\mathcal{O}(\{a_k^\dagger\}, \{a_k\}):\rangle = \int \varphi(\{z_k\})\mathcal{O}(\{z_k^*\}, \{z_k\})\,d\mu(\{z_k\}) \qquad \text{(8-235)}$$

In particular, the normal ordered generating functional (8-23) is given by

$$C_N(\{u_k\}) \equiv \left\langle \exp\left(\sum_1^\infty u_k a_k^\dagger\right) \exp\left(-\sum_1^\infty u_k^* a_k\right)\right\rangle$$
$$= \int \varphi(\{z_k\}) \exp\left[\sum_1^\infty (u_k z_k^* - u_k^* z_k)\right] d\mu(\{z_k\}) \quad (8\text{-}236a)$$

On comparison with (8-190a) we see that

$$C_N(\{u_k\}) = \lim_{N\to\infty} \tilde{\varphi}_N(-x_1, \ldots, -x_N; -k_1, \ldots, -k_N)$$
$$\equiv \tilde{\varphi}(\{-x_k\}, \{-k_k\}) \quad (8\text{-}236b)$$

where $u_k \equiv (x_k + ik_k)/\sqrt{2\hbar}$.

We need not repeat the derivation of the several counting distributions $P(m, T + t, t)$, etc., which were carried out earlier. The reader may readily convince himself that the operators which, through their mean values, determine $P(m, T + t, t)$ and $Q(\lambda, T + t, t)$ in (8-132) and (8-133), for example, are in fact bounded operators. Indeed, an operator whose mean value in any state is at most unity (as P or Q must fulfill on physical grounds) is by definition a bounded operator whose norm is at most unity. Thus our present discussion serves to make our earlier derivation precise.

There are direct analogs in the field case of the convolution combinations and double-integral representation discussed for the single degree of freedom, but we need not explicitly include the rather obvious generalizations that are involved.

Let us conclude this chapter with the remark that the diagonal representation enables one to formulate the quantum theory of optical coherence in a language formally equivalent in essentially all respects to the language of the classical theory as expressed in terms of analytic signals. It is this remarkable result which is the essence of the optical equivalence theorem.[12]

[12] The optical equivalence theorem was discovered by Sudarshan [8-7].

CHAPTER 9

SPECIAL STATES OF THE RADIATION FIELD

9-1 CHAOTIC AND THERMAL STATES

The overwhelming majority of macroscopic fields that are naturally produced are thermal-like in their properties. It is important that we analyze this basic example in some detail. We begin with a derivation of the states in question; later we discuss some properties of the solutions.

A. Quantum Central Limit Theorem

CLASSICAL CENTRAL LIMIT THEOREM. A fundamental result of classical probability theory states that the distribution of a random variable

$$x = N^{-1/2} \sum_{n=1}^{N} x_n \tag{9-1}$$

which is the sum of independent and "similarly" distributed random variables x_n, is for large N, Gaussian. As Eq. (3-9) shows such a distribution is determined by its mean and variance which, respectively, are

$$\langle x \rangle = N^{-1/2} \sum_{n=1}^{N} \langle x_n \rangle \tag{9-2a}$$

$$\begin{aligned}\langle (\Delta x)^2 \rangle &= N^{-1} \sum_{n,m=1}^{N} [\langle x_n x_m \rangle - \langle x_n \rangle \langle x_m \rangle] \\ &= N^{-1} \sum_{n=1}^{N} [\langle x_n{}^2 \rangle - \langle x_n \rangle^2]\end{aligned} \tag{9-2b}$$

Since Gaussian distributions necessarily have finite mean and variance, it is necessary that $\langle x_n \rangle$ and $\langle x_n^2 \rangle$ both exist for x to approach a normal distribution. The presence of the factor N guarantees that the variance converges for large N in the case of "similarly"—and thus, in particular, identically—distributed variables x_n. If the mean $\langle x \rangle$ vanishes we can assume, without loss of generality, that each variable x_n has mean zero. As we shall now show, an analogous central limit theorem holds in the quantum theory under similar and very mild assumptions. We begin our analysis with a study of the case for a single degree of freedom.

Quantum Analog for a Single Degree of Freedom. As we discussed in Chapter 7, the state of a single degree of freedom (*not* necessarily a normal mode) is transformed from the ground state $|0\rangle\langle 0|$ to a coherent state $|z\rangle\langle z|$ due to the presence of an external driving source characterized by z. In turn, if we imagine z to be composed of a large number N of contributions, then we can set

$$|z\rangle\langle z| = |N^{-1/2}\Sigma z_n\rangle\langle N^{-1/2}\Sigma z_n| \tag{9-3}$$

Intuitively, a thermal or chaotic field is one whose wave amplitude is composed of a myriad number of minute contributions each of which may be assumed to be independently distributed.

Let us define $r_n(z_n)$ as the distribution (in the sense of Chapter 8) describing the elementary contribution z_n. Allowing for fluctuations in each of the contributions, z_n leads us, heuristically, to study the operator

$$\begin{aligned} \rho &= \int \varphi(z)|z\rangle\langle z| \, d\mu(z) \\ &\equiv \int \left|N^{-1/2} \sum z_n\right\rangle \left\langle N^{-1/2} \sum z_n\right| \prod_{n=1}^{N} r_n(z_n) \, d\mu(z_n) \end{aligned} \tag{9-4}$$

It follows that $\varphi(z)$ is given by a multiple convolution integral similar to the type discussed in Chapter 8. Guided by Eq. (8-204) and taking account of the factors $N^{1/2}$, we learn that the Fourier transform $\tilde{\varphi}(x, k)$ of the proposed weight in (9-4) is given by

$$\tilde{\varphi}(x, k) = \prod_{n=1}^{N} \tilde{r}_n(x/N^{1/2}, k/N^{1/2}) \tag{9-5}$$

This equation is a simple inductive generalization of the type of multiple convolution considered in (8-205). Therefore, we are assured that if $r_n(z_n)$ is the diagonal weight for a density operator ρ_n for all n (as we assume), then $\varphi(z)$ is a bona fide diagonal weight leading to a true density operator ρ for all N. As such it follows from (8-149b) that we must have

$$|\tilde{\varphi}(x, k)| \leq \exp\left[\frac{1}{4\hbar}(x^2 + k^2)\right] \tag{9-6}$$

since $\|\rho\|_1 = \text{Tr}(\rho) = 1$; but this is an elementary consequence of (9-5) coupled with the relation

$$|\tilde{r}_n(x, k)| \leq \exp\left[\frac{1}{4\hbar}(x^2 + k^2)\right] \tag{9-7}$$

To focus on the essentials, let us now specialize to the case where all distributions $\tilde{r}_n$ are, in fact, identical, $\tilde{r}_n \equiv \tilde{r}$. Then we explicitly have

$$\tilde{\varphi}(x, k) = [\tilde{r}(x/N^{1/2}, k/N^{1/2})]^N \tag{9-8}$$

Intuitively, if we assume that

$$\tilde{r}(x, k) \simeq 1 - \frac{A}{2\hbar}(x^2 + k^2) \tag{9-9}$$

for small enough x and k, then we have

$$\tilde{\varphi}(x, k) \simeq \left[1 - \frac{A}{2\hbar N}(x^2 + k^2)\right]^N$$

which for indefinitely large N becomes

$$\tilde{\varphi}(x, k) = \exp\left[-\frac{A}{2\hbar}(x^2 + k^2)\right] \tag{9-10}$$

and is valid for all x and k. In order for this conclusion to be true it suffices that $\tilde{r}$ be twice differentiable at the origin and have vanishing first derivatives there. [Alternatively stated this is a condition on the first two moments of r; more precisely that $\langle a \rangle = 0$, $\langle a^\dagger a \rangle < \infty$ with the density operator determined by $r(z)$.] Henceforth we adopt these conditions on $\tilde{r}$. We emphasize that $\tilde{r}(x, k)$ is not necessarily assumed to be a function only of $x^2 + k^2$. For example, the next term in a possible power series for $\tilde{r}$ could be $(x^2 + 2k^2)^2 + x^4$. Nevertheless, the resultant function $\tilde{\varphi}$ is strictly a function of $(x^2 + k^2)$. Moreover, it follows that [cf. (8-190a)]

$$\begin{aligned} \langle a^\dagger a \rangle &= \int r(z)|z|^2\, d\mu(z) \\ &= -\frac{\hbar}{2}\left(\frac{\partial^2}{\partial x^2} + \frac{\partial^2}{\partial k^2}\right)\tilde{r}(x, k)\bigg|_{x=k=0} = A \end{aligned} \tag{9-11}$$

which shows that $A \geq 0$. If $A = 0$, then $\tilde{\varphi}(x, k) \equiv 1$ and the resultant density operator $\rho = |0\rangle\langle 0|$. We may, therefore, exclude this case and assume $A > 0$. It follows then that the weight function $\tilde{\varphi}(x, k)$ is a standard Gaussian and so, therefore, is the diagonal weight $\varphi(p, q)$. Specifically

$$\varphi(p, q) = A^{-1} \exp\left[-\frac{1}{2\hbar A}(p^2 + q^2)\right] \tag{9-12}$$

which in complex form reads

$$\varphi(z) = \frac{1}{\langle N \rangle} \exp(-|z|^2/\langle N \rangle) \tag{9-13}$$

where we have set $A = \langle |z|^2 \rangle = \langle N \rangle$. The normal distribution (9-13) for $\varphi(z)$ was derived in a similar way by Glauber [8-1].

General Solution. Equation (9-13) is the basic result of this section but our discussion so far has only scratched its basic nature! We continue to assume that all contributions z_n have the same distribution r so that Eq. (9-8) still applies. Again we assume $\tilde{r}$ to be twice differentiable at the origin with vanishing first derivatives, but we now replace (9-9) by an expression with a general quadratic,

$$\tilde{r}(x, k) \simeq 1 - \frac{1}{2\hbar}(Bx^2 + 2Cxk + Dk^2) \tag{9-14}$$

assumed valid for small x and k. Similar reasoning as before then shows for arbitrarily large N that

$$\tilde{\varphi}(x, k) = \exp\left[-\frac{1}{2\hbar}(Bx^2 + 2Cxk + Dk^2)\right] \tag{9-15}$$

which holds for all x and k. But unlike the case (9-10) there is no guarantee that the quadratic form in the exponent is positive. In other words, $\tilde{\varphi}$ may, in fact, grow in some directions [in a manner consistent with (9-6), of course]. Indeed, one may readily cite examples of diagonal distributions $\tilde{r}(x, k)$ (which, in fact, are test functions in $\mathcal{S}_2$!) for which the resultant "thermal" distribution (9-15) has negative B. Such cases are possible because $\tilde{\varphi}(x, k)$ is ultimately sensitive *only* to the behavior of $\tilde{r}(x, k)$ near the origin which in the x direction, say, may temporarily rise above unity before falling to zero with rapid decrease.

It is important to observe that in spite of such curious behavior the resultant distributions are truly thermal! Let us assume first that $C = 0$ since the relevant features are present in this simpler case. Therefore, for small enough x and k, we let

$$\tilde{r}(x, k) \simeq 1 - \frac{1}{2\hbar}(Bx^2 + Dk^2) \tag{9-16}$$

Now for some density operator ρ_0 we have [cf. (8-169) and (8-178)]

$$\begin{aligned}\mathrm{Tr}\{\rho_0 U^\dagger[k, x]\} &= \tilde{r}(x, k)\exp\left[-\frac{1}{4\hbar}(x^2 + k^2)\right] \\ &\simeq 1 - \frac{1}{2\hbar}[(B + \tfrac{1}{2})x^2 + (D + \tfrac{1}{2})k^2]\end{aligned} \tag{9-17}$$

the latter form holding for small enough x and k. If we now invoke the uncertainty principle applied to (9-17) we discover that

$$\langle P^2\rangle\langle Q^2\rangle = \hbar^2(B + \tfrac{1}{2})(D + \tfrac{1}{2}) \geq \tfrac{1}{4}\hbar^2 \tag{9-18}$$

Due to the positive nature of the individual factors, we conclude that

$$B + \tfrac{1}{2} > 0 \quad D + \tfrac{1}{2} > 0 \quad \text{and} \quad (B + \tfrac{1}{2})(D + \tfrac{1}{2}) \geq \tfrac{1}{4} \tag{9-19}$$

If $B = D$, then $B \geq 0$ follows; but if $B \neq D$, then either B or D may possibly be negative (e.g., $B = -\frac{1}{8}$, $D = 2$). If we set

$$b = 1 + 2B \qquad d = 1 + 2D \tag{9-20}$$

then

$$b > 0 \quad d > 0 \quad \text{and} \quad bd \geq 1 \tag{9-21}$$

Now it follows quite generally from (8-169) and (8-178) that

$$\tilde{\varphi}(x, k) = \mathrm{Tr}\{\rho U^\dagger[k, x]\}\exp\left[\frac{1}{4\hbar}(x^2 + k^2)\right] \tag{9-22}$$

where $\tilde{\varphi}$ is the weight associated with the density operator ρ. In the present context we are led by (9-15) and (9-20) to the specific relation

$$\mathrm{Tr}\{\rho U^\dagger[k, x]\} = \exp\left[-\frac{1}{4\hbar}(bx^2 + dk^2)\right] \tag{9-23}$$

It is readily shown that the above conditions on b and d imply that ρ is a true density operator given by

$$\rho \equiv e^{-\beta'\mathcal{H}'}/\mathrm{Tr}(e^{-\beta'\mathcal{H}'}) \tag{9-24}$$

Here the "Hamiltonian"

$$\mathcal{H}' = \tfrac{1}{2}(P^2 + \omega'^2 Q^2 - \hbar\omega') \equiv \hbar\omega' N' \tag{9-25}$$

the "angular frequency"

$$\omega' \equiv (b/d)^{1/2} \tag{9-26}$$

and the "inverse temperature" β' is determined from the relation [cf. (5-56)]

$$\langle N' \rangle = \frac{1}{e^{\beta' \hbar \omega'} - 1} = \tfrac{1}{2}[(bd)^{1/2} - 1] \qquad (9\text{-}27)$$

If $b = d$ (i.e., $B = D$) we recover the special thermal distributions covered by Eq. (9-10) where $A = \langle N' \rangle$. When $b \neq d$ we obtain other thermal distributions. In fact, an example where $b \neq d$ was previously given in (8-198) in which $b = \omega$ and $d = \omega^{-1}$. Since then $BD = -(4\omega)^{-1}(1 - \omega)^2 \leq 0$, either B or D must be negative if $\omega \neq 1$. Clearly for this example $\omega' = \omega$ and $\beta' = \infty$, i.e., ρ' is the degenerate thermal ensemble at zero "temperature" which is just the projection operator onto the ground state of $\mathcal{H}'$ [which correctly characterizes the example chosen for (8-198)].

Entirely similar conclusions would apply if the factor C in (9-15) differs from zero. In this case the relevant oscillator Hamiltonian $\mathcal{H}'$ would contain cross-terms between P and Q.

In summary we observe that under very general conditions (essentially just twofold differentiability of $\tilde{r}$ or, equivalently, the existence of the first two moments of r) the quantum mechanical density operator for an indefinitely large number of similarly distributed contributions is strictly thermal.

The curious property that B or D may become negative is by no means wrong. However, its appearance would reflect the fact that we had not expanded the density operator in the most "favorable" set of "coherent states" for the chaotic source in question. For example, if we would re-expand the state ρ_ω of (8-198) in terms of coherent states adapted to the frequency ω we would find the result $\tilde{\varphi}(x, k) = 1$. This result is clearly more perspicuous than the alternative choice which grows exponentially. More generally, by exploiting arbitrary linear transformations on P and Q consistent with $[Q, P] = i\hbar$ and by employing the associated coherent states determined thereby, we can recast all thermal state weights of the form (9-15) into the basic Gaussian form (9-10) with non-negative variance.

If we assume that a transformation to "favorable" coherent states has been carried out whenever necessary, then we can summarize our results by the observation that in the presence of a myriad of independent and similarly distributed driving terms the density operator for a single degree of freedom is characterized by

$$\tilde{\varphi}(x, k) = \exp\left[-\frac{1}{2\hbar} A(x^2 + k^2)\right]$$

which leads to the canonical, diagonal, weight function

$$\varphi(z) = \frac{1}{\langle N\rangle} \exp(-|z|^2/\langle N\rangle) \tag{9-28}$$

with $A = \langle|z|^2\rangle = \langle N\rangle$. In the case $\langle N\rangle = 0$ this result is to be interpreted as $\varphi(z) = \pi\,\delta(z)$ for the two-dimensional δ function defined in (8-137). It is an important consequence that the resultant canonical distribution is phase invariant, $\varphi(z) = \varphi(|z|)$, no matter how it started out.

It should be fairly clear that the same $\varphi(z)$ applies even in cases where the individual distributions $r_n(z_n)$ are not all identical but are sufficiently "similar" to one another (in ways analogous to those necessary to derive the classical central limit theorem). We shall not carry out the parallel derivation in the present context.

Let us conclude our single degree of freedom examples by directly demonstrating that the Gaussian weight $\varphi(z)$ leads to the familiar density operator for a thermal state. Specifically

$$\begin{aligned}
\rho &= \frac{1}{\pi}\int \varphi(z)|z\rangle\langle z|\, d^2z \\
&= \frac{1}{\pi\langle N\rangle}\int \exp\,[-|z|^2(1+\langle N\rangle^{-1})] \sum_{n,m=0}^{\infty} \frac{z^n z^{*m}}{(n!m!)^{1/2}}\,|n\rangle\langle m|\, d^2z \\
&= \frac{1}{\langle N\rangle}\sum_{n=0}^{\infty}\frac{1}{n!}\int |z|^{2n}\exp[-|z|^2(1+\langle N\rangle^{-1})]|n\rangle\langle n|\, d|z|^2 \\
&= \frac{1}{\langle N\rangle}\sum_{n=0}^{\infty}(1+\langle N\rangle^{-1})^{-n+1}|n\rangle\langle n| \\
&= \frac{1}{1+\langle N\rangle}\sum_{n=0}^{\infty}\left(\frac{\langle N\rangle}{1+\langle N\rangle}\right)^n |n\rangle\langle n|
\end{aligned} \tag{9-29}$$

which has the geometric form characteristic of a Bose-Einstein distribution. If we define

$$e^{-\beta\hbar\omega} \equiv \langle N\rangle/(1+\langle N\rangle) \tag{9-30}$$

then

$$\rho = (1 - e^{-\beta\hbar\omega}) \sum_{n=0}^{\infty} e^{-n\beta\hbar\omega}|n\rangle\langle n| \tag{9-31}$$

Since the oscillator energy levels $E_n = n\hbar\omega$, Eq. (9-31) is, as we explicitly verify below, the form of the equilibrium thermal state:

B. Extension to Finitely Many Degrees of Freedom

As a preparatory to obtaining thermal or chaotic states for the radiation field, let us first indicate the straightforward generalizations to finitely many degrees of freedom of our preceding analysis. As before it is not necessary to assume that these are normal modes of the radiation field. If $r(\{z_k\})$, $k = 1, \ldots, K$, denotes the diagonal distribution governing the identically distributed elementary contributions, then the Fourier transforms $\tilde{r}$ and $\tilde{\varphi}$ fulfill an equation analogous to (9-8), namely,

$$\tilde{\varphi}(\{x_k\}, \{k_k\}) = [\tilde{r}(\{x_k/N^{1/2}\}, \{k_k/N^{1/2}\})]^N \tag{9-32}$$

Under suitable conditions on $\tilde{r}$ similar to those discussed earlier, this function has a limit for infinitely large N given quite generally by

$$\tilde{\varphi}(\{x_k\}, \{k_k\}) = \exp\left\{-\frac{1}{2\hbar}\Sigma_{r,s}(x_r B_{rs} x_s + 2x_r C_{rs} k_s + k_r D_{rs} k_s)\right\} \tag{9-33}$$

for suitable matrices B, C, and D. Specifically

$$B_{rs} = B_{sr} = \frac{1}{\hbar}\langle P_r P_s\rangle - \tfrac{1}{2}\,\delta_{rs} \tag{9-34a}$$

$$D_{rs} = D_{sr} = \frac{1}{\hbar}\langle Q_r Q_s\rangle - \tfrac{1}{2}\,\delta_{rs} \tag{9-34b}$$

$$C_{rs} = -\frac{1}{2\hbar}\langle P_r Q_s + Q_s P_r\rangle \tag{9-34c}$$

which, as mean values of Hermitian variables, are all real elements. In a self-evident matrix notation the exponent in (9-33) can be written

$$(x\ k)\begin{pmatrix} B & C \\ C^T & D\end{pmatrix}\begin{pmatrix} x \\ k\end{pmatrix}$$

where C^T is the transpose of the matrix C. In this form it is clear that the overall quadratic form is real and symmetric and may, thus, be diagonalized by an orthogonal transformation on the x and k variables. If, after such a transformation we call the new variables x and k again, then (9-33) reads

$$\tilde{\varphi}(\{x_k\}, \{k_k\}) = \exp\left\{-\frac{1}{2\hbar}\Sigma_k(B_k x_k^2 + D_k k_k^2)\right\}$$

Finally, scale changes which preserve $[Q_s, P_r] = i\hbar\,\delta_{rs}$ bring this result into the canonical form

$$\tilde{\varphi}(\{x_k\}, \{k_k\}) = \exp\left\{-\frac{1}{2\hbar}\Sigma_k A_k(x_k^2 + k_k^2)]\right\} \tag{9-35}$$

where $A_k \geq 0$ for each k as follows from our earlier discussion. The essence of these remarks is the following: By exploiting the freedom available in the choice of angular frequencies ω_k and in the canonical variables we can, as before, always choose "favorable" coherent states in the diagonal representation for a chaotic field such that $\tilde{\varphi}$ always has the canonical form (9-35). For such favorable coherent states it follows that the diagonal weight function in complex form reads

$$\varphi(\{z_k\}) = \prod_{k=1}^{K} \frac{1}{\langle N_k \rangle} \exp(-|z_k|^2/\langle N_k \rangle) \tag{9-36}$$

where $A_k = \langle |z_k|^2 \rangle = \langle N_k \rangle$. Again, if $\langle N_k \rangle = 0$ for some k, then evidently we interpret the factor in (9-36) as $\pi\, \delta(z_k)$.

As a last step before taking up the limit $K \to \infty$ we note that (9-36) leads to

$$\begin{aligned} \langle \{z_k'\} | \rho | \{z_k'\} \rangle &= \int \varphi(\{z_k\}) |\langle \{z_k'\} | \{z_k\} \rangle|^2 \, d\mu(\{z_k\}) \\ &= \prod_{k=1}^{K} \int \frac{1}{\langle N_k \rangle} \exp(-|z_k|^2/\langle N_k \rangle - |z_k' - z_k|^2) \, d\mu(z_k) \\ &= \prod_{k=1}^{K} \frac{1}{1 + \langle N_k \rangle} \exp[-|z_k'|^2/(1 + \langle N_k \rangle)] \end{aligned} \tag{9-37}$$

As emphasized in Chapter 7 these diagonal elements serve to determine the operator ρ uniquely.

C. *Chaotic and Thermal Radiation Fields*

It was proved in Chapter 8 that every density operator for the radiation field may be represented in the form of (8-231) as the limit of a sequence of diagonally represented operators each involving a finite number of degrees of freedom. In the present application it would appear natural to adopt

$$\varphi_K(\{z_{k,K}\}) = \prod_{k=1}^{K} \frac{1}{\langle N_k \rangle} \exp(-|z_k|^2/\langle N_k \rangle) \tag{9-38}$$

as the truncated diagonal weight for K degrees of freedom, and to define

$$\begin{aligned} \rho &= \lim_{K \to \infty} \rho_K \\ &= \lim_{K \to \infty} \int \varphi_K(\{z_{k,K}\}) |\{z_{k,K}\}\rangle\langle \{z_{k,K}\}| \, d\mu(\{z_{k,K}\}) \end{aligned} \tag{9-39}$$

as the density operator for a chaotic field. As was noted in Chapter 5, however, it cannot be expected that every sequence of mean occupancies $\langle N_k\rangle$ defines a bona fide density operator ρ by such a procedure. One argument to select suitable sequences is to note that

$$\begin{aligned}\langle\{z_k\}|\rho|\{z_k\}\rangle &= \lim_{K\to\infty} \langle\{z_{k,K}\}|\rho_K|\{z_{k,K}\}\rangle \\ &= \prod_{k=1}^{\infty} \frac{1}{1+\langle N_k\rangle} \exp[-|z_k|^2/(1+\langle N_k\rangle)]\end{aligned} \tag{9-40}$$

as follows from (9-37). Evidently,

$$\langle\{z_k\}|\rho|\{z_k\}\rangle \le \langle 0|\rho|0\rangle = \prod_{k=1}^{\infty} \frac{1}{1+\langle N_k\rangle} \tag{9-41}$$

If this infinite multiple product converges to zero, then *all* diagonal coherent-state elements of ρ vanish and, consequently, ρ itself vanishes. Since this is clearly undesirable the multiple product must converge to a nonzero number, the condition for which is simply

$$\sum_{k=1}^{\infty} \langle N_k\rangle < \infty \tag{9-42}$$

[as may be inferred from remarks made in connection with (5-95)].

In virtue of the condition (9-42) on allowable sequences $\langle N_k\rangle$, it follows not only that ρ is an honest density operator but, moreover, the convergence in (9-39) is in trace-class norm, $\|\rho - \rho_K\|_1 \to 0$. This has as a particular consequence that for *any* bounded operator B

$$\begin{aligned}\langle B\rangle &= \mathrm{Tr}(\rho B) = \lim_{K\to\infty} \mathrm{Tr}(\rho_K B) \\ &= \lim_{K\to\infty} \int \varphi_K(\{z_{k,K}\})\langle\{z_{k,K}\}|B|\{z_{k,K}\}\rangle\, d\mu(\{z_{k,K}\})\end{aligned} \tag{9-43}$$

Specifically, the normal order, generating function $C_N(\{u_k\})$ is given through (8-236) and (9-35) as

$$\begin{aligned}C_N(\{u_k\}) &= \mathrm{Tr}\left(\rho \exp\left[\sum_1^{\infty} u_k a_k^\dagger\right] \exp\left[-\sum_1^{\infty} u_k^* a_k\right]\right) \\ &= \exp\left(-\sum_1^{\infty} \langle N_k\rangle |u_k|^2\right)\end{aligned} \tag{9-44}$$

If we introduce the operator

$$J^\dagger \equiv \sum_{k=1}^{\infty} u_k a_k^\dagger \tag{9-45}$$

then we note that (9-44) has a rather simple structure given by

$$\langle e^{J\dagger}e^{-J}\rangle = e^{-\langle J\dagger J\rangle} \tag{9-46}$$

This formula is particularly convenient for it permits us to state immediately the result for

$$J^{\dagger} \equiv \int \mathbf{S}(\mathbf{r}, t) \cdot \mathbf{A}^{(-)}(\mathbf{r}, t)\, d^4x \tag{9-47}$$

which in view of the free-field equations is an operator of the type (9-45). In this case the normal ordered, generating functional for the transverse potential reads

$$\begin{aligned} C_N\{\mathbf{S}\} &= \langle e^{J\dagger}e^{-J}\rangle = e^{-\langle J\dagger J\rangle} \\ &= \exp\{-\Sigma \textstyle\int S_j(\mathbf{r}, t)G_{jk}(\mathbf{r}, t; \mathbf{r}', t')S_k{}^*(\mathbf{r}', t')\, d^4x\, d^4x'\} \end{aligned} \tag{9-48}$$

where $j, k = 1, 2, 3$ and

$$G_{jk}(\mathbf{r}, t; \mathbf{r}', t') \equiv \langle A_j^{(-)}(\mathbf{r}, t)A_k^{(+)}(\mathbf{r}', t')\rangle \tag{9-49}$$

is just the second-order correlation function. It is important to note again that the second-order correlation function determines the entire distribution in the present examples.

It follows from (7-179a) that we can alternatively represent these expressions in terms of the radiation field normal modes as

$$\begin{aligned} &G_{jk}(\mathbf{r}, t; \mathbf{r}', t') \\ &\quad = \frac{1}{L^3}\Sigma_{\mathbf{k},\mathbf{k}'}\frac{\hbar}{2(\omega\omega')^{1/2}}\{\exp[i(\mathbf{k}'\cdot\mathbf{x}' - \mathbf{k}\cdot\mathbf{x}) - i(\omega't' - \omega t)] \\ &\qquad\qquad \times \langle a_j{}^{\dagger}(\mathbf{k})a_k(\mathbf{k}')\rangle\} \end{aligned} \tag{9-50}$$

which for arbitrarily large quantization volumes approaches the suggestive integral relation $[\Sigma_k \to (L/2\pi)^3 \int d^3k]$

$$G_{jk}(\mathbf{r}, t; \mathbf{r}'\, t') = \frac{L^3}{(2\pi)^6}\int\!\!\int d^3k\, d^3k'\, \frac{\hbar}{2(\omega\omega')^{1/2}}\{\text{as above}\} \tag{9-51}$$

If we introduce

$$\tilde{\mathbf{S}}(\mathbf{k}, \nu) = \Sigma_\lambda \mathbf{e}_\lambda(\mathbf{k})\tilde{S}_\lambda(\mathbf{k}, \nu) = (2\pi)^{-3/2}\textstyle\int e^{-i\mathbf{k}\cdot\mathbf{x}+i\omega t}\mathbf{S}(\mathbf{x}, t)\, d^4x \tag{9-52}$$

then we can alternatively write

$$\begin{aligned} C_N\{\mathbf{S}\} = \exp\Big\{-\frac{L^3}{(2\pi)^3}\sum\int \frac{\hbar}{2(\omega\omega')^{1/2}}\tilde{S}_\lambda(\mathbf{k}, \nu)\langle a_\lambda{}^{\dagger}(\mathbf{k})a_{\lambda'}(\mathbf{k}')\rangle\tilde{S}^*_{\lambda'}(\mathbf{k}', \nu') \\ \times\, d^3k\, d^3k'\Big\} \end{aligned} \tag{9-53}$$

Clearly only the transverse parts of $\tilde{\mathbf{S}}(\mathbf{k}, \nu)$ contribute in (9-53) and we hereafter assume that $\mathbf{S}$ is transverse. These relations apply quite generally, and there is no requirement that the state be stationary, or homogeneous and isotropic in space, etc.

In cases where the state can be treated sensibly as stationary, homogeneous, and isotropic, however, Eq. (9-53) can be considerably simplified. In such a case we have

$$\frac{L^3}{(2\pi)^3}\langle a_\lambda{}^\dagger(\mathbf{k})a_{\lambda'}(\mathbf{k}')\rangle \simeq \delta_{\lambda\lambda'}\,\delta(\mathbf{k}-\mathbf{k}')N(\nu) \tag{9-54}$$

where

$$N(\nu) \equiv \langle a_\lambda{}^\dagger(\mathbf{k})a_\lambda(\mathbf{k})\rangle \tag{9-55}$$

for any polarization λ and $\mathbf{k}$ satisfying $|\mathbf{k}| = \omega = 2\pi\nu$. Making use of these properties we find

$$C_N\{\mathbf{S}\} = \exp\left\{-\int \frac{\hbar}{2\omega}|\tilde{\mathbf{S}}(\mathbf{k}, \nu)|^2 N(\nu)\,d^3k\right\} \tag{9-56}$$

Suppose we confine our further questions to a limited class of test functions suitable for a detector sensibly localized at a point $\mathbf{R}$ and which is sensitive to photons of arbitrary polarization. In particular, let us restrict the test functions such that

$$\tilde{\mathbf{S}}(\mathbf{k}, \nu) \equiv (2\pi)^{-3/2}\mathbf{e}_\lambda(\mathbf{k})e^{i\mathbf{k}\cdot\mathbf{R}}\tilde{S}(\nu) \tag{9-57}$$

in which case C_N becomes independent of $\mathbf{k}$, $\mathbf{R}$, and λ. Thus we can regard C_N as a functional depending on $\tilde{S}(\nu)$. If we use the substitution $d^3k \rightarrow 4\pi k^2\,dk$, $k = 2\pi\nu$, and define

$$\tilde{\Gamma}(\nu) \equiv \hbar\nu N(\nu) \tag{9-58}$$

we readily find that

$$C_N\{\tilde{S}(\nu)\} = \exp\left\{-\int_0^\infty |\tilde{S}(\nu)|^2\tilde{\Gamma}(\nu)\,d\nu\right\} \tag{9-59}$$

This integral expression achieves exact validity in the infinite volume limit.

This is an important characterization of an important set of states. We emphasize that the analysis of chaotic fields presented above leads to a Gaussian stochastic process but the variance is not predetermined. Even in the stationary, homogeneous, and isotropic case characterized by (9-59) the specific (real, nonnegative) function $\tilde{\Gamma}(\nu)$ remains arbitrary.

It is noteworthy that the normal ordered characteristic functions for chaotic fields have the same general structure as we observed for the classical fields in Chapter 3. The only appearance that $\hbar$ can make is in the function G_{jk} in the general relation (9-48), or in the function $\tilde{\Gamma}(\nu)$ in the special relation (9-59).

Stationary States. Of particular importance in various considerations are the multitude of states of the radiation field which are stationary. In a Schrödinger picture—in which only the density operator changes with time—the desired time-independence condition may be stated

$$\rho(t) = e^{-i\mathcal{H}t/\hbar}\rho e^{i\mathcal{H}t/\hbar} = \rho \tag{9-60}$$

namely, that ρ commutes with $\mathcal{H}$. Let us imagine our field confined again to a large but finite quantization volume L^3 with periodic boundary conditions. Then the spectrum of $\mathcal{H}$ is discrete and has finite multiplicity. Let us introduce the orthonormal eigenstates of $\mathcal{H}$,

$$\mathcal{H}|E_n, \alpha_m\rangle = E_n|E_n, \alpha_m\rangle \tag{9-61}$$

where E_n labels the energy eigenvalues, and the degeneracy parameter α_m labels states of a fixed energy. Stationary density operators are those which are diagonal in the energy representation, and thus have the canonical form

$$\rho = \Sigma_{n,m}\beta_{nm}|E_n, \alpha_m\rangle\langle E_n, \alpha_m| \tag{9-62}$$

where

$$\beta_{nm} \equiv \langle E_n, \alpha_m|\rho|E_n, \alpha_m\rangle \tag{9-63}$$

satisfies $0 \leq \beta_{nm} \leq 1$ and

$$\Sigma_{n,m}\beta_{nm} = 1 \tag{9-64}$$

Two additional points are worth emphasizing. Equation (9-62) does not generally imply that $\rho = F(\mathcal{H})$ for this would require that

$$\beta_{nm} = \langle E_n, \alpha_m|F(\mathcal{H})|E_n, \alpha_m\rangle = F(E_n) \tag{9-65}$$

which is completely independent of the variable m. Furthermore, stationary states of the type (9-62) include far more cases than just the stationary chaotic fields discussed above.

Entropy and the Equilibrium Thermal Distribution. Let us now single out those states of the radiation field that correspond to equilibrium thermal distributions. The equilibrium condition implies that the state does not change under time evolution, i.e., that ρ is a stationary state. The thermal nature has to do with the most disordered or maximum entropy state.

The entropy $S(\rho)$ of a general state of a system is defined by the equation[1]

$$S(\rho) = -\mathrm{Tr}(\rho \ln \rho) \tag{9-66}$$

[1] See, e.g., von Neumann [5-4].

In the canonical diagonal form, where

$$\rho = \sum_{n=1}^{\infty} \beta_n |\psi_n\rangle\langle\psi_n| \tag{9-67}$$

$$0 \leq \beta_n \leq 1 \qquad \sum_{n=1}^{\infty} \beta_n = 1$$

the above equation reads

$$\begin{aligned} S(\rho) &= -\mathrm{Tr}\left\{\sum_{n=1}^{\infty} \beta_n \ln \beta_n |\psi_n\rangle\langle\psi_n|\right\} \\ &= -\sum_{n=1}^{\infty} \beta_n \ln \beta_n \end{aligned} \tag{9-68}$$

For any *pure* state we can choose $\beta_1 = 1$, $\beta_n = 0$, $n > 1$, and it follows that $S(\rho) = 0$. For any *mixed* state $S(\rho) > 0$.

Intuitively, as our knowledge about the state diminishes the entropy rises. Consider the case of 2×2 matrices, as discussed in Chapter 5 for the example of polarization of a monochromatic beam. If $\beta_1 \equiv \beta$ and $\beta_2 \equiv 1 - \beta$, then the density operator

$$\rho = \begin{pmatrix} \beta & 0 \\ 0 & 1 - \beta \end{pmatrix}$$

has entropy

$$S(\rho) \equiv S(\beta) = -\beta \ln \beta - (1 - \beta) \ln(1 - \beta)$$

The maximum entropy occurs when

$$S'(\beta) = -1 - \ln \beta + 1 + \ln(1 - \beta) = 0$$

namely, for $\beta = \frac{1}{2}$, which shows the most entropy belongs to the least informative density operator $\rho = \frac{1}{2}$.

We note quite generally for two density operators ρ_1 and ρ_2 and parameter α, $0 \leq \alpha \leq 1$, that

$$S(\alpha\rho_1 + (1 - \alpha)\rho_2) \geq \alpha S(\rho_1) + (1 - \alpha)S(\rho_2) \tag{9-69}$$

which shows that the entropy of a mixture exceeds the weighted sum of the entropy of its constituent components. Moreover, if we consider a *composite* system conveniently described by a double-index sequence for which

$$\rho = \Sigma_{n,m}\gamma_{n,m}|\psi_{n,m}\rangle\langle\psi_{n,m}|$$

then clearly

$$S(\rho) = -\Sigma_{n,m}\gamma_{n,m} \ln \gamma_{n,m}$$

In the special case that the two systems are *independent*, characterized in particular by

$$\gamma_{n,m} \equiv \lambda_n \mu_m$$
$$\Sigma_n \lambda_n = \Sigma_m \mu_m = 1$$

then

$$\begin{aligned} S(\rho) &= -\Sigma_{n,m} \lambda_n \mu_m \ln(\lambda_n \mu_m) \\ &= -\Sigma_n \lambda_n \ln \lambda_n - \Sigma_m \mu_m \ln \mu_m \end{aligned} \tag{9-70}$$

which is the sum of the entropy of each system computed individually. In a suggestive notation (signifying the independent but product nature of the combined system) we see that

$$S(\rho_1 \otimes \rho_2) = S(\rho_1) + S(\rho_2) \tag{9-71}$$

We now define the equilibrium thermal state as the state ρ that maximizes the entropy $S(\rho)$ for a given mean value of the energy $E = \langle \mathcal{H} \rangle = \mathrm{Tr}(\rho \mathcal{H})$. To find this state we may appeal to the general representation (9-62) for equilibrium states and consider

$$\begin{aligned} \bar{S}(\rho) &= -\mathrm{Tr}(\rho \ln \rho) - \beta[\mathrm{Tr}(\rho \mathcal{H}) - E] + \mu[\mathrm{Tr}(\rho) - 1] \\ &= -\Sigma_{n,m} \beta_{nm} \ln \beta_{nm} \\ &\quad -\beta(\Sigma_{n,m} \beta_{nm} E_n - E) + \mu(\Sigma_{n,m} \beta_{nm} - 1) \end{aligned} \tag{9-72}$$

Here β and μ are Lagrange multipliers which ensure the requisite constraints and permit extremization of $\bar{S}$ by an independent variation of each β_{nm}. Hence we require

$$\frac{\partial}{\partial \beta_{nm}} \bar{S}(\rho) = -1 - \ln \beta_{nm} - \beta E_n + \mu = 0$$

which leads to the solution

$$\beta_{nm} = \exp(\mu - 1 - \beta E_n) \equiv Z^{-1} \exp(-\beta E_n) \tag{9-73}$$

independent of m [hence $\rho = F(\mathcal{H})$].

By imposing the constraint $\mathrm{Tr}(\rho) = 1$ we find that

$$Z = \Sigma_{n,m} \exp(-\beta E_n) = \Sigma_n N_n \exp(-\beta E_n) \tag{9-74}$$

where N_n is the degeneracy of the level E_n. The quantity Z is called the partition function and is an important parameter. On the basis of earlier remarks we clearly find that

$$Z = \mathrm{Tr}(e^{-\beta \mathcal{H}}) \tag{9-75}$$
$$\rho = Z^{-1} e^{-\beta \mathcal{H}} \tag{9-76}$$

The energy constraint is expressed as

$$\begin{aligned} E &= \mathrm{Tr}(\rho\mathcal{H}) = Z^{-1}\,\mathrm{Tr}(e^{-\beta\mathcal{H}}\mathcal{H}) \\ &= \Sigma_{n,m}\beta_{nm}E_n = Z^{-1}\Sigma_{n,m}\exp(-\beta E_n)E_n \end{aligned} \tag{9-77a}$$

Alternatively we see that

$$E = -\frac{\partial}{\partial\beta}\ln Z(\beta) = \frac{\mathrm{Tr}(\mathcal{H}e^{-\beta\mathcal{H}})}{\mathrm{Tr}(e^{-\beta\mathcal{H}})} \tag{9-77b}$$

For the radiation field we may extend (5-75) to deduce that

$$E = \Sigma_{\lambda,\mathbf{k}}\frac{\hbar|\mathbf{k}|}{e^{\beta\hbar|\mathbf{k}|}-1} \tag{9-78}$$

which, for large (but finite) quantization volume L^3, may be approximated by

$$\begin{aligned} E &= 2\frac{L^3}{(2\pi)^3}\int d^3k\,\frac{\hbar|\mathbf{k}|}{e^{\beta\hbar|\mathbf{k}|}-1} \\ &= \frac{L^3}{\pi^2\hbar^3\beta^4}\int_0^\infty \frac{x^3}{e^x-1}\,dx \end{aligned} \tag{9-79}$$

The last integral may be shown[2] to equal $\pi^4/15$ which leads us to the classic solution ($\beta \equiv 1/\kappa T$)

$$E = \frac{\pi^2}{15}\frac{L^3}{\hbar^3\beta^4} = \frac{\pi^2}{15}\frac{(\kappa T)^4L^3}{\hbar^3} \tag{9-80}$$

where κ is Boltzmann's constant and T is the absolute temperature. We further note that integration of (9-77b) leads to the approximate evaluation that

$$Z(\beta) = \exp[(\pi^2/45)(L/\hbar\beta)^3] \tag{9-81}$$

the normalization coming from the condition $Z(\infty) = 1$. It follows from (9-80) that E uniquely determines β and thereby fully determines the equilibrium thermal state.

It is clear that the thermal state we have determined is a special case of the chaotic states described by (9-56) for which $N(\nu) = (e^{\beta\hbar\omega} - 1)^{-1}$. In fact—in an instance of the tail wagging the dog—the thermal state is so basic and fundamental that the various chaotic states are often loosely called "thermal." This is partially justified since quite general chaotic states can be and most frequently are made as "filtered" thermal states, as happens, for example, in atmospheric absorption of the sun's radiation.

[2] See, e.g., Landau and Lifshitz [9-1].

D. Counting Distributions for Chaotic Fields

Because of the especially simple formulas that emerge we should like to confine our principal discussion to a detector sensibly localized at a point **R** in the presence of a stationary radiation field. In order to compare with formulas derived by other workers we assume also that only one mode of polarization is present described by $\mathbf{e}_\lambda$. If we set

$$A^{(+)}(t) \equiv \mathbf{e}_\lambda \cdot \mathbf{A}^{(+)}(\mathbf{R}, t) \tag{9-82a}$$
$$V(t) \equiv \mathbf{e}_\lambda \cdot \mathbf{V}(\mathbf{R}, t) \tag{9-82b}$$

then Eq. (8-124) with $t \equiv -\frac{1}{2}T$ coupled with the diagonal representation implies that

$$\begin{aligned} Q(\lambda, T) &= \left\langle :\exp\left[-\lambda\alpha\int_{-T/2}^{T/2} A^{(-)}(t')A^{(+)}(t')\,dt'\right]:\right\rangle \\ &= \int \varphi(\{z_k\})\exp\left[-\lambda\alpha\int_{-T/2}^{T/2} V^*(t')V(t')\,dt'\right]d\mu(\{z_k\}) \end{aligned} \tag{9-83}$$

Here $\mathbf{A}^{(+)}$ and $\mathbf{V}$ are related in the usual way through Eq. (7-181a), and $\varphi(\{z_k\})$ is a normal distribution which in a favorable coherent-state expansion has the form implicit in (9-38). Computation of the mean involved in (9-83) for such normal distributions is a standard task in noise theory.

Rather than employ (9-83) directly it is most convenient to derive a distribution suitable for the present application directly from (9-59). Since we are only interested in the time interval $-\frac{1}{2}T$ to $+\frac{1}{2}T$ in forming $Q(\lambda, T)$ we may specialize Eq. (9-59) to functions $\tilde{S}(\nu)$ for which $S(t)$ vanishes when $|t| \geq \frac{1}{2}T$. This restriction permits us to expand all relevant quantities in a Fourier series over the time interval T. Specifically let us set

$$S(t) \equiv T^{-1/2}\Sigma_l s_l \exp(-2\pi i\nu_l t) \tag{9-84a}$$
$$V(t) \equiv T^{-1/2}\Sigma_l v_l \exp(-2\pi i\nu_l t) \tag{9-84b}$$
$$\Gamma(t) \equiv T^{-1}\Sigma_l \Gamma_l \exp(-2\pi i\nu_l t) \tag{9-84c}$$

where $\nu_l = l/T$. Since both $V(t)$ and $\Gamma(t)$ are analytic signals, the sums in question run from $l = 0$ to $l = +\infty$. If we focus our interest on a distribution θ for the variables v_l then using (9-59) and simple consequences of (9-84) we can write

$$\begin{aligned} C_N\{\tilde{S}\} &= \exp[-\Sigma_l(s_l^* s_l \Gamma_l)] \\ &= \langle\exp[\Sigma_l(s_l^* v_l - s_l v_l^*)]\rangle \\ &\equiv \lim_{L\to\infty}\int \theta_L(\{v_l\})\exp\left[\sum_0^L (s_l^* v_l - s_l v_l^*)\right]\prod_0^L d\mu(v_l) \end{aligned} \tag{9-85}$$

where as usual $d\mu(v) = \pi^{-1}\, d^2v$. If we note that

$$\int \frac{1}{\Gamma} \exp[-|v|^2/\Gamma + (sv^* - s^*v)]\pi^{-1}\, d^2v = \exp(-|s|^2\Gamma)$$

(break into two real integrals) it follows that

$$\theta_L(\{v_l\}) = \prod_{l=0}^{L} \frac{1}{\Gamma_l} \exp(-|v_l|^2/\Gamma_l) \tag{9-86}$$

which characterizes the desired weight function for the variables v_l. It is important to note that this is generally a different distribution than (9-38). Lastly the observation that

$$\int \frac{1}{\Gamma} \exp(-|v|^2/\Gamma - \lambda\alpha|v|^2)\pi^{-1}\, d^2v = \frac{1}{1 + \lambda\alpha\Gamma}$$

(which is a simple consequence of normalization and a change of variables!) permits us to compute $Q(\lambda, T)$ by the requisite average given by

$$\begin{aligned} Q(\lambda, T) &= \langle \exp(-\lambda\alpha\Sigma_l v_l^* v_l)\rangle \\ &= \lim_{L\to\infty} \int \theta_L(\{v_l\}) \exp\left(-\lambda\alpha \sum_{l=0}^{L} v_l^* v_l\right) \prod_{l=0}^{L} d\mu(v_l) \\ &= \Pi_l \frac{1}{1 + \lambda\alpha\Gamma_l} = \exp[-\Sigma_l \ln(1 + \lambda\alpha\Gamma_l)] \end{aligned} \tag{9-87}$$

The convergence criterion for this calculation simply reads $\Sigma_l\Gamma_l < \infty$. The important quantities Γ_l appearing in this result are given in terms of $\Gamma(t)$ by the relation

$$\Gamma_l = \int_{-T/2}^{T/2} \Gamma(t) \exp(2\pi i l t/T)\, dt \tag{9-88}$$

The general and exact relation (9-87) has several simple limiting forms. In the limit when T is extremely short compared to the coherence time we may replace $\Gamma(t)$ by $\Gamma(0) \exp(-2\pi i \nu_0 t)$, where ν_0 is the center frequency of the radiation. In our periodic analysis treatment [cf. (9-84c)] $\nu_0 = l_0/T$ for some $l_0 \gg 1$. Hence (9-88) shows that $\Gamma_{l_0} = T\Gamma(0)$ with all other Γ_l vanishing. This gives rise to

$$Q(\lambda, T) = \frac{1}{1 + \lambda\alpha\Gamma_{l_0}} = \frac{1}{1 + \lambda\alpha T\Gamma(0)} \tag{9-89}$$

which is recognized as the generating function for a geometric or Bose-Einstein counting distribution as discussed in Eq. (2-20). It follows from (2-19) that

$$P(m, T) = (1 + \bar{m})^{-1}(1 + \bar{m}^{-1})^{-m}$$

where $\bar{m} = \alpha T\Gamma(0)$.

In the next approximation for small T we can account for a slow variation of the modulus of $\Gamma(t)$. In particular, if we set

$$\Gamma(t) \equiv \Gamma_0(t) \exp(-2\pi i\nu_0 t) \equiv \Gamma(0)\gamma_0(t) \exp(-2\pi i\nu_0 t) \qquad (9\text{-}90)$$

where $\Gamma_0(t) \simeq \Gamma(0)$ in the interval $|t| \leq \frac{1}{2}T$, then the largest term in (9-88) is

$$\Gamma_{l_0} = \int_{-T/2}^{T/2} \Gamma_0(t)\, dt$$

while the remaining terms

$$\Gamma_{l_0+l} = \int_{-T/2}^{T/2} \Gamma_0(t)e^{2\pi i l t/T}\, dt$$

are assumed very small for all $l \neq 0$. For these latter terms we may expand the logarithm to first order so as to obtain

$$\begin{aligned} Q(\lambda, T) &= \frac{1}{1 + \lambda\alpha\Gamma_{l_0}} \exp(-\Sigma'\lambda\alpha\Gamma_{l+l_0}) \\ &\equiv \frac{1}{1 + \lambda\bar{m}_1} \exp(-\lambda\bar{m}_2) \end{aligned} \qquad (9\text{-}91)$$

where the prime signifies that the term $l = 0$ is omitted from the sum. However, we need not explicitly carry out the sum in the exponent to determine the relevant parameters. It follows from

$$Q(\lambda, T) = \sum_{m=0}^{\infty} (1 - \lambda)^m P(m, T) \qquad (9\text{-}92)$$

and Eq. (3-39) that quite generally

$$\bar{m} = -\frac{\partial}{\partial\lambda} Q(\lambda, T)\bigg|_{\lambda=0} = \alpha T\Gamma(0) \qquad (9\text{-}93)$$

Hence, from (9-91) we learn that

$$\bar{m} = \bar{m}_1 + \bar{m}_2 = \alpha T\Gamma(0) \qquad (9\text{-}94)$$

which when coupled with (9-90) shows that

$$\bar{m}_1 \equiv \alpha \int_{-T/2}^{T/2} \Gamma_0(t)\, dt = \alpha\Gamma(0) \int_{-T/2}^{T/2} \gamma_0(t)\, dt \qquad (9\text{-}95a)$$

and

$$\bar{m}_2 \equiv \alpha T \Gamma(0) - \bar{m}_1$$
$$= \alpha \Gamma(0) \int_{-T/2}^{T/2} [1 - \gamma_0(t)]\, dt \qquad (9\text{-}95b)$$

Equation (9-91) is recognized as the product of two generating functions—one for a Bose-Einstein distribution and the other for a Poisson distribution. It follows that the resultant counting distribution is given by (2-35) as a convolution,

$$P(m, T) = \sum_{n=0}^{m} P_1(m - n, T) P_2(n, T) \qquad (9\text{-}96)$$

where

$$P_1(m, T) \equiv (1 + \bar{m}_1)(1 + \bar{m}_1{}^{-1})^m \qquad (9\text{-}97a)$$

$$P_2(m, T) \equiv \frac{(\bar{m}_2)^m e^{-\bar{m}_2}}{m!} \qquad (9\text{-}97b)$$

characteristic of these two distributions. The variance of the resultant distribution is given by

$$\sigma^2 = \overline{(\Delta m)^2} = \bar{m} + \bar{m}_1{}^2 = \bar{m} + (1 + r)^{-2}\bar{m}^2 \qquad (9\text{-}98)$$

where $r \equiv \bar{m}_2/\bar{m}_1$.

As an example of the preceding equations, suppose that $\gamma_0(t) = \exp(-\gamma|t|)$. It then follows that

$$\bar{m}_1 = \alpha\Gamma(0) T(\tfrac{1}{2}\gamma T)^{-1}[1 - e^{-1/2\gamma T}] \simeq \alpha\Gamma(0) T[1 - \tfrac{1}{4}\gamma T] \qquad (9\text{-}99a)$$

and

$$\bar{m}_2 = \alpha\Gamma(0) T - \bar{m}_1 \simeq \tfrac{1}{4}\alpha\Gamma(0)\gamma T^2 \qquad (9\text{-}99b)$$

The latter terms apply in our approximation where $\gamma T \ll 1$. In (9-98) the factor $r \simeq \frac{1}{4}\gamma T$.

In the other limiting form for Eq. (9-87) that we wish to consider the time T is *long* compared to the coherence time. In such a regime we can regard Γ_l as a slowly varying function of l. As such we may pass to a continuum approximation and replace Σ_l by $T \int d\nu$ in much the same way as we did for a large quantization volume in deriving (9-79). In such a case

$$Q(\lambda, T) = \exp[-\Sigma_l \ln(1 + \lambda\alpha\Gamma_l)]$$
$$= \exp\left\{-T \int_0^\infty d\nu \ln[1 + \lambda\alpha\tilde{\Gamma}(\nu)]\right\} \qquad (9\text{-}100)$$

where we can sensibly choose [cf. (9-88)]

$$\tilde{\Gamma}(\nu) = \int_{-\infty}^{\infty} \Gamma(t) e^{2\pi i \nu t}\, dt \qquad (9\text{-}101)$$

namely, just the power spectrum characteristic of the stationary Gaussian process.

In general the complete counting distribution $P(m, T)$ will depend on the power spectrum in an involved way. From the definition (9-92) we may note two ways to determine the counting distribution: The first method is given simply by

$$P(m, T) = \frac{(-1)^m}{m!} \frac{\partial^m}{\partial \lambda^m} Q(\lambda, T)\bigg|_{\lambda=1} \tag{9-102}$$

whereas if we set $(1 - \lambda) = e^{is}$, then a second method is given by the integral

$$P(m, T) = (2\pi)^{-1} \int_{-\pi}^{\pi} \exp\{-ism - T \int_0^\infty d\nu \ln[1 + (1 - e^{is})\alpha\tilde{\Gamma}(\nu)]\} \, ds \tag{9-103}$$

We can simplify our latter expression under the following reasonable conditions. The expressions we have derived have validity for large T and relatively broad spectrum $\tilde{\Gamma}(\nu)$ both of which conspire to make $\bar{m} \gg 1$. It is then reasonable to assume that $P(m, T)$ is a slowly varying function of m and that we can approximate $P(m, T)$ by a smooth density function $p(x, T)$ interpolated on the basis of the points $p(x_m, T) \simeq \bar{m}P(m, T)$, where $x_m \equiv m/\bar{m}$. This normalization is such that, to all intents and purposes,

$$\int_0^\infty p(x, T)\, dx = \sum_{m=0}^{\infty} p(x_m, T) \frac{1}{\bar{m}} = 1 \tag{9-104}$$

To proceed further we note first that

$$\begin{aligned} \bar{m}P(m, T) &= (2\pi)^{-1}\bar{m} \int_{-\pi}^{\pi} \exp\left\{-is\bar{m}x_m - T \int_0^\infty d\nu \ln [1 + (1 - e^{is})\alpha\tilde{\Gamma}(\nu)]\right\} ds \\ &= (2\pi)^{-1} \int_{-\pi\bar{m}}^{\pi\bar{m}} \exp\left\{-iyx_m - T \int_0^\infty d\nu \ln [1 + (1 - e^{iy/\bar{m}})\alpha\tilde{\Gamma}(\nu)]\right\} dy \end{aligned} \tag{9-105}$$

The smooth approximation we adopt is obtained by replacing the integration limits for $y(= s\bar{m})$ by $\pm\infty$, and retaining only the first term in an expansion of y in the logarithm. Specifically, we choose

$$p(x, T) \equiv (2\pi)^{-1} \int_{-\infty}^{\infty} \exp\left\{-iyx - T \int_0^\infty d\nu \ln [1 - i\bar{m}^{-1}y\alpha\tilde{\Gamma}(\nu)]\right\} dy \tag{9-106}$$

Since Eq. (9-106) may alternatively be viewed as the limit of (9-105) as $\bar{m} \to \infty$, $m \to \infty$, $\tilde{\Gamma}(\nu) \to \infty$, $x_m \to x$, and $\bar{m}^{-1}\tilde{\Gamma}(\nu)$ remaining fixed, it is intuitively evident that $p(x, T)$ vanishes for $x < 0$ and that $p(x, T) \geq 0$ for $x \geq 0$. The former condition is plausible as well on the basis of a well-behaved integrand (analytic in the upper-half y plane). Clearly the resultant distribution satisfies the normalization condition (9-104). For all practical purposes, when $\bar{m} \gg 1$ we may adopt as the counting distribution

$$P(m, T) \equiv (\bar{m})^{-1}p(m/\bar{m}, T) \tag{9-107}$$

where $p(x, T)$ is defined by (9-106).

Let us now illustrate the preceding long-time equations by two examples. Suppose first of all that the spectrum of $\tilde{\Gamma}(\nu)$ is rectangular, i.e., of uniform amplitude b over some positive frequency interval of width γ. We may relate αb to the mean number of counts by (9-94) such that

$$\bar{m} = \alpha T \int \tilde{\Gamma}(\nu)\, d\nu = \alpha T b \gamma$$

Let us also introduce the mean counting rate $w \equiv \bar{m}/T$. Consequently, the parameter

$$\alpha b = w/\gamma \equiv \mu$$

which is, thus, expressed in terms of measurable quantities. Armed with these definitions we may write

$$\begin{aligned} Q(\lambda, T) &= e^{-T\gamma \ln[1+\lambda\alpha b]} \\ &= e^{-(\bar{m}/\mu)\ln[1+\lambda\mu]} = (1 + \lambda\mu)^{-(\bar{m}/\mu)} \end{aligned} \tag{9-108}$$

Since

$$\overline{m(m-1)} = \frac{\partial^2}{\partial\lambda^2} Q(\lambda, T)\bigg|_{\lambda=0} = \bar{m}(\mu + \bar{m})$$

it follows that the counting variance

$$\sigma^2 = \overline{(\Delta m)^2} = \bar{m}(1 + \mu) = \bar{m}\left(1 + \frac{\bar{m}}{\gamma T}\right) \tag{9-109}$$

On comparison with (3-40) we learn that the coherence time [cf. (3-38)]

$$\xi(\infty) \equiv 2 \int_0^\infty |\gamma(\tau)|^2\, d\tau \tag{9-110}$$

has the value γ^{-1} in the present case. A straightforward expansion by the binomial theorem shows that

$$\begin{aligned} P(m, T) &= \frac{(1+\mu)^{-(\bar{m}/\mu)}}{m!}\left(\frac{\mu}{1+\mu}\right)^m \frac{\Gamma(m + \bar{m}/\mu)}{\Gamma(\bar{m}/\mu)} \\ &= \frac{(1+\mu)^{-(\bar{m}/\mu)}}{m!}\left(\frac{\mu}{1+\mu}\right)^m \prod_{p=1}^{m}\left(p + \frac{\bar{m}}{\mu} - 1\right) \end{aligned} \tag{9-111}$$

We note that, if $\mu = \bar{m}$, then

$$P(m, T) = (1 + \mu)^{-1}[\mu/(1 + \mu)]^m$$

characteristic of a Bose-Einstein distribution.

We can use Eq. (9-106) to find a suitable smooth function to characterize the distribution when $\bar{m} \gg 1$. In the present case we find

$$\begin{aligned} p(x, T) &= (2\pi)^{-1}\int \exp\{-iyx - (\bar{m}/\mu) \ln[1 - iy(\mu/\bar{m})]\} \, dy \\ &= (2\pi)^{-1}\int[1 - iy(\mu/\bar{m})]^{-(\bar{m}/\mu)}e^{-iyx} \, dy \\ &= (\bar{m}/\mu)[\Gamma(\bar{m}/\mu)]^{-1}(x\bar{m}/\mu)^{(\bar{m}/\mu)-1}e^{-(x\bar{m}/\mu)} \end{aligned} \tag{9-112a}$$

Consequently, from (9-107),

$$P(m, T) = \mu^{-1}[\Gamma(\bar{m}/\mu)]^{-1}(m/\mu)^{(\bar{m}/\mu)-1}e^{-(m/\mu)} \tag{9-112b}$$

Our second example, which is perhaps physically more interesting, corresponds to the Lorentzian line shape

$$\tilde{\Gamma}(\nu) = \frac{b'}{(\omega - \omega_0)^2 + \gamma^2} \tag{9-113}$$

with $\omega_0 \gg \gamma$. The constant $\alpha b'$ is related to the mean count through

$$\bar{m} \equiv wT = \alpha T \int \tilde{\Gamma}(\nu) \, d\nu = \tfrac{1}{2}\alpha T b'/\gamma$$

in which we have extended the lower limit to $-\infty$. Hence, $\alpha b' = 2w\gamma$, so that we may set

$$Q(\lambda, T) = \exp\{-(2\pi)^{-1}T\int d\omega \ln[1 + 2\lambda w\gamma/(\omega - \omega_0)^2 + \gamma^2]\} \tag{9-114}$$

With the aid of the general integral

$$\int_{-\infty}^{\infty} \ln\left(\frac{a^2 + x^2}{b^2 + x^2}\right) dx = 2\pi(a - b)$$

Eq. (9-114) can be evaluated in the form

$$Q(\lambda, T) = \exp\{-T[(\gamma^2 + 2\lambda w\gamma)^{1/2} - \gamma]\} \tag{9-115a}$$

which was first shown by Grenander, Pollak, and Slepian [9-2], and rederived in the context of quantum optics by Glauber [8-2]. Once again we may introduce $\mu = w/\gamma$ so that

$$Q(\lambda, T) = \exp\{-(\bar{m}/\mu)[(1 + 2\lambda\mu)^{1/2} - 1]\} \tag{9-115b}$$

In the present example, if we note for a Lorentzian line shape that $|\gamma(\tau)| = \exp(-\gamma|\tau|)$, then the coherence time

$$\xi(\infty) = 2\int_0^{\infty} |\gamma(\tau)|^2 \, d\tau = 2\int_0^{\infty} e^{-2\gamma\tau} \, d\tau = \gamma^{-1} \tag{9-116}$$

Thus the counting variance is the same as that given in (9-109). The counting distribution that follows from (9-115) is rather involved, and we shall only quote the result (given by Glauber [8-1]) that

$$P(m, T) = \frac{1}{m!}\left(\frac{2\Omega T}{\pi}\right)^{1/2}\left(\frac{\gamma w T}{\Omega}\right)^{m} K_{m-1/2}\,(\Omega T)\, e^{\gamma T} \qquad (9\text{-}117)$$

Here we have introduced the abbreviation

$$\Omega \equiv (\gamma^2 + 2w\gamma)^{1/2}$$

and $K_{m-1/2}$ is a modified Hankel function of half-integral order.

More transparent than (9-117) is the simple asymptotic form for the smooth function $p(x, T)$ which characterizes this distribution for large $\bar{m}$. It follows from (9-106) that

$$\begin{aligned} p(x, T) &= (2\pi)^{-1}\int \exp\{-iyx - T\int d\nu \ln[1 - i\bar{m}^{-1}y\alpha\tilde{\Gamma}(\nu)]\}\, dy \\ &= (2\pi)^{-1}\int \exp\{-iyx - (\bar{m}/\mu)[(1 - 2iy\mu/\bar{m})^{1/2} - 1]\}\, dy \qquad (9\text{-}118) \end{aligned}$$

which is a tabulated Fourier transform that leads to the relation

$$p(x, T) = \left(\frac{\bar{m}}{2\pi\mu x^3}\right)^{1/2} \exp\left[-\frac{\bar{m}}{2\mu}\left(\sqrt{x} - \frac{1}{\sqrt{x}}\right)^2\right] \qquad (9\text{-}119\text{a})$$

which was given by Grenander, Pollak, and Slepian [9-2]. Consequently, from (9-107) we find

$$P(m, T) = \frac{\bar{m}}{(2\pi\mu m^3)^{1/2}} \exp\left[-\frac{1}{2\mu}\left(\sqrt{m} - \frac{\bar{m}}{\sqrt{m}}\right)^2\right] \qquad (9\text{-}119\text{b})$$

which was obtained by Glauber [9-3] from an asymptotic form of (9-117).

Photocounting experiments for light of thermal character have been performed by Freed and Haus [9-4]; see Fig. 9.1. Their data has been compared with several theoretical formulas, the most successful being that which follows from the exact relation (9-87) for a Lorentzian spectrum as computed by Barakat and Glauber [9-5]. The counting interval in these experiments is too short for either Eqs. (9-117) or (9-119b) to be applicable.

The expressions for the counting distributions and their generating functions we have derived hold for geometries other than the point detector we have assumed. For example, Glauber has shown similar expressions to hold for plane polarized waves incident on a thin planar detector. If the detector is more complicated in structure or if the field cannot over the time interval T be treated as stationary, then much more complicated equations emerge. In any case, the requisite generating function Q is given by a multivariate Gaussian integral leading to the

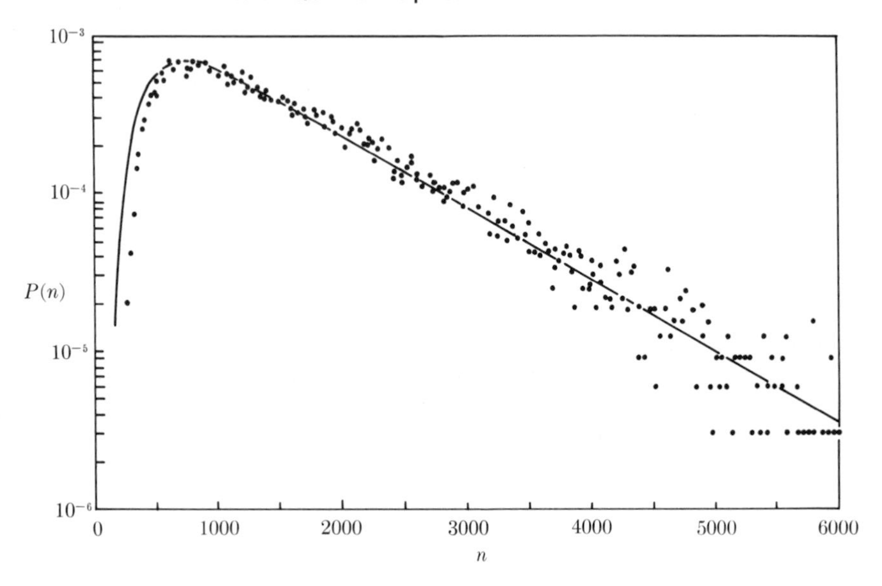

Fig. 9-1 Probability distribution versus number of photons. The dots represent the experimental results for photoelectron counts from a thermal-like source approximated by a laser operating below threshold. The counting interval T is 10^{-3} sec, and there were 13,093 samples. The solid curve is the theoretical prediction that follows from the exact relation Eq. (9-87) assuming a Lorentzian line shape. [Experimental data: After C. Freed and H. Haus, *Phys. Rev. Letters* **15**, 942 (1965); reprinted with permission. Theoretical curve: After R. Barakat and R. J. Glauber (unpublished calculations); reprinted with permission.]

inverse of an infinite rank determinant. Only in the special case of Eq. (9-87) was it straightforward to diagonalize this determinant so that its evaluation became simply a product over its eigenvalues. Such simplicity is the exception in problems of this kind rather than the rule!

9-2 PHENOMENOLOGICAL LASER MODELS

On the basis of plausible physical idealizations it is possible to give a phenomenological description of a laser. Such a description may be based on semiclassical arguments to derive the weight in the diagonal representation for the density operator. The essential idea is not unlike that which was at the core of our derivation of general chaotic fields, and, just as before, the source z driving the radiation field is decomposed into several components z_n with suitable averages being taken over their individual distributions. Although for several of these models one can introduce very simple, equivalent model Hamiltonians, we shall not explicitly follow such an approach here. The value of these simple models lies in their intuitive relation to classical stochastic theory and we shall approach them in such a vein. In the next section brief mention will be made of more realistic models in which a full quantum treatment is warranted.

We begin with the remark that if a single normal mode is excited by a stabilized, external source z_0, then the requisite state of the system is $|z_0\rangle\langle z_0|$. This also corresponds to a diagonal weight given by

$$\varphi(z) = \pi\,\delta(z - z_0) = \pi\,\delta(x - x_0)\,\delta(y - y_0)$$

where $z \equiv x + iy$. We note further that in a Schrödinger picture

$$\rho(t) = |\exp(-i\omega_0 t)z_0\rangle\langle\exp(-i\omega_0 t)z_0|$$

which is not a stationary state since, e.g., $\langle a(t)\rangle = \exp(-i\omega_0 t)z_0$ varies with t.

A. Ideal Model

At optical frequencies we are unlikely to have any certaintude about the initial phase of an oscillator, and we should average the preceding density operator over the phase θ_0 of $z_0 = \exp(i\theta_0)|z_0|$. A reference to the expansion (7-1) shows that the resultant density operator has the form

$$\rho = \exp(-|z_0|^2) \sum_{n=0}^{\infty} \frac{1}{n!} |z_0|^{2n}\,|n\rangle\langle n| \tag{9-120}$$

which is evidently stationary. It is convenient to characterize this state also with a diagonal weight given by

$$\varphi(z) = (2\pi)^{-1} \int_{-\pi}^{\pi} \pi\,\delta(z - \exp(i\theta_0)|z_0|)\,d\theta_0$$

Recall, when $x + iy \equiv re^{i\theta}$ that we may set

$$\delta(x - x_0)\,\delta(y - y_0) = r^{-1}\,\delta(r - r_0)\,\delta(\theta - \theta_0)$$

for angles in the interval $-\pi < \theta \leq \pi$; the factor r^{-1} is present merely to knock out the r in the invariant planar measure $dx\,dy = r\,dr\,d\theta$. It follows, therefore, that

$$\begin{aligned}\varphi(z) &= (2)^{-1} \int_{-\pi}^{\pi} |z|^{-1}\,\delta(|z| - |z_0|)\,\delta(\theta - \theta_0)\,d\theta_0 \\ &= (2|z|)^{-1}\,\delta(|z| - |z_0|) = \delta(|z|^2 - |z_0|^2)\end{aligned} \tag{9-121}$$

We may refer to this as the ideal laser distribution. It is evident in this model that there are no amplitude fluctuations, and thus the counting statistics are Poisson. Moreover, *all* even-order correlation functions coincide with those for pure coherent states as, e.g., in the case

$$\langle a^\dagger(t)a(0)\rangle = \exp(i\omega_0 t)|z_0|^2$$

B. Phase-Diffusion Model

For our next example let us focus our attention on the correlation functions

$$G = \langle a^\dagger(t_1) \cdot\cdot\cdot a^\dagger(t_n)a(t_{n+1}) \cdot\cdot\cdot a(t_{2n})\rangle \tag{9-122}$$

for our single mode. If the state in question is a coherent state $|z_0\rangle$ and the mode in question is a normal mode with frequency ω_0, then

$$G = \exp\left(i\sum_1^n \omega_0 t_l - i\sum_{n+1}^{2n} \omega_0 t_l\right)|z_0|^{2n} \tag{9-123}$$

In the present model, although we assume that $|z_0|$ is stabilized, we want to allow for time-varying *phase* fluctuations. Suppose, first of all, that instead of $a(t) = \exp(-i\omega_0 t)a$, we set

$$a(t) = \exp\left[-i\int_0^t \omega(t')\,dt'\right]a_0 \tag{9-124}$$

where $\omega(t')$ is some prescribed function which is approximately ω_0. Such frequency changes might arise, for example, by fluctuations in the resonant cavity, which, in turn, influence the resonant frequency.

Quantum mechanically, a phenomenological Hamiltonian for such a system would have the form $\mathcal{H} = \hbar\omega(t')a^\dagger a$ which depends explicitly on time. This picture is, of course, highly contrived but we might understand this model as follows. Since the full radiation Hamiltonian contains a superposition over a multitude of oscillators, fluctuations in the cavity walls—slow on a scale of the optical frequencies involved—could, in a manner of speaking, adiabatically pass the resonance from one oscillator to another. Insofar as we neglect amplitude fluctuations in such a model we can let *one* oscillator variable do the work of many.

If we account for possible randomness in the frequency histories $\omega(t')$, then the relevant G is obtained as an ensemble average over these histories. Denoting this average by angular brackets, the quantity we seek to study is thus

$$\begin{aligned} G &= \left\langle \exp\left[i\sum_1^n \int_0^{t_l} \omega(t')\,dt' - i\sum_{n+1}^{2n} \int_0^{t_l} \omega(t')\,dt'\right]\right\rangle |z_0|^{2n} \\ &\equiv \langle \exp[i\textstyle\int s(t')\omega(t')\,dt']\rangle\,|z_0|^{2n} \end{aligned} \tag{9-125}$$

Here

$$s(t') \equiv -\int_{-\infty}^{t'} \left[\sum_{1}^{n} \delta(t - t_l) - \sum_{n+1}^{2n} \delta(t - t_l) \right] dt \tag{9-126}$$

is a function that vanishes if t' is less than or greater than all times $t_1, \ldots, t_{2n}$ and assumes integral values in between. For example, if $n = 1$ and $t_1 > t_2$, then

$$\begin{aligned} s(t') &= 0 \qquad (t' < t_2) \\ s(t') &= 1 \qquad (t_2 < t' < t_1) \\ s(t') &= 0 \qquad (t_1 < t') \end{aligned} \tag{9-127}$$

The quantity of direct physical interest here is recognized as the characteristic functional of the stochastic process and not, as is more usually the case, the probability distribution.

The mean required in (9-125) is similar to that which arises in a number of physical problems of diverse origin. The desired answer can be simply formulated for a very large class of stationary stochastic processes, which includes as special cases those processes most commonly assumed in physics. Each of the distributions we consider here is characterized by two real functions $f(t)$ and $\hat{G}(t)$; the latter function plays the role of a causal Green's function in the sense that

$$\hat{G}(t) \equiv 0 \qquad (t < 0)$$

The characteristic functional for each process is given—for general smooth functions $s(t)$—by the expression

$$\langle e^{i\int s(t')\omega(t')\,dt'} \rangle = \exp\{ i\omega_0 \int s(t')\,dt' - \int f[\int s(t'')\hat{G}(t'' - t')\,dt'']\,dt' \} \tag{9-128}$$

For present purposes we may regard $f(y)$ as a rather general function[3] for which $f(y) = f(-y) \geq 0$, and $f(0) = f'(0) = 0$.

For orientation purposes we quote without proof a few basic properties of the above distributions. Quite generally, it follows from (9-128) that

$$\langle \omega(t) \rangle = \omega_0 \tag{9-129a}$$

$$C(t) \equiv \langle \Delta\omega(t)\,\Delta\omega(0) \rangle = f''(0) \int_0^\infty \hat{G}(t')\hat{G}(t + t')\,dt' \tag{9-129b}$$

[3] Specifically, $-f(y)$ must be the exponent of a so-called infinitely divisible process. A broad enough class of such functions to indicate their generality is given by the representation

$$f(y) = ky^2 + \int [1 - \cos(\lambda y)]\,\sigma(\lambda)\,d\lambda$$

where $k \geq 0$ and $\lambda^2\sigma(\lambda)/(1 + \lambda^2)$ is nonnegative and integrable. The example given in (3-30) is essentially of this type with $\sigma(\lambda)$ a Gaussian. For further details see Lukacs [3-1] or Gel'fand and Vilenkin [3-6].

where $\Delta\omega(t) \equiv \omega(t) - \langle\omega(t)\rangle$. These results may be deduced from first-order expansion terms in b and c when $s(t') = b\,\delta(t'-t) + c\,\delta(t')$ is used in (9-128). When $f(y) = ky^2$, the process is Gaussian and (9-129) determines the entire ensemble [cf. (3-13)]. If, for general f, we assume that

$$\begin{aligned}\hat{G}(t) &\equiv Ae^{-Rt} \qquad (t > 0)\\ &\equiv 0 \qquad (t < 0)\end{aligned} \tag{9-130}$$

then

$$\langle\Delta\omega(t)\,\Delta\omega(0)\rangle = e^{-Rt}f''(0)A^2/2R \tag{9-131}$$

and the process is Markoffian; for all other $\hat{G}(t)$ the process is non-Markoffian. Of special interest in the Markoffian case is the conditional distribution

$$P(\omega, t|\omega_1) = (2\pi)^{-1}\int \exp[iy(\omega - \omega_1 e^{-Rt}) - iy\omega_0(1 - e^{-Rt}) - \int_0^t f(Aye^{-Rt'})\,dt']\,dy \tag{9-132}$$

which may be deduced from (9-128). The stationary Markoff-Gaussian process is more commonly known to physicists as the Ornstein-Uhlenbeck process.

Short Correlation Time. With Eq. (9-128) the exact form of the normal ordered correlation functions for a whole host of processes is reduced to quadrature. A significant simplification occurs when the correlation time of the process $\omega(t)$ is extremely short. In the Markoffian case, this occurs when R is a very fast rate. More generally, this occurs when $\hat{G}(t)$ is highly localized. On the assumption that

$$\tau \equiv \int_0^\infty \hat{G}(t')\,dt' \neq 0 \tag{9-133}$$

we may adopt the replacement $\hat{G}(t) \simeq \tau\,\delta(t)$ for purposes of Eq. (9-128), which thus leads to

$$\langle e^{i\int s(t')\omega(t')\,dt'}\rangle = \exp\{i\omega_0\int s(t')\,dt' - \int f[\tau s(t')]\,dt'\} \tag{9-134}$$

In the special case $n = 1$, $s(t')$ is given by (9-127). If we set $t_1 = t > 0$ and $t_2 = 0$, then

$$\left\langle\exp\left[i\int_0^t \omega(t')\,dt'\right]\right\rangle = \exp[i\omega_0 t - tf(\tau)]$$

The result for $t < 0$ may be deduced from stationarity simply by

$$\begin{aligned}\left\langle\exp\left[i\int_0^{-t} \omega(t')\,dt'\right]\right\rangle &= \left\langle\exp\left[i\int_t^0 \omega(t')\,dt'\right]\right\rangle\\ &= \left\langle\exp\left[-i\int_0^t \omega(t')\,dt'\right]\right\rangle = \left\langle\exp\left[i\int_0^t \omega(t')\,dt'\right]\right\rangle^*\end{aligned}$$

which shows for general t that

$$\left\langle \exp\left[i \int_0^t \omega(t')\,dt'\right]\right\rangle = \exp\left[i\omega_0 t - |t| f(\tau)\right] \tag{9-135}$$

Inevitably, then, under these conditions one is led to a Lorentzian spectral profile for the correlation function $\langle a^\dagger(t)a(0)\rangle$ with a line width $f(\tau)$.

The Lorentzian line width $f(\tau)$ may be given a physically more transparent rendition in the case that τ can be viewed as a "small" argument of f. It follows from (9-129b) that

$$\begin{aligned}\int C(t)\,dt &= f''(0)\int\int \widehat{G}(t')\widehat{G}(t+t')\,dt\,dt' \\ &= f''(0)[\int \widehat{G}(t)\,dt]^2 = f''(0)\tau^2\end{aligned} \tag{9-136}$$

We say that τ is small if in a power series expansion of $f(\tau)$ we may set

$$f(\tau) \simeq f(0) + \tau f'(0) + \tfrac{1}{2}\tau^2 f''(0) = \tfrac{1}{2}\int C(t)\,dt \tag{9-137}$$

where we have retained only the first nonvanishing term. For Gaussian diffusion, Eq. (9-137) is exactly valid. Under these circumstances, it follows from (9-135) that

$$\langle a^\dagger(t)a(0)\rangle = \exp(i\omega_0 t - \zeta|t|)|z_0|^2 \tag{9-138}$$

where the line width is given by

$$\zeta = \tfrac{1}{2}\int C(t)\,dt = \int_0^\infty \langle \Delta\omega(t)\,\Delta\omega(0)\rangle\,dt \tag{9-139}$$

Namely, ζ is just the time integral of the autocorrelation of the frequency fluctuations.

The special examples above should serve to illustrate the various correlations contained in (9-128). However, it must be emphasized that this whole analysis has assumed only phase fluctuations so there are still no correlations in the photon counting statistics.

C. Signal-Plus-Noise Model

A simple physical model possessing amplitude fluctuations (and thus counting correlations!) is the following. Suppose at any fixed time we represent the amplitude of our normal mode by

$$z(t) = \exp(-i\omega_0 t + i\theta_0)z_0 + z_n(t) \tag{9-140}$$

Here z_0 and ω_0 are regarded as fixed, θ_0 is distributed uniformly, and z_n is an independent noise source with Gaussian distribution. The diagonal weight φ appropriate to such a sum is determined as a convolution of the constituent distributions. In particular, Eq. (8-203a) shows that

$$\begin{aligned}\varphi(z) &= \int \varphi_1(z')\varphi_2(z - z')\, d\mu(z') \\ &= \frac{1}{\pi\langle N\rangle} \iint (2|z'|)^{-1}\, \delta(|z'| - |z_0|) \\ &\quad \times \exp(-|z - e^{i\theta'}|z'|\,|^2/\langle N\rangle)|z'|d|z'|\, d\theta' \\ &= (2\pi\langle N\rangle)^{-1} \int_{-\pi}^{\pi} \exp(-|z - e^{i\theta'}|z_0|\,|^2/\langle N\rangle)\, d\theta'\end{aligned}$$

Let us expand the exponent in the integrand explicitly:

$$\begin{aligned}|z - e^{i\theta'}|z_0|\,|^2 &= |z|^2 + |z_0|^2 - |z_0|(z^*e^{i\theta'} + ze^{-i\theta'}) \\ &= |z|^2 + |z_0|^2 - 2|z_0|\,|z| \cos(\theta' - \theta)\end{aligned}$$

When we recall the definition

$$I_0(x) = (2\pi)^{-1} \int_{-\pi}^{\pi} e^{x \cos\theta}\, d\theta$$

for a modified Bessel function of the first kind, we can easily see that[4]

$$\varphi(z) = \langle N\rangle^{-1} I_0(2|z|\,|z_0|/\langle N\rangle) \exp[-(|z|^2 + |z_0|^2)/\langle N\rangle] \tag{9-141}$$

Counting Distribution. For small times T, short compared to the coherence time, the generating function $Q(\lambda, T)$ for the counting distribution is given by [cf. (8-101)]

$$\begin{aligned}Q(\lambda, T) &= \langle : \exp(-\lambda\alpha T a^\dagger a) : \rangle \\ &= \int \varphi(z) \exp(-\lambda\alpha T|z|^2)\, d\mu(z) \\ &= \langle N\rangle^{-1} \int_0^\infty I_0(2|z|\,|z_0|/\langle N\rangle) \\ &\quad \times \exp[-\lambda\alpha T|z|^2 - (|z|^2 + |z_0|^2)/\langle N\rangle]\, d|z|^2\end{aligned} \tag{9-142}$$

With the aid of the known integral

$$\int_0^\infty I_0(2\sqrt{bx})e^{-ax}\, dx = \frac{1}{a} e^{b/a}$$

Eq. (9-142) may be written

$$Q(\lambda, T) = \frac{1}{1 + \lambda\alpha T\langle N\rangle} \exp\left[-\frac{\lambda\alpha T|z_0|^2}{1 + \lambda\alpha T\langle N\rangle}\right] \tag{9-143}$$

Evidently as $\langle N\rangle \to 0$ the counting distribution is Poisson, while as $|z_0|^2 \to 0$ it becomes geometric (Bose-Einstein).

[4] This result was obtained first by Rice [3-3].

To derive the general counting distribution, let us first set

$$r = \frac{\alpha T\langle N\rangle}{1 + \alpha T\langle N\rangle} \qquad s = \frac{\alpha T|z_0|^2}{1 + \alpha T\langle N\rangle}$$

and rewrite the denominator of (9-143) as

$$\begin{aligned} 1 + \lambda\alpha T\langle N\rangle &= 1 + \alpha T\langle N\rangle - (1 - \lambda)\alpha T\langle N\rangle \\ &= (1 + \alpha T\langle N\rangle)[1 - (1 - \lambda)r] \end{aligned}$$

Thus, we have

$$Q(\lambda, T) = \frac{1}{1 + \alpha T\langle N\rangle}\frac{1}{1 - (1 - \lambda)r}\exp\left[-\frac{\lambda s}{1 - (1 - \lambda)r}\right]$$

Now if we use the identity

$$\lambda s \equiv -rs(1 - \lambda)(r^{-1} - 1) + s[1 - (1 - \lambda)r]$$

it follows that

$$Q(\lambda, T) = \frac{e^{-s}}{1 + \alpha T\langle N\rangle}\frac{1}{1 - (1 - \lambda)r}\exp\left[\frac{s(r^{-1} - 1)(1 - \lambda)r}{1 - (1 - \lambda)r}\right]$$

Let us now recall the generating function for the Laguerre polynomials [defined in (2-25)]

$$\frac{1}{1 - t}\exp\left(\frac{-xt}{1 - t}\right) = \sum_{m=0}^{\infty} t^m L_m(x)$$

In view of (9-92) it follows that the desired counting distribution reads

$$\begin{aligned} P(m, T) &= \frac{e^{-s}}{1 + \alpha T\langle N\rangle} r^m L_m(-s(r^{-1} - 1)) \\ &= \frac{(\alpha T\langle N\rangle)^m}{(1 + \alpha T\langle N\rangle)^{m+1}}\exp\left[-\frac{\alpha T|z_0|^2}{1 + \alpha T\langle N\rangle}\right] \\ &\quad \times L_m\left(-\frac{|z_0|^2}{\langle N\rangle(1 + \alpha T\langle N\rangle)}\right) \end{aligned} \tag{9-144}$$

as was first shown by Glauber [9-3]. This distribution may be re-expressed as a function of its own mean and variance with the help of the relations

$$\bar{m} = \alpha T(\langle N\rangle + |z_0|^2) \tag{9-145a}$$

$$\sigma^2 = \overline{(\Delta m)^2} = \bar{m} + \alpha^2 T^2\langle N\rangle[2|z_0|^2 + \langle N\rangle] \tag{9-145b}$$

Photocounting experiments for an He–Ne laser, operating just above threshold, were carried out by Freed and Haus [9-4] and by Magill and

Soni [9-10], and compared with the preceding expressions (see Fig. 9-2 and Fig. 9-3). Both groups found satisfactory agreement with the distribution given by (9-144), and measurable departures from Poisson statistics were observed for observation times such that $\alpha T\langle N\rangle \gtrsim 1$ but small compared to the coherence time so as not to invalidate (9-142). In the experiments of Magill and Soni these times fell in the range 10^{-4} sec $\lesssim T \lesssim 10^{-1}$ sec. For times $T \lesssim 10^{-4}$ sec, the observed distribution followed a Poisson law, whereas for times $T \gtrsim 10^{-1}$ sec the results disagreed with (9-144). It was estimated that $\langle N\rangle/|z_0|^2 \simeq 5 \times 10^{-5}$ in their experiment.

9-3 COUPLED-SYSTEM LASER MODEL

A number of authors have treated idealized interacting systems as models for lasers. Extensive studies have been carried out by Lax [9-11], Scully and Lamb [9-14], Haken [9-12], Sauerman [9-13], and others. Soluble models have been examined by Schwabl and Thirring [9-15].

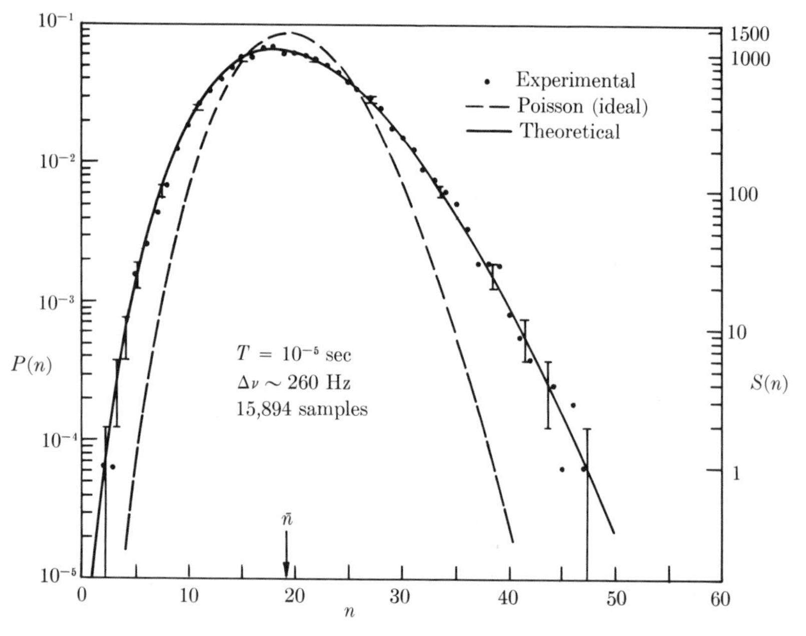

Fig. 9-2 Probability distribution versus photoelectron count for a He-Ne laser operating just above threshold and for a counting interval 10^{-5} sec. The experimental results are shown by dots and associated error bars, while the theoretical results based on the signal-plus-noise model of Eq. (9-144) are shown by the solid curve. For comparison, the Poisson distribution is indicated by a dashed curve. [After C. Freed and H. A. Haus, *IEEE J. Quantum Electron.*, QE-2, No. 8, 190 (1966); reprinted with permission.]

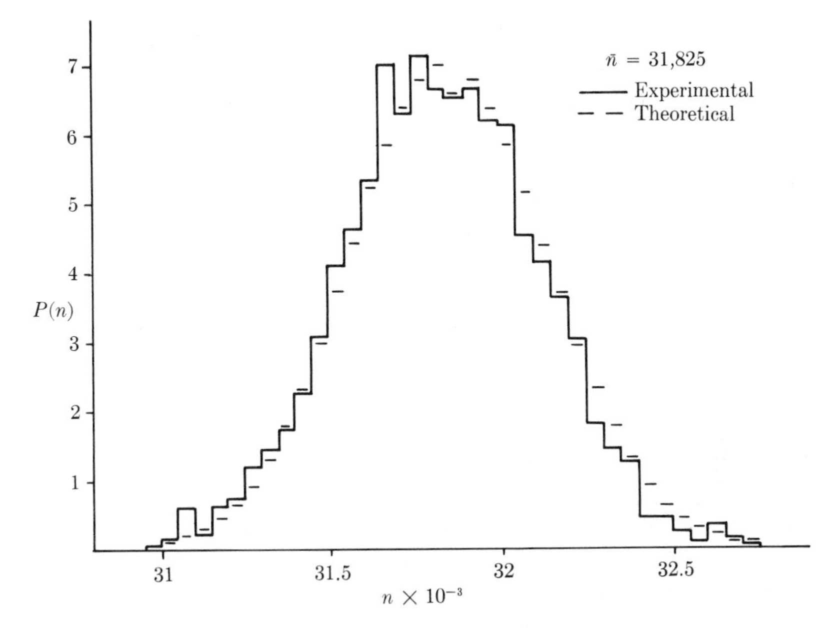

Fig. 9-3 Probability distribution versus photoelectron count for a He-Ne laser operating just above threshold for a counting interval $T = 10^{-2}$ sec. The experimental results are shown in the histogram with the solid curve, while the theoretical results based on the signal-plus-noise model of Eq. (9-144) are shown in the histogram with dashed lines. [After P. J. Magill and R. P. Soni, *Phys. Rev. Letters* 16, 911 (1966); reprinted with permission.]

Several simplified dynamical models for devices of various sorts are given in the last chapter of Louisell's book [7-2].

We cannot hope to do justice to all this work by any means. Rather, we should like to focus on one basic model, primarily for its own sake, but also partly as a vehicle to bring to the reader's attention one general feature of such problems which we feel is inadequately represented in the existing literature. This feature deserves future study, not only for the laser problem but for other quantum statistical problems as well.

The essence of our remarks may be stated rather generally and in advance of our specific analysis. In the cases where the problem at hand is sensibly Markoffian, even in the presence of "reservoir" forces, it is possible to adopt an equation for the complete density operator which is first order in time. If we represent the density operator in the diagonal representation by means of the weight $\varphi = \varphi(t)$, then we can seek a first-order equation of motion to describe the time evolution of φ. To the extent that φ behaves like a classical distribution such a first-order equation corresponds to the stochastic equation (or, as it is often called, generalized Fokker-Planck equation) as discussed in Chapter 4. As we have seen in detail in Chapter 8, the diagonal weights φ are frequently distributions rather than "good old" classical-like probability densities. This feature can reflect itself in unusual stochastic equations in which some of the diffusion coefficients are *negative*, or the diffusion matrix in a diffusion approximation [e.g., restricting the sum in (4-46) to $n \leq 2$] is *not positive*. This behavior is not peculiar to the laser problem but occurs in very simple models and can be expected to be quite general. It is our opinion that such stochastic equations deserve study in their own right, especially since they provide a particularly convenient c-number equation encompassing the complete quantum problem.

A. Laser Model

The model we shall briefly describe has been studied by several authors, notably by Lax [9-11]. In this model it is assumed that there is a single, important, radiation field mode described by the annihilation operator b. Also it is assumed that there are $N (N \gg 1)$ three-level atoms described by annihilation operators a_{jm}, $j = 0, 1, 2$, $m = 1, \ldots, N$. These atoms are treated in interaction with the field but not with each other. Both the field and atoms are affected by individual "reservoirs" simulating the effects of other radiation modes, phonons in the cavity walls, the pump, etc.

In the Schrödinger picture, the density operator for the combined field and atom system fulfills the equation of motion given by

$$\begin{aligned}\dot{\rho} = &-\frac{i}{\hbar}[(\mathcal{H}_a + \mathcal{H}_b), \rho] + \mu[(Mb^\dagger - M^\dagger b), \rho] \\ &+ \sum_{m=1}^{N} \sum_{i,j=0}^{2} w_{ij}\{(a_{im}^\dagger a_{jm})\rho(a_{jm}^\dagger a_{im}) \\ &- \tfrac{1}{2}(a_{jm}^\dagger a_{jm})\rho - \tfrac{1}{2}\rho(a_{jm}^\dagger a_{jm})\} \\ &- \frac{\gamma}{2}\{[\bar{n}bb^\dagger + (\bar{n}+1)b^\dagger b]\rho + \rho[\bar{n}bb^\dagger + (\bar{n}+1)b^\dagger b]\} \\ &+ \gamma\{(\bar{n}+1)b\rho b^\dagger + \bar{n}b^\dagger \rho b\}\end{aligned} \tag{9-146}$$

In this equation

$$\mathcal{H}_b = \hbar\omega_b b^\dagger b \qquad \mathcal{H}_a = \sum_{m,j} \epsilon_j a_{jm}^\dagger a_{jm} \tag{9-147}$$

which are the free radiation and free atomic Hamiltonians, respectively, with ϵ_j the energy of atomic level j. The term

$$i\hbar\mu(Mb^\dagger - M^\dagger b) \tag{9-148}$$

is the basic interaction between the field and the polarization

$$M = \sum_{m=1}^{N} a_{1m}^{\dagger} a_{2m} \tag{9-149}$$

the strength of which is determined by μ (roughly the atomic dipole moment). It must be understood that terms such as Mb and $M^{\dagger}b^{\dagger}$ properly belong in the interaction, but for quasi-monochromatic radiation these terms are far-off resonance and are neglected in the rotating wave approximation [cf. the discussion pertaining to (6-65)].

The laser model is completed by specifying the effects of the reservoirs which account for the remaining terms in (9-146). The first additional terms correspond to reservoir-induced transitions from level i to level j which are governed by the rate w_{ij} for such transitions. The negative terms of this type give the decrease in population of level j caused by transitions to level i, and may be shown to provide for the decay of the atomic polarization. Lastly, γ is the field decay constant. In an occupation number representation for the field mode, it may be seen that the negative terms yield a decay of ρ_{nm} proportional to ρ_{nm}, whereas the positive terms yield an increase in ρ_{nm} proportional to $\rho_{n+1,m+1}$ and $\rho_{n-1,m-1}$. The parameter $\bar{n}$ is the mean photon number in equilibrium with the reservoir. For further discussion and justification of the present model we refer to the articles of Lax, especially "Quantum Noise IV" [9-11].

An interesting approach to these equations has been developed by Gordon [9-16]. His method exploits the diagonal representation for the field mode and a conceptually similar representation for the atomic system. In view of the equal treatment accorded each atom, the net influence on the atomic system can be summarized with the aid of four macroscopic parameters. Let us set

$$\sigma_m = N^{-1}[(N - \mathfrak{N}_1 - \mathfrak{N}_2)a_{0m}^{\dagger}a_{0m} + \mathfrak{N}_1 a_{1m}^{\dagger}a_{1m} + \mathfrak{N}_2 a_{2m}^{\dagger}a_{2m} + \mathfrak{M} a_{2m}^{\dagger}a_{1m} + \mathfrak{M}^* a_{1m}^{\dagger}a_{2m}] \tag{9-150}$$

as an elementary density operator for the mth atom, and set

$$\sigma_a = \prod_{m=1}^{N} \sigma_m \tag{9-151}$$

as a canonical density operator for the N atoms. Each elementary density operator is described by the same parameters $\mathfrak{N}_1$, $\mathfrak{N}_2$, $\mathfrak{M}$, and $\mathfrak{M}^*$, which we may abbreviate simply as $\mathfrak{X}_k$, $k = 1, 2, 3, 4$. Combining the canonical operator (9-151) with the notion of the diagonal representation for the field mode, Gordon is led to consider

$$\rho(t) \equiv \int \varphi(z, \mathfrak{X}_k, t)\sigma(z, \mathfrak{X}_k)\, d\mu(z, \mathfrak{X}_k) \tag{9-152}$$

where

$$\sigma(z, \mathfrak{X}_k) \equiv |z\rangle\langle z|\sigma_a \tag{9-153a}$$

and

$$d\mu(z, \mathfrak{X}_k) \equiv d\mu(z)\, d^4\mathfrak{X}_k \equiv \pi^{-1}\, d(\text{Re } z)\, d(\text{Im } z)\, d\mathfrak{N}_1\, d\mathfrak{N}_2\, d(\text{Re } \mathfrak{M})\, d(\text{Im } \mathfrak{M}) \tag{9-153b}$$

Equation (9-152) is a reasonable extension of the philosophy of diagonal representations to include the atomic variables for the model under study.

The reduced density operator for the single radiation field mode alone is given by a partial trace over the atomic density operators. In turn, each of these is defined such that

$$\text{Tr}_m\, \sigma_m \equiv \sum_{j=0}^{2} \langle jm|\sigma_m|jm\rangle = 1 \tag{9-154}$$

Here $|jm\rangle = a^\dagger_{jm}|0\rangle$ is a single-particle state signifying that atom m is in level j; these fulfill the relation

$$a^\dagger_{j''m} a_{jm}|j'm\rangle = \delta_{jj'}|j''m\rangle \tag{9-155}$$

Evidently, the reduced density operator for the single-field mode b becomes

$$\begin{aligned} \rho_b(t) &= \int \varphi(z, \mathfrak{X}_k, t)|z\rangle\langle z|\, d\mu(z, \mathfrak{X}_k) \\ &\equiv \int \varphi(z, t)|z\rangle\langle z|\, d\mu(z) \end{aligned} \tag{9-156}$$

where

$$\varphi(z, t) \equiv \int \varphi(z, \mathfrak{X}_k, t)\, d^4\mathfrak{X}_k \tag{9-157}$$

Equation (9-157) represents the diagonal weight of interest for questions concerned with the radiation field mode alone.

It is plausible that the basic equation (9-146) for the density operator can be cast into an equation of motion for the weight $\varphi(z, \mathfrak{X}_k, t)$. Such an equation is clearly linear in the weight φ and is composed of a sum of terms corresponding to those in (9-146). To win such an equation each operation on the right side of (9-146) may (*1*) first be carried out as if the density operator were the elementary operator $\sigma(z, \mathfrak{X}_k)$, (*2*) next averaged with φ, (*3*) and finally the resultant operator re-expressed in the form of (9-152). In practice, the operations in (9-146) can be realized as partial differential operators in the variables z and $\mathfrak{X}_k$ on the elementary density operator σ, which can then, by partial integration, be cast back as derivatives acting on the weight φ. In this way one is led to a differential equation for φ which summarizes Eq. (9-146). We shall not carry out the necessary evaluation but only quote the result obtained by Gordon [9-16] in the physically interesting case that $N \gg |\mathfrak{X}_k|$ for any of the variables $\mathfrak{X}_k$. Thus the level $j = 0$ is macroscopically occupied and acts as an atom reservoir.

Let us first introduce the abbreviations $\hbar\omega_a = \epsilon_2 - \epsilon_1$ for the energy spacing between levels 1 and 2, and also $R_i = Nw_{i0}$ and

$$\Gamma_i = \sum_{j(\neq i)} w_{ji} \quad (i = 1, 2) \tag{9-158a}$$

$$\Gamma_{12} = \frac{1}{2} \sum_j (w_{j1} + w_{j2}) \tag{9-158b}$$

for various rates involved in the problem. Then the basic equation for $\varphi(z, \mathfrak{X}_k, t)$ reads

$$\begin{aligned}\frac{\partial\varphi}{\partial t} = \Bigg\{ &- \frac{\partial}{\partial z}\left[\mu\mathfrak{M} - \left(\frac{\gamma}{2} + i\omega_b\right) z\right] - \frac{\partial}{\partial z^*}\left[\mu\mathfrak{M}^* - \left(\frac{\gamma}{2} - i\omega_b\right) z^*\right] \\ &- \frac{\partial}{\partial\mathfrak{M}}\left[\mu z(\mathfrak{N}_2 - \mathfrak{N}_1) - (\Gamma_{12} + i\omega_a)\mathfrak{M}\right] \\ &- \frac{\partial}{\partial\mathfrak{M}^*}\left[\mu z^*(\mathfrak{N}_2 - \mathfrak{N}_1) - (\Gamma_{12} + i\omega_a)\mathfrak{M}^*\right] \\ &- \frac{\partial}{\partial\mathfrak{N}_1}\left[R_1 + w_{12}\mathfrak{N}_2 - \Gamma_1\mathfrak{N}_1 + \mu(z^*\mathfrak{M} + z\mathfrak{M}^*)\right] \\ &- \frac{\partial}{\partial\mathfrak{N}_2}\left[R_2 + w_{21}\mathfrak{N}_1 - \Gamma_2\mathfrak{N}_2 - \mu(z^*\mathfrak{M} + z\mathfrak{M}^*)\right] \\ &+ \frac{\partial^2}{\partial z\,\partial z^*}\bar{n}\gamma + \left(\frac{\partial^2}{\partial z\,\partial\mathfrak{M}^*} + \frac{\partial^2}{\partial z^*\,\partial\mathfrak{M}}\right)\mu\mathfrak{N}_2 \\ &+ \frac{\partial^2}{\partial\mathfrak{N}_1\,\partial z}\mu\mathfrak{M} + \frac{\partial^2}{\partial\mathfrak{N}_1\,\partial z^*}\mu\mathfrak{M}^*\Bigg\}\varphi\end{aligned} \tag{9-159}$$

Although this equation is of the Fokker-Planck form, it is rather clear that the diffusion coefficients are not all positive; indeed, several diagonal terms are missing altogether.

In principle, the solution of (9-159) would yield a very general formula for the model laser under discussion. So far, however, solutions to this equation have not yet been determined. Somewhat simpler equations arise under those special circumstances when one or another rate is considerably faster than other rates in the problem. In such a case the variable in question can be assumed to be determined *instantaneously* (rather than dynamically) in terms of the remaining variables and, then, eliminated in favor of them. This is an adiabatic type of approximation familiar in many branches of physics.

One favorite choice for an adiabatic elimination is the assumption that $\Gamma_{12} \gg \gamma/2$ which enables us to eliminate the polarization $\mathfrak{M}$ (and thus $\mathfrak{M}^*$) as a dynamical variable in favor of the remaining quantities. We quote without proof the equation that follows from (9-159) on the basis of this assumption. Let us first define

$$\alpha \equiv \frac{\omega_a - \omega_b}{\Gamma_{12} + \gamma/2} \tag{9-160}$$

and the rate

$$\pi \equiv \frac{2\mu^2}{\Gamma_{12}(1 + \alpha^2)} \tag{9-161}$$

Then the modified equation reads

$$\begin{aligned}\frac{\partial \varphi}{\partial t} = \Bigg\{ &-\frac{\partial}{\partial z}[\pi(\mathfrak{N}_2 - \mathfrak{N}_1) - \gamma](1 - i\alpha)(z/2) \\ &- \frac{\partial}{\partial z^*}[\pi(\mathfrak{N}_2 - \mathfrak{N}_1) - \gamma](1 + i\alpha)(z^*/2) \\ &- \frac{\partial}{\partial \mathfrak{N}_1}[R_1 + (w_{12} + \pi + \pi z^* z)\mathfrak{N}_2 - (\Gamma_1 + \pi z^* z)\mathfrak{N}_1] \\ &- \frac{\partial}{\partial \mathfrak{N}_2}[R_2 - (\Gamma_2 + \pi + \pi z^* z)\mathfrak{N}_2 + (w_{21} + \pi z^* z)\mathfrak{N}_1] \\ &+ \frac{\partial^2}{\partial z\, \partial z^*}[\gamma \bar{n} + \pi \mathfrak{N}_2] \\ &+ \frac{\partial^2}{\partial \mathfrak{N}_1\, \partial z}[\pi z \mathfrak{N}_2 - \tfrac{1}{2}\pi(1 - i\alpha) z \mathfrak{N}_1] \\ &+ \frac{\partial^2}{\partial \mathfrak{N}_1\, \partial z^*}[\pi z^* \mathfrak{N}_2 - \tfrac{1}{2}\pi(1 + i\alpha) z^* \mathfrak{N}_1] \\ &+ \frac{\partial^2}{\partial \mathfrak{N}_2\, \partial z}[-\tfrac{1}{2}\pi(1 + i\alpha) z \mathfrak{N}_2] + \frac{\partial^2}{\partial \mathfrak{N}_2\, \partial z^*}[-\tfrac{1}{2}\pi(1 - i\alpha) z^* \mathfrak{N}_2] \\ &- \frac{\partial^3}{\partial \mathfrak{N}_1\, \partial z\, \partial z^*}[\pi \mathfrak{N}_2] \Bigg\} \varphi\end{aligned} \tag{9-162}$$

This relation is seen to involve partial derivatives up to the third order. The "cost" of adiabatic elimination of $\mathfrak{M}$ has been an increase in the order of the equation.

It is especially convenient to introduce

$$z \equiv I^{1/2}e^{-i\theta} \tag{9-163}$$

as an alternative parameterization for the mode amplitude z. Here $I = |z|^2$ is just the intensity, whereas θ is the phase of the wave. It is a straightforward matter to transcribe (9-162) into an equation of motion for $\varphi(I, \theta, \mathfrak{N}_1, \mathfrak{N}_2, t)$, which is given by

$$\begin{aligned}\frac{\partial\varphi(I, \theta, \mathfrak{N}_1, \mathfrak{N}_2, t)}{\partial t} = \Bigg\{ & -\frac{\partial}{\partial I}[\pi(I+1)\mathfrak{N}_2 - \pi I\mathfrak{N}_1 + \gamma(\bar{n} - I)] \\ & -\frac{\partial}{\partial\theta}\left[\frac{\alpha}{2}\{\pi(\mathfrak{N}_2 - \mathfrak{N}_1) - \gamma\}\right] \\ & -\frac{\partial}{\partial\mathfrak{N}_1}[R_1 + \{w_{12} + \pi(I+1)\}\mathfrak{N}_2 - (\Gamma_1 + \pi I)\mathfrak{N}_1] \\ & -\frac{\partial}{\partial\mathfrak{N}_2}[R_2 - \{\Gamma_2 + \pi(I+1)\}\mathfrak{N}_2 + (w_{21} + \pi I)\mathfrak{N}_1] \\ & +\frac{\partial^2}{\partial I^2}[I(\gamma\bar{n} + \pi\mathfrak{N}_2) + \frac{\partial^2}{\partial\theta^2}\left[\frac{1}{4I}(\gamma\bar{n} + \pi\mathfrak{N}_2)\right] \\ & +\frac{\partial^2}{\partial\mathfrak{N}_1\,\partial I}[\pi(2I+1)\mathfrak{N}_2 - \pi I\mathfrak{N}_1] + \frac{\partial^2}{\partial\mathfrak{N}_2\,\partial I}[-\pi I\mathfrak{N}_2] \\ & +\frac{\partial^2}{\partial\mathfrak{N}_1\,\partial\theta}\left[-\frac{\pi}{2}\alpha\mathfrak{N}_1\right] + \frac{\partial^2}{\partial\mathfrak{N}_2\,\partial\theta}\left[\frac{\pi}{2}\alpha\mathfrak{N}_2\right] \\ & -\frac{\partial^3}{\partial\mathfrak{N}_1\,\partial I^2}[\pi I\mathfrak{N}_2] - \frac{\partial^3}{\partial\mathfrak{N}_1\,\partial\theta^2}[\pi\mathfrak{N}_2/4I]\Bigg\}\varphi\end{aligned} \tag{9-164}$$

We may carry out yet another elimination of atomic variables to obtain an effective equation for the field mode alone. If we assume that Γ_1 and Γ_2 are large compared with the rates w_{12}, w_{21}, and π, then we may eliminate the atomic populations $\mathfrak{N}_1$ and $\mathfrak{N}_2$. Unfortunately, an exact elimination of these variables leads to a generalized Fokker-Planck equation with arbitrarily high orders of derivatives. We quote only the "diffusion approximation" for such an elimination in which at most second-order derivatives are retained. To facilitate writing this relation let us first define

$$\mathfrak{D} \equiv \Gamma_1\Gamma_2 + \pi I(\Gamma_1 + \Gamma_2) \tag{9-165a}$$

$$A_2 \equiv \mathfrak{D}^{-1}[\Gamma_1 R_2 + \pi I(R_1 + R_2)] \tag{9-165b}$$

$$A_1 \equiv \mathfrak{D}^{-1}[\Gamma_2 R_1 + \pi I(R_1 + R_2)] \tag{9-165c}$$

Physically, A_2 and A_1 are the adiabatic mean values of $\mathfrak{N}_2$ and $\mathfrak{N}_1$, respectively. In terms of these variables the approximate equation for the diagonal weight $\varphi(z, t) \equiv \varphi(I, \theta, t)$ is given by

$$\frac{\partial\varphi}{\partial t} = \left\{ -\frac{\partial}{\partial I}[\pi(I+1)A_2 - \pi I A_1 + \gamma(\bar{n} - I)] \right.$$
$$- \frac{\partial}{\partial\theta}\left[\frac{\alpha}{2}\{\pi(A_2 - A_1) - \gamma\}\right]$$
$$+ \frac{\partial^2}{\partial I^2}[\gamma\bar{n}I + \mathfrak{D}^{-1}\pi I\Gamma_2\{\Gamma_1 A_2 - \pi I(A_2 - A_1)\}]$$
$$+ \frac{\partial^2}{\partial\theta^2}\left[\frac{1}{4I}(\gamma\bar{n} + \pi A_2) + \mathfrak{D}^{-1}\left(\frac{\pi\alpha}{2}\right)^2(\Gamma_1 A_2 + \Gamma_2 A_1)\right]$$
$$\left. + \frac{\partial^2}{\partial\theta\,\partial I}[-\mathfrak{D}^{-1}\pi^2\alpha I\Gamma_2(A_2 - A_1)] \right\} \varphi \tag{9-166}$$

In this form we have reduced the problem to an effective equation for the field mode alone. The approximate density operator is given in terms of the solution to (9-166) by

$$\rho_b(t) = \int \varphi(z, t)|z\rangle\langle z|\, d\mu(z) \tag{9-167}$$

coupled with the definition $z \equiv I^{1/2}e^{-i\theta}$. We need no longer integrate out any variables, as in (9-157), to win $\rho_b(t)$.

The effect of saturation at large intensity I on the main diffusion terms is rather interesting. For the phase term, the minimum coefficient arises "on resonance" when $\alpha = 0$, or from (9-160), when $\omega_b = \omega_a$. For large intensity it follows from (9-165) that the coefficient of $\partial^2/\partial\theta^2$ becomes

$$\frac{1}{4I}(\gamma\bar{n} + \pi A_2) \simeq \frac{1}{4I}\left[\gamma\bar{n} + \frac{\pi(R_1 + R_2)}{(\Gamma_1 + \Gamma_2)}\right] \tag{9-168}$$

For the coefficient of $\partial^2/\partial I^2$ several cancellations arise at high intensity leading to the value given by

$$\gamma\bar{n}I + \mathfrak{D}^{-1}\pi I\Gamma_2\{\Gamma_1 A_2 - \pi I(A_2 - A_1)\} \simeq \gamma\bar{n}I + \frac{\Gamma_2 R_1}{\Gamma_1 + \Gamma_2} \tag{9-169}$$

This is a value lower than otherwise might be expected since R_2, the basic pumping rate from level 0 to level 2, does not appear.

We may see some of these properties in another fashion. In the equilibrium solution to (9-166), whatever it may be, let us compute $\langle I\rangle$ and $\langle I^2\rangle$. This we may simply do by setting $\partial\varphi/\partial t = 0$, multiplying (9-166) by I or I^2 and integrating by parts, assuming the surface terms make no contribution. For $\langle I\rangle$ only the first term contributes and, if we use the values of A_1 and A_2 appropriate to high intensities, it follows that

$$\langle I \rangle = \bar{n} + \frac{(R_2\Gamma_1 - R_1\Gamma_2)}{\gamma(\Gamma_1 + \Gamma_2)} \tag{9-170a}$$

For $\langle I^2 \rangle$ we find in the same approximation

$$\langle I^2 \rangle = \langle I \rangle^2 + \bar{n}\langle I \rangle + \frac{R_1\Gamma_2}{\gamma(\Gamma_1 + \Gamma_2)} \tag{9-170b}$$

Now we can achieve a high mean intensity if R_2 is large, and, in addition, a small intensity fluctuation if $\bar{n}$ and R_1 are comparatively small.

Finally, let us derive an approximate relation for the spectral width due to phase diffusion. In this case we do not assume an equilibrium distribution but instead we seek to find the time behavior of $\langle e^{-i\theta} \rangle$. Evidently only those terms on the right side of (9-166) will contribute in which no $\partial/\partial I$ terms appear. If we choose $\alpha = 0$ $(\omega_b = \omega_a)$ and use (9-168) for large-intensity behavior, then

$$\frac{\partial}{\partial t}\langle e^{-i\theta} \rangle = -\left\langle e^{-i\theta}\frac{1}{4I}\left[\gamma\bar{n} + \frac{\pi(R_1 + R_2)}{(\Gamma_1 + \Gamma_2)}\right]\right\rangle$$

Assuming that the distribution is roughly the equilibrium distribution as far as the intensities go, it follows from (9-170) that

$$\begin{aligned}
\frac{\partial}{\partial t}\langle e^{-i\theta} \rangle &= -\frac{1}{4}\left[\gamma\bar{n} + \frac{\pi(R_1 + R_2)}{(\Gamma_1 + \Gamma_2)}\right]\left\langle \frac{1}{I} e^{-i\theta} \right\rangle \\
&\simeq -\frac{1}{4}\left[\gamma\bar{n} + \frac{\pi(R_1 + R_2)}{(\Gamma_1 + \Gamma_2)}\right]\frac{1}{\langle I \rangle}\langle e^{-i\theta} \rangle \\
&= -\frac{\gamma}{4}\frac{[\gamma\bar{n}(\Gamma_1 + \Gamma_2) + \pi(R_1 + R_2)]}{[\gamma\bar{n}(\Gamma_1 + \Gamma_2) + (R_2\Gamma_1 - R_1\Gamma_2)]}\langle e^{-i\theta} \rangle \\
&\equiv -\Lambda\langle e^{-i\theta} \rangle
\end{aligned} \tag{9-171}$$

Here we have made use of the assumed small-intensity fluctuations. The solution of this relation,

$$\langle e^{-i\theta} \rangle_t = e^{-\Lambda t}\langle e^{-i\theta} \rangle_0 \tag{9-172}$$

implies that the phase diffuses at a constant rate Λ and has a Lorentzian line width not unrelated to the pure phase-diffusion model discussed earlier.

There are, of course, a number of other possible questions and approximations that can be studied in this vein. Moreover, new variables are sometimes called for to make certain features more apparent. For further discussion of these questions we refer the reader to the literature on laser models.

In spite of the value to be gained from studying truncated diffusion-approximation equations, there seems to be no reason that the exact, second-order stochastic equation (9-159) could not be profitably studied in its own right. As remarked earlier, the nonpositivity of the diffusion matrix can, in part, be attributed to the use of the diagonal representation for ρ. Our discussion of related nonpositive matrices in the study of chaotic states should suggest that "their bark is worse than their bite." It would seem at the present time that a study of such equations and some of their general features would be a very useful undertaking.

CHAPTER 10

INTENSITY INTERFEROMETRY IN QUANTUM OPTICS

10-1 INTENSITY INTERFEROMETRY: LOWEST-ORDER CORRELATION

A. Counting Correlation

We return now to reconsider the question of intensity correlations which we discussed in Chapter 3. For counting correlations in two counters we may adopt Eqs. (3-46) and (3-52) as our starting point. For localized, fast detectors these relations state that

$$\bar{n}_j = \alpha_j \int_0^T \langle \mathbf{V}_j^*(t') \cdot \mathbf{V}_j(t') \rangle \, dt' \tag{10-1a}$$

$$\overline{n_j n_k} = \alpha_j \alpha_k \int_0^T \int_0^T \langle \mathbf{V}_j^*(t') \cdot \mathbf{V}_j(t') \mathbf{V}_k^*(t'') \cdot \mathbf{V}_k(t'') \rangle \, dt' \, dt'' \tag{10-1b}$$

Here j, $k = 1, 2$ label the two detectors, and $\mathbf{V}_j(t') \equiv \mathbf{V}(\mathbf{r}_j, t')$, where $\mathbf{r}_j$ denotes the detector location. We do not exclude the idealization that $\mathbf{r}_1 = \mathbf{r}_2$. In view of the formal equivalence admitted by the optical equivalence theorem, these equations may be regarded as fully quantum mechanical if we but carry out the requisite mean with aid of the appropriate diagonal weight $\varphi(\{z_\lambda(\mathbf{k})\}) \equiv \varphi\{\mathbf{V}\}$.

For counting correlations of the type examined by Hanbury Brown and Twiss [3-9], we may study the quantity

$$\overline{n_1 n_2} = \bar{n}_1 \bar{n}_2 + \alpha_1 \alpha_2 \int_0^T \int_0^T \langle \Delta I_1(t') \, \Delta I_2(t'') \rangle \, dt' \, dt'' \tag{10-2}$$

where

$$\Delta I_j(t') \equiv I_j(t') - \langle I_j(t') \rangle$$

In analogy to the definition appropriate to thermal fields, let us introduce

$$\eta_{12}(T) \equiv T \frac{\alpha_1\alpha_2}{\bar{n}_1\bar{n}_2} \int_0^T \int_0^T \langle \Delta I_1(t') \, \Delta I_2(t'') \rangle \, dt' \, dt'' \tag{10-3a}$$

which for stationary fields reduces to

$$\eta_{12}(T) = \frac{2}{T\langle I_1(0)\rangle\langle I_2(0)\rangle} \int_0^T (T - \tau)\langle \Delta I_1(\tau) \, \Delta I_2(0)\rangle \, d\tau \tag{10-3b}$$

In any case it follows that

$$\overline{n_1 n_2} - \bar{n}_1\bar{n}_2 = \bar{n}_1\bar{n}_2[\eta_{12}(T)/T] \tag{10-4}$$

reminiscent of (3-55). For long times T we may assume, in the case of stationary fields, that

$$\eta_{12}(T) \simeq \eta_{12}(\infty) \equiv \frac{2}{\langle I_1(0)\rangle\langle I_2(0)\rangle} \int_0^\infty \langle \Delta I_1(\tau) \, \Delta I_2(0)\rangle \, d\tau \tag{10-5}$$

For the thermal fields discussed in Chapter 3 the quantity $\eta_{12}(T) \equiv \xi_{12}(T)$ was positive and had the bounds $0 \leq \xi_{12}(T) \leq T$. This remark remains true in the quantum treatment of thermal or general chaotic fields as well since the diagonal weight is still a Gaussian. However, in our enlightened frame of mind we need no longer confine our attention to Gaussian fields. When other distributions are considered we may even anticipate that $\eta_{12}(T)$ may become negative, thus showing a negative counting correlation. One need not seek negative or ill-behaved diagonal weights to achieve this. For example, if we let $W \equiv I_1(t)$ and $X \equiv I_2(0)$, then

$$\sigma(W, X) = \tfrac{1}{2}[\delta(W) \, \delta(X - 2) + \delta(X) \, \delta(W - 2)] \tag{10-6}$$

is a distribution for which

$$\begin{aligned} \langle \Delta I_1(t) \, \Delta I_2(0)\rangle &= \langle I_1(t) I_2(0)\rangle - \langle I_1(t)\rangle\langle I_2(0)\rangle \\ &= \langle WX\rangle - \langle W\rangle\langle X\rangle = -1 \end{aligned}$$

Here the latter angular brackets denote an average computed with the aid of $\sigma(W, X)$.

Effects peculiar to quantum theory may (but not necessarily!) arise if one probes the field within a correlation volume, i.e., in a spatial and temporal volume small enough such that

$$\sigma(W, X) \simeq \sigma(X) \, \delta(W - X)$$

In this case it follows from (8-73) that

$$\langle I_1(t) I_2(0)\rangle = \langle X^2\rangle \geq \langle X\rangle^2 = \langle I_1(t)\rangle\langle I_2(0)\rangle$$

Deviation from this behavior requires a suitably negative diagonal weight in the diagonal representation. The basic example where such behavior occurs is when there is only *one* photon in the field. In that case, the mean $\overline{n_1 n_2}$ for two-photon coincidences necessarily vanishes.

For a chaotic field the general behavior of the intensity correlation may be deduced from (9-48) or (9-53). For present purposes let us assume a spatially homogeneous, polarized and stationary field, which amounts to the assumption that

$$\frac{L^3}{(2\pi)^3} \langle a_\lambda{}^\dagger(\mathbf{k}) a_{\lambda'}(\mathbf{k}') \rangle \simeq \delta_{\lambda 1}\, \delta_{\lambda' 1}\, \delta(\mathbf{k} - \mathbf{k}') \frac{2\omega}{\hbar} \tilde{\Gamma}(\mathbf{k}, \nu) \qquad (10\text{-}7)$$

This is a slight generalization of (9-54). On combination with (9-48) or (9-56) (and dropping the polarization subscript), we may write

$$C_N\{S\} = \exp\{-\textstyle\int\int S^*(\mathbf{r}', t')\Gamma(\mathbf{r}' - \mathbf{r}; t' - t) S(\mathbf{r}, t)\, d^4x\, d^4x'\} \qquad (10\text{-}8)$$

It follows from (3-49) that

$$\langle \Delta I(\mathbf{r}', t')\, \Delta I(\mathbf{r}, t) \rangle = |\Gamma(\mathbf{r}' - \mathbf{r}; t' - t)|^2 \qquad (10\text{-}9)$$

Hence, in the quantum case, there is *no* qualitative departure from the counting mean as it is given in (3-55), only a quantitative one since the present Γ depends on $\hbar$. This is particularly apparent in the true quantum thermal distribution at a temperature T for which

$$\tilde{\Gamma}(\mathbf{k}, \nu) = (2\pi)^{-1} \hbar\omega / (e^{\hbar\omega/\kappa T} - 1) \qquad (10\text{-}10)$$

In the fully classical limit ($\hbar \to 0$) this expression collapses to $\tilde{\Gamma}(\mathbf{k}, \nu) = \kappa T / 2\pi$. An uncritical acceptance of this distribution would lead to no spatial or temporal correlations other than those inherent in the spectral limitations of the detectors themselves.

For an ideal laser field, on the other hand, in which no intensity fluctuations arise, it is evident that $I(t) = \langle I(t) \rangle$ so that $\eta_{12}(T) \equiv 0$. Consequently, no counting correlations are observed, $\overline{n_1 n_2} = \bar{n}_1 \bar{n}_2$. It is clear in the general case that it would be inappropriate to call $\eta_{12}(\infty)$ the "coherence time."

Spectral Profile by Counting Correlation. Certain information about the field is contained in the second-order intensity correlation. Through the time dependence of the mean counting coincidence (10-4) the function $\eta_{12}(T)$ may be determined. In the stationary field case, it follows from (10-3b) that

$$\frac{1}{2} \frac{\partial^2}{\partial T^2} \{T \eta_{12}(T)\} = \frac{\langle \Delta I_1(T)\, \Delta I_2(0) \rangle}{\langle I_1(0) \rangle \langle I_2(0) \rangle} \equiv |\chi_{12}(T)|^2 \qquad (10\text{-}11)$$

Experimentally, however, it is more convenient to determine the intensity correlation directly by delayed coincidence measurements. Specifically, the joint probability per unit (time)^2 that a photon is observed at $t = 0$ and another at $t = \tau$ is given by

$$\begin{aligned} p_{12}(\tau) &= \alpha^2\langle I_1(\tau)I_2(0)\rangle \\ &= \alpha^2[\langle I_1(0)\rangle\langle I_2(0)\rangle + \langle \Delta I_1(\tau)\, \Delta I_2(0)\rangle] \\ &= \alpha^2\langle I_1(0)\rangle\langle I_2(0)\rangle[1 + |\chi_{12}(\tau)|^2] \\ &\equiv (\text{const.})[1 + |\chi_{12}(\tau)|^2] \end{aligned} \tag{10-12}$$

Here $|\chi_{12}(\tau)|$ is the analog of $|\gamma_{12}(\tau)|$ in the thermal case. Experiments to determine the second-order intensity correlations have been carried out by several workers. In order for this to be feasible the sought-for variations in $p_{12}(\tau)$ must lie within the resolving time of the circuitry. For normal thermal light $|\chi_{12}(\tau)| = |\gamma_{12}(\tau)|$ falls to zero in a reciprocal bandwidth which, in general, is impractically short. Thus one must resort to special sources.

Arecchi, Gatti, and Sona [10-1] have measured the time dependence of $p_{12}(\tau)$ for both coherent and chaotic sources (Fig. 10-1). In the coherent case, based on radiation from an He–Ne laser, $p_{12}(\tau) = p_{12}(0)$ to within experimental errors consistent with zero-intensity fluctuations. In their chaotic source experiment, $|\chi_{12}(\tau)| = |\gamma_{12}(\tau)|$ falls smoothly from unity to zero in the order of 10^{-3} sec. To achieve such a narrow bandwidth the chaotic source used by these workers is made by passing the coherent radiation from their He–Ne laser through a rotating ground glass disk. As noted in Chapter 2, Arecchi [2-4] has shown for such artificially synthesized sources that the distribution of photons in the resultant field follows a geometric law characteristic of a chaotic source.

Another experiment of this type was carried out by Morgan and Mandel [10-3]. For a low-pressure Hg^{198} discharge lamp—with a line width of 200 Mc/sec ascertainable by other means—they were able to determine that $|\gamma_{12}(\tau)| \simeq \exp(-|\tau|/T_c)$, where $T_c \simeq 1.7 \times 10^{-9}$ sec, consistent with a Lorentzian line of 200 Mc/sec (see Fig. 10-2). This experiment is not quite as straightforward as our discussion might imply and the interested reader is encouraged to study the original literature for himself.

B. *Spatial Intensity Correlation*

Let us return again to Eq. (10-1) and consider these relations for small times T, short compared to the appropriate coherence time. We focus now not on the time dependence but rather on the space dependence, so we shall explicitly reinsert the dependence on $\mathbf{r}$. Consequently, if $m(\mathbf{r}')$

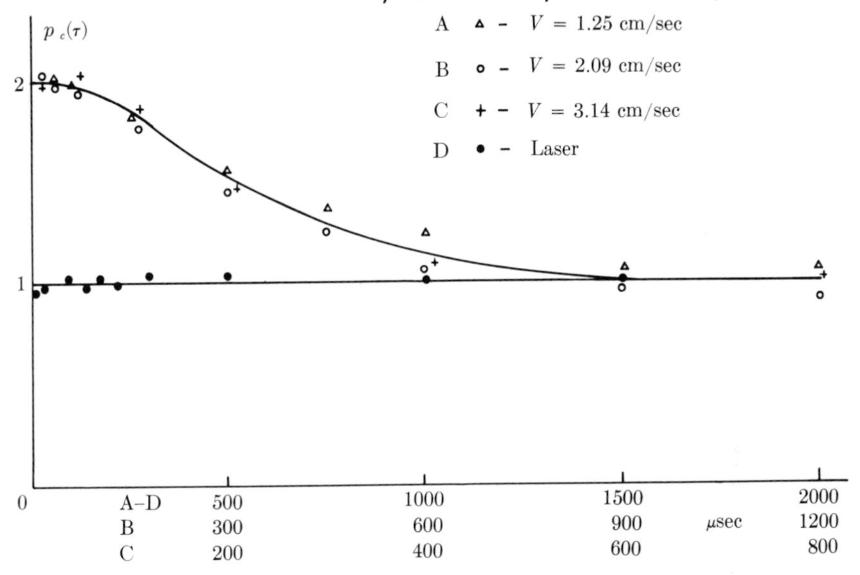

Fig. 10-1 The relative intensity correlation versus time for thermal and coherent sources. Experimental results apply to a laser and to an artificially synthesized chaotic source created by passing the laser radiation through ground glass which is rotated at speeds of 1.25 cm/sec, 2.09 cm/sec, and 3.14 cm/sec, respectively. The relative intensity correlation decays from 2 to 1 in a time characteristic of the spectral bandwidth of the chaotic radiation. The equilibrium value of unity is reached in a shorter time interval for a higher rate of rotation of the ground glass indicating thereby a correspondingly wider band of frequencies. In the case of laser light, essentially no intensity correlation was observed compatible with the absence of intensity fluctuations. [After F. T. Arecchi, E. Gatti, and A. Sona, *Phys. Rev. Letters* **20**, 27 (1966); reprinted with permission.]

denotes the random counting variable at time t and for the short interval T, then

$$\overline{m(\mathbf{r}')} = \alpha T\langle \mathbf{V}^*(\mathbf{r}') \cdot \mathbf{V}(\mathbf{r}')\rangle \tag{10-13a}$$

$$\overline{m(\mathbf{r}')m(\mathbf{r}'')} = \alpha^2 T^2\langle \mathbf{V}^*(\mathbf{r}') \cdot \mathbf{V}(\mathbf{r}')\mathbf{V}^*(\mathbf{r}'') \cdot \mathbf{V}(\mathbf{r}'')\rangle \tag{10-13b}$$

Here we have assumed the detector efficiencies are spatially independent, and we have suppressed the dependence on the common time variable t.

The expressions (10-13) relate to the spatial variation of mean counts or mean intensities. If we consider a (sensibly) spatially homogeneous field (but not necessarily a stationary one!), then it follows that $\overline{m(\mathbf{r}')} = \bar{m}$ independent of $\mathbf{r}$, whereas

$$\overline{m(\mathbf{r}')m(\mathbf{r}'')} = \overline{m(\mathbf{r}' - \mathbf{r}'')m(0)} \tag{10-14}$$

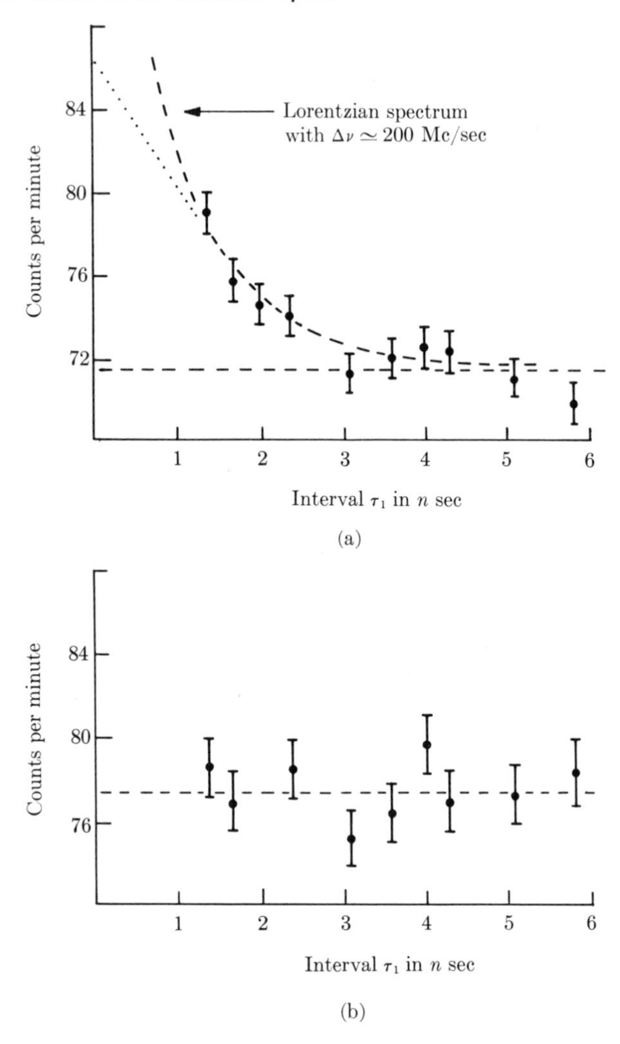

Fig. 10-2 The relative intensity correlation versus time for two thermal sources. The experimental results are shown by dots and vertical error bars. Part (a) is based on light from a highly monochromatic mercury arc lamp and is compatible with a mutual coherence function having a bandwidth of approximately 200 Mc/sec. Part (b) is based on light from a conventional tungsten lamp whose wide frequency spectrum leads to intensity correlations in an immeasurably short time interval. [After B. L. Morgan and L. Mandel, *Phys. Rev. Letters* **16**, 1012 (1966); reprinted with permission.]

To make the analogy with the time correlation even closer, let us define

$$\eta(\mathbf{R}) \equiv \frac{R}{\bar{m}^2} \overline{\Delta m(\mathbf{R}) \, \Delta m(0)} \tag{10-15}$$

where $\Delta m(\mathbf{R}) = m(\mathbf{R}) - \overline{m(\mathbf{R})}$, and $R = |\mathbf{R}|$. Consequently, we may set

$$\overline{m(\mathbf{R})m(0)} - \bar{m}^2 = \bar{m}^2[\eta(\mathbf{R})/R] \tag{10-16}$$

For thermal radiation it follows directly that $\eta(\mathbf{R}) = R|\gamma(\mathbf{R})|^2$ expressed in terms of the degree of coherence. Thus $\eta(\mathbf{R})$ fulfills the conditions $0 \leq \eta(\mathbf{R}) \leq R$. However, for a general radiation field this need not be the case. For ideal laser radiation there are correlations neither in time nor in space; hence $\eta(\mathbf{R}) \equiv 0$. If we simply reinterpret $m(\mathbf{R}) \equiv W$ and $m(0) \equiv X$, then the distribution given in (10-6) leads to a negative value for $\eta(\mathbf{R})$. However, if $\mathbf{R}$ lies in a correlation volume, then quantum effects exhibited by suitably negative diagonal weights are necessary to make $\eta(\mathbf{R}) < 0$. In a one-photon state, again, it follows that $\overline{m(\mathbf{R})m(0)}$ necessarily vanishes.

Spatial correlation effects of the kind implicit in (10-16) are, in principle, present in a number of fields. In most thermal fields, however, they are difficult if not impractical to observe. This is due principally to the low number of photons available in a coherence volume. Although thermal fields may have spatial coherence lengths of the order of meters, if there is only a negligible number of available photons in a coherence volume no effect can be observed. The relevant degeneracy factor δ here according to (2-18) is the mean occupancy $\bar{n}$. From the Planck formula

$$\delta = \bar{n} = \frac{1}{e^{\hbar\omega/\kappa T} - 1}$$

which leads to $\delta \simeq 10^{-3}$ for the best thermal sources.

To overcome this difficulty Magyar and Mandel [10-4] observed the light incident from two independent laser sources. Since lasers have a degeneracy factor $\delta \simeq 10^{12}$, an effect, if present, should be more observable.

It may be thought that the two independently generated fields may combine in one of two rather obvious fashions. For simplicity, let us illustrate these two combinations with just two modes present. On the one hand, let us assume that precise amplitudes add as in

$$z = z_1 + z_2 \tag{10-17}$$

Then the distribution is characterized by

$$\pi^2\,\delta(z - z_1) * \delta(z - z_2)$$

with a suitable phase average carried out subsequently. This leads to a diagonal weight given by

$$(2|z|)^{-1}\,\delta(|z| - |z_1 + z_2|) = \delta(|z|^2 - |z_1 + z_2|^2) \tag{10-18}$$

characteristic of an ideal laser mode with amplitude $|z_1 + z_2|$. In such a combination there would be no amplitude fluctuations, and $\eta(\mathbf{R})$ would vanish. On the other hand, if the states add *incoherently*, characteristic of their independence and individual phase uncertainty, then the appropriate state is given by

$$\varphi(z) = \delta(|z|^2 - |z_1|^2) * \delta(|z|^2 - |z_2|^2)$$

A straightforward calculation shows that this convolution is given by

$$\varphi(z) = \mathrm{Re}\{2[|z|^2|z_1|^2 + |z|^2|z_2|^2 + |z_1|^2|z_2|^2] - |z|^4 - |z_1|^4 - |z_2|^4\}^{-1/2} \tag{10-19}$$

This expression is nonvanishing in the region

$$|\,|z_1| - |z_2|\,| \le |z| \le |z_1| + |z_2| \tag{10-20}$$

as befits an incoherent superposition. Indeed, if we parameterize $|z|$ in accord with (10-20) in the manner

$$|z|^2 = |z_1|^2 + |z_2|^2 + 2|z_1|\,|z_2| \cos \Phi$$

where Φ is real, then it follows directly from (10-19) that

$$\varphi(z) = (2|z_1|\,|z_2| \sin \Phi)^{-1} \tag{10-21}$$

This relation vividly displays a range of nonvanishing values for $\varphi(z)$ which leads quite naturally to amplitude fluctuations.

In the experiments of Magyar and Mandel [10-4], a transient intensity pattern was observed. Though transient, the "geometry" of the fringe pattern is dictated by the geometry of the interference experiment and the wavelength of the light. Although the average intensity at any point was uniform, indicating the spatial homogeneity, the recognition of a *pattern* makes implicit use of intensity correlations and consequently is sensitive to $\overline{m(\mathbf{R})m(0)}$.

Thus we see that spatial correlations as well as temporal correlations may be observed in intensity phenomena. In fact, the lowest-order spatial or temporal correlations we have considered are just two of a whole host of intensity correlations that exist in principle.

10-2 INTENSITY INTERFEROMETRY WITH INDEPENDENT SOURCES

With the background of the preceding section it is not difficult to indicate the general features of coincident counting from independent sources. We confine our discussion to two independent sources S_1 and S_2 and to two counters C_1 and C_2; the generalization to M independent sources and N counters is straightforward. Our presentation will draw on relations and concepts discussed in several earlier chapters.

We work with the generating function that governs the counting distribution (8-135) in the case of two counters. We may write this generating function in the form

$$\begin{aligned} Q \equiv Q(\lambda_1, \lambda_2; \tau_1, \tau_2; t_1, t_2) &= \sum_{n_1, n_2 = 0}^{\infty} (1 - \lambda_1)^{n_1}(1 - \lambda_2)^{n_2} P(n_1, n_2; \tau_1, \tau_2; t_1, t_2) \\ &= \int \exp\left\{-\Sigma_j \lambda_j \alpha_j \int_{t_j}^{\tau_j} |\mathbf{V}(\mathbf{r}, t)|^2 \sigma_j(\mathbf{r})\, d^3r\, dt\right\} \\ &\quad \times \varphi(\{z_\lambda(\mathbf{k})\})\, d\mu(\{z_\lambda(\mathbf{k})\}) \end{aligned} \tag{10-22}$$

Here we have assumed the detector admittance tensors are of the simple type (8-128) and, in particular, are insensitive to polarization.

The concept of independent, random sources was used in Chapter 9 in our discussion of general chaotic fields. Intuitively, in such a case the field $\mathbf{V}(\mathbf{r}, t)$ is composed of a linear sum of terms each of which has an independent distribution in the diagonal representation. Let us recall that spatial propagation relations of the form (6-83) and (6-84) apply to any field obeying the free wave equation outside the sources. In particular, we can relate the analytic-signal wave field $\mathbf{V}(\mathbf{r}, t)$ in this fashion to its values at the sources. Specifically, with the kernel K given by (6-82) [in terms of the generic Green's function (6-80)] we have

$$\begin{aligned} \mathbf{V}(\mathbf{x}, t) &= \iint_S K(\mathbf{x}, \mathbf{y}, t - t')\mathbf{V}(\mathbf{y}, t')\, dS\, dt' \\ &= \Sigma_j \iint_{S_j} K(\mathbf{x}, \mathbf{y}, t - t')\mathbf{V}(\mathbf{y}, t')\, dS_j\, dt' \end{aligned} \tag{10-23}$$

Here, in the last relation we have recognized in the present application that the "surface" of the sources is in reality two separate surfaces. The essential point is that the field at a general point $\mathbf{x}$ and time t is given by the values assumed on the two source surfaces S_1 and S_2.

Schematically, let us write (10-23) in the form

$$\mathbf{V}(\mathbf{x}, t) \equiv K_1\mathbf{V}_1 + K_2\mathbf{V}_2 \tag{10-24}$$

where $\mathbf{V}_1$ and $\mathbf{V}_2$ are field values on the source surfaces and K_1 and K_2 are linear propagation kernels. In this form it is convenient to regard the diagonal weight in (10-22) as a functional of the fields $\mathbf{V}_1$ and $\mathbf{V}_2$,

$$\varphi(\{z_\lambda(\mathbf{k})\}) = \varphi\{\mathbf{V}_1, \mathbf{V}_2\} \tag{10-25}$$

as confined to the surfaces S_1 and S_2. As is traditional in probability theory, independence of the sources is taken to mean factorization of the distribution:

$$\varphi\{\mathbf{V}_1, \mathbf{V}_2\} = \varphi_1\{\mathbf{V}_1\}\varphi_2\{\mathbf{V}_2\} \tag{10-26}$$

However, as we have often emphasized, in the optical regime we generally have no knowledge of or control over the overall phase of waves emitted by a specific source. In such a case φ_1, for example, gives equal weight to the fields $\exp(i\theta_1)\mathbf{V}_1(\mathbf{y}, t)$, for all real θ_1; or, in other words, φ_1 is independent of the overall phase θ_1. As in Chapter 3 we may call these cases phase-uncertain distributions. For quasi-monochromatic radiation, for which effectively

$$\mathbf{V}_1(\mathbf{y}, t) = \mathbf{v}_1(\mathbf{y}, t) \exp(-2\pi i\bar{\nu}_1 t)$$

with $\mathbf{v}_1$ slowly varying, phase-uncertain and stationary distributions are equivalent. In general, however, these are not fully equivalent, and we shall treat only the phase-uncertain distributions here. Analogous discussions pertain to the stationary cases as well.

If we now assume that each independent source is properly described by a phase-uncertain diagonal weight,

$$\varphi_j\{\exp(i\theta_j)\mathbf{V}_j\} = \varphi_j\{\mathbf{V}_j\} \tag{10-27}$$

then we may readily deduce the consequences for the joint counting distribution or, more specifically, for its generating function. Evidently, from our preceding remarks, we may formally write

$$Q = \iint \exp\left\{-\Sigma_j\lambda_j\alpha_j \int_{t_j}^{T_j} |\Sigma_k K_k \mathbf{V}_k|^2\sigma_j(\mathbf{x})\, d^3x\, dt\right\} \times \varphi_1\{\mathbf{V}_1\}\varphi_2\{\mathbf{V}_2\}\, d\mu\{\mathbf{V}_1\}\, d\mu\{\mathbf{V}_2\} \tag{10-28}$$

Let us expand out the terms in the exponent and explicitly insert an additional phase θ between the fields $\mathbf{V}_1$ and $\mathbf{V}_2$. In this case, we find generically the form

$$\begin{aligned} Q = \iint \exp\{&-\mathbf{V}_1{}^* \cdot A_1\mathbf{V}_1 - \mathbf{V}_2{}^* \cdot A_2\mathbf{V}_2 \\ &- [e^{i\theta}(\mathbf{V}_1{}^* \cdot B\mathbf{V}_2) + e^{-i\theta}(\mathbf{V}_1{}^* \cdot B\mathbf{V}_2)^*]\} \\ &\times \varphi_1\{\mathbf{V}_1\}\varphi_2\{\mathbf{V}_2\}\, d\mu\{\mathbf{V}_1\}\, d\mu\{\mathbf{V}_2\} \end{aligned} \tag{10-29}$$

Here A_j and B are linear operators involving spatial and temporal integrations, which depend linearly on the factors λ_1 and λ_2; they may readily be deduced from (10-28). The important point is the simple fact that although Q is defined with an auxiliary parameter θ it is, in fact, independent thereof due to the individual phase uncertainty of each source. Thus we may freely average Q over θ without changing its value. Using the relation for the Bessel function $I_0(x)$ leading to (9-141), we find that

$$Q = \iint \exp\{-\mathbf{V}_1^* \cdot A_1\mathbf{V}_1 - \mathbf{V}_2^* \cdot A_2\mathbf{V}_2\} I_0(|\mathbf{V}_1^* \quad B\mathbf{V}_2|) \times \varphi_1\{\mathbf{V}_1\}\varphi_2\{\mathbf{V}_2\}\, d\mu\{\mathbf{V}_1\}\, d\mu\{\mathbf{V}_2\} \qquad (10\text{-}30)$$

It is also useful to exhibit explicitly the linear dependence of A_j and B on λ_k by defining

$$A_j \equiv \Sigma_k \lambda_k A_{kj} \qquad (10\text{-}31\text{a})$$

$$B \equiv \Sigma_k \lambda_k B_k \qquad (10\text{-}31\text{b})$$

where A_{kj} and B_k are independent of λ_k. If we insert these expansions into (10-30) we are led to the relation given by

$$Q = \iint \exp\{-\Sigma_{k,j}\lambda_k(\mathbf{V}_j^* \cdot A_{kj}\mathbf{V}_j)\} I_0(|\Sigma_k\lambda_k\mathbf{V}_1^* \cdot B_k\mathbf{V}_2|) \times \varphi_1\{\mathbf{V}_1\}\varphi_2\{\mathbf{V}_2\}\, d\mu\{\mathbf{V}_1\}\, d\mu\{\mathbf{V}_2\} \qquad (10\text{-}32)$$

There are correlations of several sorts implicit in this expression. Even if the factor I_0 were ineffective, e.g., if $\mathbf{V}_1$ and $\mathbf{V}_2$ had orthogonal polarizations, there would generally be counting correlations in the two counters since $Q(\lambda_1, \lambda_2)$ would not factor in the form $Q_1(\lambda_1)Q_2(\lambda_2)$. [Generally for such a factorization to occur $A_{kj} = 0$, $k \neq j$, which implies that counter number 1 does not see any radiation from source number 2 and vice versa; if this is the case $B_k = 0$ automatically. Physically, this is just as if a "wall" had been set up separating one source and its counter (S_1 and C_1) entirely from the other pair (S_2 and C_2).]

There is, however, an important exception to the preceding remarks which permits the factor I_0 to "steal the show completely." If the radiation from S_1 and S_2 are each without intensity fluctuations, then only the I_0 term leads to correlations. Specifically, if we regard $\varphi_j\{\mathbf{V}j\}$ as δ functional-like, peaked about one specific field (apart from overall phase uncertainty), then we may readily evaluate (10-32). For simplicity, let us denote the preferred wave field by $\mathbf{V}$ again. Then we find that

$$Q = \exp\{-\Sigma_{k,j}\lambda_k(\mathbf{V}_j^* \cdot A_{kj}\mathbf{V}_j)\} I_0(|\Sigma_k\lambda_k\mathbf{V}_1^* \cdot B_k\mathbf{V}_2|) \qquad (10\text{-}33)$$

If the I_0 term is ineffective (e.g., orthogonal polarizations again) the resultant Q has the form $Q_1(\lambda_1)Q_2(\lambda_2)$ leading to *no* coincident counting correlations. Thus all correlations that arise come about from the factor I_0.

It should be noted that even if we ignore the second counter C_2, the two independent sources give rise to non-Poisson counting statistics in C_1. According to (10-22), we need only set $\lambda_2 = 0$ in (10-33) to exhibit this property. Namely, suppressing all the time variables, we find

$$\begin{aligned} Q(\lambda_1) &= \sum_{n_1=0}^{\infty} (1-\lambda_1)^{n_1} P(n_1) \\ &= \exp\{-\lambda_1 \Sigma_j (\mathbf{V}_j{}^* \cdot A_{1j}\mathbf{V}_j)\} I_0(\lambda_1 |\mathbf{V}_1{}^* \cdot B_1 \mathbf{V}_2|) \\ &\equiv \exp\{-\lambda_1 E\} I_0(\lambda_1 C) \end{aligned} \tag{10-34}$$

From here [cf. (2-8)] we can discover that $E = \bar{n}_1$ while C is a measure of the departure from Poisson statistics given by $C = \{2(\sigma_1{}^2 - \bar{n}_1)\}^{1/2}$. The counting distribution corresponding to (10-34) is implicitly determined by (2-7) but is not very simply expressed. However we may deduce the distribution $p(U)$ for the integrated intensity [cf. (2-4)]

$$U \equiv \int_{t_1}^{T_1} I_1(t')\, dt' \tag{10-35}$$

by using Eq. (2-6). Specifically,

$$\begin{aligned} p(U) &= \frac{\alpha}{2\pi} \int_{-\infty}^{\infty} e^{i\lambda\alpha U} Q(i\lambda)\, d\lambda \\ &= \frac{\alpha}{2\pi} \int_{-\infty}^{\infty} e^{i\lambda(\alpha U - E)} J_0(\lambda C)\, d\lambda \\ &= \tfrac{1}{2}\alpha \operatorname{Re}\{C^2 - [\alpha U - E]^2\}^{-1/2} \\ &= \tfrac{1}{2}\alpha \operatorname{Re}\{|\mathbf{V}_1{}^* \cdot B_1 \mathbf{V}_2|^2 - [\alpha U - \Sigma_j(\mathbf{V}_j{}^* \cdot A_{1j}\mathbf{V}_j)]^2\}^{-1/2} \end{aligned} \tag{10-36}$$

This relation determines the distribution for U as a function of the observation times, and the fields and geometry of the sources. Fluctuations in U exist so long as $C > 0$.

In the previous discussion we have treated the counting statistics in counters illuminated by independent sources. Of course, it is not necessary that all (or any!) of the sources be really independent of one another. There are a number of other forms of source correlations that may be envisaged as well. All these possibilities are implicitly contained in the formulas we have developed for a general, multiple counting distribution coupled with any special source correlations that might apply.

10-3 CONCLUSION AND OUTLOOK

In the present text we have studied the classical and quantum theories of partially coherent, freely propagating waves as a branch of classical and quantum statistical theories, respectively. We have seen the utility of the analytic-signal formulation in the classical theory, particularly for quasi-monochromatic fields. In turn, the normal order of the field operators, shown to characterize the multiple coincidence rates in quantum theory, makes the coherent states a very convenient and natural framework in which to present the quantum discussion. As eigenvectors of the annihilation operators these states likewise involve analytic signals, establishing a close relationship to the classical formulation. The systematic study of the coherent states has shown how, and in what sense to use the diagonal representation for density operators so as to exploit this formal classical connection. The utility of such representations, both conceptually and analytically, should be apparent from our discussion and examples. It is worth while to conclude by pointing to a few other broad topics of interest which are undergoing research and development at the present time.

Although we have alluded to the problems caused by atmospheric distortion, the general aspects of light propagation in nonfree space, in random media, in nonlinear media, etc.—apart from the questions of detection and generation—are of increasing importance in practical applications. Such topics raise the questions of signal degradation and, as in communication theory, of transmission through noisy channels. In addition there remain numerous unsolved problems in developing more exact treatments of the detection process so as to account more properly for the nonlinear processes that take place there.

We have discussed, especially in the present chapter, how multiple counters react in the presence of multiple sources. Evidently, to a certain extent this problem may be turned around so as to use counting information to deduce statistical properties of the source. If, in turn, we regard one or more of the "sources" as *scatterers* in the illuminated field of other sources, then we may learn about the scattering properties of these objects. In particular, relative phase information unavailable in single-counter techniques may be found in suitable multiple-counter studies. These questions have been extensively discussed by Goldberger, Lewis, and Watson [10-6].

Another topic worthy of a few general remarks is the description of statistical states for infinitely many degrees of freedom. In both classical and quantum contexts we have emphasized the utility of characteristic functionals as a means of description. Whether the problem is classical or quantum, whether the distribution does or does not have finite moments, the characteristic functional is a well-defined and continuous function of its arguments. This is especially significant in the quantum context, for the formulation of problems with an infinite number of degrees of freedom is not without difficulties. We have attempted to mitigate these problems by quantizing the radiation field in a "box." If, for example, one quantizes the radiation field *ab initio* in an infinite volume, then to discuss the equilibrium thermal state—or any state having spatial-translational invariance, for that matter—a representation of the annihilation and creation operators is required which is *unitarily inequivalent* to the familiar one we have used (i.e., the so-called Fock representation). Indeed, the representations are all inequivalent with one another for different temperatures or for changes in any other macroscopic parameter involved. A crude physical reason for this behavior is the simple fact that no practical device (more technically a "Hamiltonian" whose evolution operator could mediate the unitary equivalence) could be invented to change a macroscopic feature uniformly over all space. In the box quantization method these questions do not arise, and in the characteristic functional approach they remain properly in the background. It is, of course, desirable to get rid of the box (so as to have one less irrelevent parameter!), and this desire makes the study of "boxless" states of the field from an operator point of view an interesting question, although nontrivial. As we remarked in Chapter 5, research on just these questions is currently in progress.

In many ways, of course, the heart of any problem in classical or quantum optics is a discussion of its nonlinear equations of interaction, and a discovery of the appropriate states of the field from first principles. Whenever possible and practical this procedure surely yields the deepest knowledge of the coupled systems in question. A glimpse into a possible formulation of such problems was given in Chapter 4, and a brief account of an idealized laser model was given in Chapter 9. Additional systems and their particular equations, as well as current methods used to treat them, are discussed in the literature.

With the tools of a quantum theory of optics we have outlined, it should be possible to treat a number of interesting and challenging new problems in a field of physics rich in its history and in its contributions to other fields of physics, such as wave mechanics.

BIBLIOGRAPHY

CHAPTER 1

The classic text for optics in general and partial coherence in particular remains

1-1. M. Born and E. Wolf, *Principles of Optics,* Pergamon Press, Oxford, England, 3rd ed. (1965),

with a special emphasis on Chapter X. Two other recent works that deal with partial coherence are

1-2. M. J. Beran and G. B. Parrent, Jr., *Theory of Partial Coherence,* Prentice-Hall, Englewood Cliffs, New Jersey (1964);
1-3. E. L. O'Neill, *Introduction to Statistical Optics,* Addison-Wesley, Reading, Massachusetts (1963).

We assume that the reader is basically familiar with properties of Fourier transforms. Analytic signals were introduced and extensively used by

1-4. D. Gabor, *J. Inst. Elec. Engrs.* (*London*) **93,** 429 (1946).

A general reference for questions about Fourier integrals, including the properties of Hilbert transforms satisfied by analytic signals, is the text by

1-5. E. C. Titchmarsh, *Introduction to the Theory of Fourier Integrals,* Clarendon Press, Oxford, England, 2nd ed. (1948).

The concept of the degree of coherence and its relation to the visibility was discussed by

1-6. F. Zernike, *Physica* **5,** 785 (1938).

The so-called "phase problem" in the context of optics has been formulated in general by

1-7. E. Wolf, *Proc. Phys. Soc.* (*London*), **80,** 1269 (1962), and discussed for the specific case of blackbody radiation by

1-8. Y. Kano and E. Wolf, *Proc. Phys. Soc. (London)* **80,** 1273 (1962).

An interesting twist to the phase problem was proposed by

1-9. C. L. Mehta, *Nuovo Cimento* **10,** 202 (1965).

Several specific spectral shapes were studied by

1-10. H. M. Nussenzveig, *J. Math. Phys.* **8,** 561 (1967)

who demonstrated, for these examples, that the "minimal" solution to the phase problem was inadequate.

Wave equations for the mutual coherence function were first obtained by

1-11. E. Wolf, *Proc. Roy. Soc. (London)* **A230,** 246 (1955); *Proc. Phys. Soc. (London)* **71,** 257 (1958).

Wave equations in the vector case appropriate to the radiation field were given by

1-12. P. Roman and E. Wolf, *Nuovo Cimento* **17,** 462, 477 (1960).

CHAPTER 2

A semiclassical derivation of the counting distribution formula for thermal light was given by

2-1. L. Mandel, *Progress in Optics* (E. Wolf, ed.), Vol. II, North-Holland Publ., Amsterdam (1963).

A semiclassical derivation that applies to more general light distributions was given by

2-2. L. Mandel, E. C. G. Sudarshan, and E. Wolf, *Proc. Phys. Soc. (London)* **84,** 435 (1964).

A survey of probability methods and techniques is given, for example, by

2-3. H. Cramer, *Mathematical Methods of Statistics,* Princeton Univ. Press, Princeton, New Jersey (1946).

The experiments on counting distributions for thermal light and for laser light to which we refer are reported by

2-4. F. T. Arecchi, *Phys. Rev. Letters* **15,** 912 (1965).

The question of determining the intensity distribution from the counting distribution was examined in the context of quantum optics by

2-5. E. Wolf and C. L. Mehta, *Phys. Rev. Letters*, **13,** 705 (1964).

The identical mathematical problem was treated by

2-6. D. V. Widder, *Duke Math. J.* **1,** 126 (1935),

and this and other moment questions are fully discussed in

2-7. J. A. Shohat and J. D. Tamarkin, *Problem of Moments*, Am. Math. Soc., Providence, Rhode Island (1943).

CHAPTER 3

The approach to probability distributions via characteristic functions is championed by

3-1. E. Lukacs, *Characteristic Functions*, Charles Griffin, London (1960).

The literature on stochastic processes may be approached from a largely physical orientation through several of the articles reprinted in

3-2. N. Wax, ed., *Selected Papers on Noise and Stochastic Processes*, Dover, New York (1954).

Treatments rich both in physical and mathematical content are contained in this reference as well. Especially notable from the point of view of classical optics is that of

3-3. S. O. Rice, *Bell System Tech. J.* **23,** 282 (1944); **25,** 46 (1945), reprinted in Ref. 3-2.

Various applications to problems of diverse physical origin are treated by

3-4. M S. Bartlett, *An Introduction to Stochastic Processes*, Cambridge Univ. Press, London and New York (1955),

and by

3-5. A. Ramakrishnan, "Probability and Stochastic Processes," in *Handbuch der Physik* (S. Flügge, ed.), Vol. III/2, Springer, Berlin (1959).

Analyses with some emphasis on characteristic functionals are given in the readable account in

3-6. I. M. Gel'fand and N. Ya. Vilenkin, *Generalized Functions. Vol. 4: Applications of Harmonic Analysis* (translated by A. Feinstein), Academic Press, New York (1964), Chapters II and III, while a fuller mathematical treatment is given by

3-7. J. L. Doob, *Stochastic Processes,* Wiley, New York (1953).

Questions of information theory and the relation to statistical mechanics are discussed for optical coherence theory by

3-8. D. Gabor, *Progress in Optics* (E. Wolf, ed.), Vol. I, North-Holland Publ., Amsterdam (1961).

Multiple-photon coincident experiments were introduced and successfully carried out by

3-9. R. Hanbury Brown and R. Q. Twiss, *Nature* **177,** 27 (1956); *Proc. Roy. Soc. (London)* **A242,** 300 (1957); *Proc. Roy. Soc. (London)* **A243,** 291 (1957).

The classical explanation of these effects in terms of second-order intensity correlations was also discussed by

3-10. E. M. Purcell, *Nature* **178,** 1449 (1956),

and a comprehensive review is given by Mandel, Ref. 2-1, and also by

3-11. L. Mandel and E. Wolf, *Rev. Modern Phys.* **37,** 231 (1965).

In the cases discussed, the application of independent, multiple, thermal distributions to approximate the distribution for the integrated intensity is due to Rice, Ref. 3-3, and its application to photon counting distributions is due to

3-12. L. Mandel, *Proc. Phys. Soc. (London)* **74,** 233 (1959).

CHAPTER 4

Coupled, nonlinear, partial differential equations with random driving terms and/or random initial conditions arise in virtually all fields of physics. In the context of quantum optics, such equations arise in media with nonlinear electric and magnetic susceptibilities as discussed by

4-1. N. Bloembergen, *Nonlinear Optics,* W. A. Benjamin, New York (1965).

In the context of equilibrium and nonequilibrium quantum statistical mechanics, similar nonlinear equations are studied by

4-2. L. P. Kadanoff and G. Baym, *Quantum Statistical Mechanics,* W. A. Benjamin, New York (1962).

Related problems in turbulence are treated by

4-3. G. K. Batchelor, *The Theory of Homogeneous Turbulence*, Cambridge Univ. Press, London and New York (1963).

A broad survey of mathematical methods and physical problems in stochastic systems is afforded by

4-4. A. T. Bharucha-Reid, *Elements of the Theory of Markov Processes and their Applications*, McGraw-Hill, New York (1960).

Functional approaches to stochastic problems are elegantly treated in classical random systems by

4-5. M. Kac, *Probability and Related Topics in Physical Sciences*, Wiley (Interscience), New York (1959),

and quite parallel techniques for quantum systems are reviewed by

4-6. Yu. V. Novozhilov and A. V. Tulub, *The Method of Functionals in the Quantum Theory of Fields*, Gordon and Breach, New York (1961).

The introduction of functional differential techniques into nonlinear dynamical equations was made by

4-7. E. Hopf, *J. Rational Mech. Anal.* **1,** 87 (1952).

Equations of motion to derive classical stochastic behavior for linear and nonlinear problems in noise theory are dealt with by

4-8. R. L. Stratonovich, *Topics in the Theory of Random Noise* (translated from the Russian by R. A. Silverman), Gordon and Breach, New York (1963);

4-9. W. B. Davenport, Jr., and W. L. Root, *Random Signals and Noise*, McGraw-Hill, New York (1958),

as well as several articles on classical noise which may be traced from

4-10. M. Lax, *Rev. Modern Phys.* **38,** 541 (1966).

The application of characteristic functional techniques to dynamical questions in quantum optics is considered by

4-11. E. C. G. Sudarshan (to be published in the *International Journal for Theoretical Physics*).

CHAPTER 5

Several standard textbooks on quantum mechanics are

5-1. P. A. M. Dirac, *The Principles of Quantum Mechanics*, Clarendon Press, Oxford, England, 4th ed. (1958);

5-2. L. I. Schiff, *Quantum Mechanics,* McGraw-Hill, New York, 2nd ed. (1955);
5-3. A. Messiah, *Quantum Mechanics,* Wiley, New York, Vol. I (1961) and Vol. II (1962).

More mathematical treatments of quantum mechanics with special emphasis on the statistical questions of concern to us are those of

5-4. J. von Neumann, *Mathematical Foundations of Quantum Mechanics* (translated from the German by R. T. Beyer), Princeton Univ. Press, Princeton, New Jersey (1955);
5-5. G. W. Mackey, *Mathematical Foundations of Quantum Mechanics,* W. A. Benjamin, New York (1963).

Fuller discussions of Hilbert space and general properties of various operators, etc., may be found in

5-6. F. Riesz and B. Sz.-Nagy, *Functional Analysis,* Fredrick Ungar, New York (1955);
5-7. A. N. Kolmogorov and S. V. Fomin, *Elements of the Theory of Functions and Functional Analysis* (translated by L. F. Boron), Vol. 2, Graylock Press, Rochester, New York (1957).

Properties of pure and mixed states of polarization for a monochromatic beam are identical to those of the classical theory as discussed in Ref. 1-1, p. 541.

The reader interested in pursuing the application of C^* algebras to quantum theory and quantum statistical mechanics—a method directly capable of treating arbitrary quantum states more general than those represented by density operators—is advised to consult the article by

5-8. I. E. Segal, *Ann. Math.* **48,** 930 (1947),

and the extensive study of

5-9. R. Haag and D. Kastler, *J. Math. Phys.* **5,** 848 (1964),

and the literature cited therein.

CHAPTER 6

Quantization of the radiation field is a basic subject in all but the most elementary quantum textbooks. In addition to Refs. 5-1, 5-2, and 5-3, the reader may consult the relevant chapters in any of the standard texts, such as

6-1. A. I. Akhiezer and V. B. Berestetsky, *Quantum Electrodynamics*, Authorized English ed., revised and enlarged by the authors. Translated from the 2nd Russian ed. by G. M. Volkoff, Interscience Publishers, New York (1965).
6-2. W. Heitler, *Quantum Theory of Radiation*, Oxford Univ. Press, New York and London (1954);
6-3. J. M. Jauch and F. Rohrlich, *The Theory of Photons and Electrons*, Addison-Wesley, Reading, Massachusetts, second printing with corrections (1959);
6-4. S. S. Schweber, *An Introduction to Relativistic Quantum Field Theory*, Harper & Row, New York (1961);
6-5. W. E. Thirring, *Principles of Quantum Electrodynamics*, Academic Press, New York (1958);
6-6. H. Umezawa, *Quantum Field Theory*, North-Holland, Publ., Amsterdam (1956).
6-7. G. Wentzel, *Quantum Theory of Fields*, Wiley (Interscience), New York (1949).

CHAPTER 7

Elementary properties of coherent states may be found in standard texts such as Refs. 5-1, 5-2, and 5-3 under the subject of minimum-uncertainty wave packets, etc. These states were introduced into quantum mechanics by

7-1. E. Schrödinger, *Naturwissenschaften* **14**, 644 (1927)

for studies of displaced and driven oscillators, and they have been used subsequently by numerous authors for many purposes. Summaries of the elementary properties of coherent states are given by

7-2. W. H. Louisell, *Radiation and Noise in Quantum Electronics*, McGraw-Hill, New York (1964);
7-3. P. Carruthers and M. M. Nieto, *Am. J. Phys.* **33**, 537 (1965).

Completeness of the coherent states was first noted by von Neumann, Ref. 5-4, p. 407. The central property of the coherent states relating to the resolution of unity was first stated in the presently used form by

7-4. J. R Klauder, *Ann. Phys. (N.Y.)* **11**, 123 (1960).

In this article the associated Hilbert space of bounded continuous functions was used implicitly, but its particular properties were not studied.

These properties were first systematically studied in the closely related Segal-Bargmann spaces by

7-5. I. E. Segal, *Illinois J. Math.* **6,** 500 (1962); *Mathematical Problems of Relativistic Physics*, Am. Math. Soc., Providence, Rhode Island (1963),

and especially by

7-6. V. Bargmann, *Communs. Pure Appl. Math.* **14,** 187 (1961).

The connection of these spaces to the associated Hilbert space of bounded, continuous functions—the "continuous representation"—was pointed out by

7-7. S. S. Schweber, *J. Math. Phys.* **3,** 831 (1962).

As Hilbert spaces with reproducing kernels, all these spaces are important special cases of the theory studied by

7-8. N. Aronszajn, *Proc. Cambridge Phil. Soc.* **39,** 133 (1943); *Trans. Am. Math. Soc.* **68,** 337 (1950).

Some of the properties of the coherent states were rediscovered in the context of quantum optics by

7-9. R. J. Glauber, *Phys. Rev.* **131,** 2766 (1963).

In the important and widely quoted work of Glauber the coherent states which we denote by $|z\rangle$ are generally denoted by $|\alpha\rangle$.

Uniqueness properties of the diagonal coherent-state matrix elements for various operators was shown most simply by

7-10. C. L. Mehta and E. C. G. Sudarshan, *Phys. Rev.* **138,** B274 (1965).

Analysis of the density operator by means of its diagonal coherent-state matrix elements is given in Ref. 7-10 as well as in

7-11. K. Husimi, *Proc. Phys. Math. Soc. Japan* **22,** 264 (1940);
7-12. Y. Kano, *J. Math. Phys.* **6,** 1913 (1965);
7-13. J. McKenna and H. L. Frisch, *Ann. Phys.* **33,** 156 (1965); *Phys. Rev.* **145,** 93 (1966).

Differential operator representations may be deduced most easily from Ref. 7-6.

Alternate differential operators as a means to yield normal ordered operator expressions were introduced into field theory by

7-14. J. L. Anderson, *Phys. Rev.* **94,** 703 (1954).

In the simpler context appropriate to quantum optics they are discussed fully in Ref. 7-2, and also in

7-15. M. Lax, *Brandeis Summer Institute Lectures* 1966, Gordon and Breach, New York (to be published).

Coherent states for infinitely many degrees of freedom were introduced formally in the earliest studies. Basic ingredients of a proper theory of such states appear in

7-16. V. Bargmann, *Proc. Natl. Acad. Sci. U.S.* **48,** 199 (1962),

where elementary use is made of a technique of functional integration thoroughly studied by

7-17. K. O. Friedrichs and H. N. Shapiro, *Integration of Functionals,* Lecture Notes, New York Univ. Inst. of Math. Sci. (1957).

It may be noted that the coherent-state representations of this chapter have many properties in common with a wider class of representations (the phase-space continuous representations) of which they are but a special case. The basic properties of these representations are discussed in

7-18. J. R. Klauder, *J. Math. Phys.* **4,** 1055, 1058 (1963); *ibid.* **5,** 177 (1964).

Rigorous analysis of these representations for finitely many degrees of freedom is given by

7-19. J. McKenna and J. R. Klauder, *J. Math. Phys.* **5,** 878 (1964),

and for infinitely many degrees of freedom by

7-20. J. R. Klauder and J. McKenna, *J. Math. Phys.* **6,** 68 (1965).

Each of these articles has a section dealing with the special cases pertaining to the coherent states.

CHAPTER 8

The proper quantum statement for multiple, coincident, counting rates as means of normally ordered, photon operators is due to

8-1. R. J. Glauber, *Phys. Rev. Letters* **10,** 84 (1963); *Phys. Rev.* **130,** 2529 (1963); *ibid.* **131,** 2766 (1963); *Quantum Electronics* (*Proc. 3rd Intern. Congr.*) (N. Bloembergen and P. Grivet, eds.), Dunod, Paris; Columbia Univ. Press, New York (1964);

8-2. R. J. Glauber, *Quantum Optics and Electronics* (C. DeWitt, A. Blandin, and C. Cohen-Tannoudji, eds.), Gordon and Breach, New York (1964).

The last-mentioned article is particularly complete and contains reprints of the two major articles in Ref. 8-1.

First-order perturbation theory and the associated formulas of "Golden Rule No. 2" are discussed, for example, in Schiff, Ref. 5-2.

The definition of fully coherent states is presented in several of the articles in Ref. 8-1. Consequences of first-order coherence are developed more fully in

8-3. U. M. Titulaer and R. J. Glauber, *Phys. Rev.* **140,** B676 (1965); *ibid.* **145,** 1041 (1966).

More general, partially coherent states are discussed by

8-4. E. C. G. Sudarshan, "Quantum Theory of Partial Coherence" (to be published in the *International Journal for Theoretical Physics*).

An heirarchy of multiple-point correlation functions normalized by the product of the individual point intensities was considered by Glauber, Ref. 8-2. Alternative normalizations, motivated in part by attempts to generalize the classical, complex degree of coherence, were considered by

8-5. C. L. Mehta, "Degree of Higher Order Optical Coherence" (to be published in the *Journal of Mathematical Physics*).

and by Sudarshan, Ref. 8-4.

The counting distribution for the quantum cases was derived for extremely special situations by

8-6. F. Ghielmetti, *Phys. Letters* **12,** 210 (1964).

and more generally by Glauber, Ref. 8-2. Our principal derivation of the counting distribution makes extensive use of the diagonal representation of density operators and, thus, although fully quantum mechanical, closely parallels the familiar derivation in the classical theory.

The remarkable possibility that every state can be given a diagonal representation and the formal classical-like structure it gives to counting rates for general states of the radiation field was first pointed out by

8-7. E. C. G. Sudarshan, *Phys. Rev. Letters* **10,** 277 (1963); *Proceedings of the Symposium on Optical Masers,* Wiley, New York, (1963), p. 45.

This diagonal representation restores the classical formulas for counting distributions in terms of ensemble densities with the understanding that this is a complete quantum mechanical description, and, consequently, that the ensemble densities need not be positive definite. In the diagonal representation the $\varphi(z)$ formally corresponds to the classical distribution. Among the possible choices for $\varphi(z)$ are those that fulfill $\varphi(z) \geq 0$, which, thus, includes all the conventional classical distributions. In particular, the thermal states are represented classically by Gaussian distributions. A quantum description of these states in terms of a linear combination of projections onto coherent states with a Gaussian weight function was given by Glauber in the first *Letter* in Ref. 8-1.

The original prescription for the diagonal weight consisted of a formal infinite series of Dirac δ functions with successively higher derivatives. Techniques to define the diagonal weight that are not based on such infinite series were introduced by

8-8. J. R. Klauder, J. McKenna, and D. G. Currie, *J. Math. Phys.* **6,** 733 (1965),

and by Mehta and Sudarshan, Ref. 7-10. In the latter article the distribution nature of the diagonal weight is characterized by means of a linear functional, while both of these articles contain well-defined prescriptions to define density operators as a limit of sequences each member of which has a diagonal representation. In Ref. 8-8 these weights were square integrable functions, whereas in Ref. 7-10 they were composed of finitely many derivatives of δ functions. Either prescription serves to uniquely characterize a density operator as a limit of diagonally represented operators. However, the limiting operations involved in Refs. 8-8 and 7-10 were convergent only in Hilbert-Schmidt norm, and thus guaranteed the correct mean values only for Hilbert-Schmidt operators. The stronger convergence properties of trace-class norm necessary to imply the correct mean values for every bounded operator, which, moreover, are generated by a sequence of diagonally represented operators having exceptionally smooth weight functions, were shown to exist independently by

8-9. J. R. Klauder, *Phys. Rev. Letters* **16,** 534 (1966);
8-10. F. Rocca, *Compt. Rend.* **262,** A547 (1966).

The original prescription for the diagonal weight was given as a sum of derivatives of δ functions for which the order was essentially determined by the maximum number of photons in the state. That such a prescription for the diagonal weight does not lead to a distribution on $\mathfrak{D}_2$ whenever an infinite number of photons are present in the state was proved by

8-11. K. E. Cahill, *Phys. Rev.* **138,** B1566 (1965).

On the other hand, it is shown by

8-12. M. M. Miller and E. A. Mishkin, "Representation of Operators in Quantum Optics" (*Phys. Rev.*, to be published); M. M. Miller "Convergence of the Sudarshan Expansion for the Diagonal Coherent State Weight Functional" (to be published),

that an infinite series of successively higher derivatives of δ functions can give rise to a distribution on $\mathcal{Z}_2$, the Fourier transform of $\mathfrak{D}_2$.

The Weyl representation of operators used in our analysis of the diagonal representation is that discussed in the classic text of

8-13. H. Weyl, *The Theory of Groups and Quantum Mechanics* (translated from the German by H. P. Robertson), Dover, New York (1931), p. 274.

These representations and their application to statistical descriptions in quantum theory have been studied in the classic article of

8-14. J. E. Moyal, *Proc. Cambridge Philosophical Society* **45,** 91 (1949),

which can be traced to the work of

8-15. E. Wigner, *Phys. Rev.* **40,** 749 (1932)

and further developed by

8-16. E. C. G. Sudarshan, *Lectures in Theoretical Physics, Vol. II,* W. A. Benjamin, New York (1961); T. F. Jordan and E. C. G. Sudarshan, *Rev. Mod. Phys.* **33,** 515 (1961).

The mathematical aspects of the Weyl representation have been thoroughly explored by

8-17. G. Loupias and S. Miracle-Sole, *Commun. Math. Phys.* **2,** 31 (1966);

8-18. J. C. T. Pool, *J. Math. Phys.* **7,** 66 (1966).

Operator properties suitable for a thorough understanding of the proofs of the diagonal representation presented in this text may be found in Ref. 3-6, pp. 26–56, or in

8-19. R. Schatten, *Norm Ideals of Completely Continuous Operators,* Springer, Berlin (1960).

Properties of distributions may be found in the classic source of

8-20. L. Schwartz, *Theorie des distributions,* Vols. I and II, Hermann, Paris (1951).

The particular distributions and test-function spaces of more direct interest to us are studied by

8-21. I. M. Gel'fand and G. E. Shilov, *Generalized Functions, Vol. 1: Properties and Operators* (translated from the Russian by E. Saletan), Academic Press, New York (1964).

More popular accounts of distributions can be found in the text by

8-22. M. J. Lighthill, *Introduction to Fourier Analysis and Generalized Functions,* Cambridge Univ. Press, London and New York (1959).

The requirement that physically meaningful diagonal weights ought to admit arbitrary convolution products and possess finite moments of arbitrary order has prompted

8-23. R. Bonifacio, L. M. Narducci, and E. Montaldi, *Phys. Rev. Letters* **16,** 1125 (1966),

to propose a certain subclass of diagonal weights as physically significant. For purposes of constructing convolution products the subclass of diagonal weights obtained in this way is unnecessarily restrictive. The "contraction" techniques used to prove readily the most general convolution formula, Eq. (8-205), are implicit in Sec. 2,E of Ref. 7-20.

CHAPTER 9

The derivation of a normal distribution for a random variable composed of a myraid of similar, independently distributed contributions is a classical application in probability theory. This standard prescription was used by Glauber in the third article of Ref. 8-1 to derive the normal distribution for the diagonal weight in the case that each of the independent contributions is uniformly distributed in phase.

Entropy in quantum theory is dealt with by von Neumann, Ref. 5-4. Classic properties of the thermal distribution for the radiation field may be found in

9-1. L. D. Landau and E. M. Lifshitz, *Statistical Physics* (translated from the Russian by E. and R. F. Peierls), Pergamon, London, and Addison-Wesley, Reading, Massachusetts (1958).

Expressions for the mean value which corresponds to the generating functional of the counting distribution with a normal field distribution were considered already by Rice, Ref. 3-3, who derived approximate relations applicable to a general class of line shapes. Exact and asymptotic expressions pertaining to certain line shapes including the Lorentzian case were derived by

9-2. U. Grenander, H. O. Pollak, and D. Slepian, *J. Soc. Ind. Appl. Math.* **7,** 374 (1959).

The counting distribution for chaotic fields with Lorentzian line shape was quoted in Glauber's earliest *Letter,* Ref. 8-1, and was derived in

Ref. 8-2. An asymptotic expression valid for large mean count was stated in

9-3. R. J. Glauber, *Physics of Quantum Electronics* (P. L. Kelley, B. Lax, and P. E. Tannenwald, eds.), McGraw-Hill, New York (1966).

Counting distributions for such fields were studied in the experiments of

9-4. C. Freed and H. A. Haus, *Phys. Rev. Letters* **15,** 943 (1965); *IEEE J. Quantum Electron.* QE-**2,** No. 8, 190 (1966).

The comparison of these data with predictions based on the exact expression (9-87) was carried out by

9-5. R. Barakat and R. J. Glauber, unpublished calculations.

The rudiments of a phase-diffusion model for a laser may be traced from

9-6. C. H. Townes, *Nuovo Cimento Suppl.* **5,** 222 (1957).

Its more detailed features have been treated by

9-7. M. Lax, Proc. Durham Conf. on Quantum Optics, 1964 (unpublished)

and by Glauber in Ref. 8-2, while the domain of its applicability has been studied by

9-8. M. Lax, *Phys. Rev.* **160,** 290 (1967).

The general class of stochastic processes we use for our discussion of phase-diffusion models are adapted from

9-9. J. R. Klauder and P. W. Anderson, *Phys. Rev.* **125,** 912 (1962),

which deals with the physically related and mathematically equivalent problems in spin diffusion. The fundamental Ornstein-Uhlenbeck process is discussed in the original papers reprinted in Ref. 3-2.

The intensity distribution for the signal-plus-noise example is due to Rice, Ref. 3-3. The counting distribution that follows from this diagonal weight was given by Glauber in Ref. 9-3. Experimental tests of this counting distribution are reported by Freed and Haus in the second article of Ref. 9-4 and by

9-10. P. J. Magill and R. P. Soni, *Phys. Rev. Letters* **16,** 911 (1966).

The literature pertaining to more realistic laser models may be traced from Ref. 7-15 and

9-11. M. Lax, *Phys. Rev.* **145,** 110 (1966);
9-12. H. Haken, *Z. Physik* **190,** 327 (1966);
9-13. H. Sauerman, *Z. Physik* **188,** 480 (1965); *ibid.* **189,** 312 (1966);
9-14. M. Scully and W. E. Lamb, *Phys. Rev. Letters* **16,** 853 (1966);
9-15. F. Schwabl and W. Thirring, *Ergeb. Exakt. Naturw.* **36,** 219 (1964).

More descriptive discussions appear in Ref. 7-2, and elsewhere.

Our presentation of a coupled-system laser model draws heavily on the manuscript of

9-16. J. P. Gordon, *Phys. Rev.* **161,** 367 (1967).

The authors thank Dr. Gordon for permission to quote material from his manuscript prior to publication.

CHAPTER 10

Direct, time-dependent counting coincidences were observed by

10-1. F. T. Arecchi, E. Gatti, and A. Sona, *Phys. Letters* **20,** 27 (1966),

with devices of the type introduced by

10-2. W. Martienssen and E. Spiller, *Am. J. Phys.* **32,** 919 (1964),

and which were refined to useful sources for these problems by Arecchi, Ref. 2-4. Similar counting coincidences were observed with more traditional thermal sources by

10-3. B. L. Morgan and L. Mandel, *Phys. Rev. Letters* **16,** 1012 (1966).

Spatial correlations in the field of two independent lasers were observed by

10-4. G. Magyar and L. Mandel, *Nature* **198,** 255 (1963),

and analyzed quantum mechanically by

10-5. L. Mandel, *Phys. Rev.* **134,** A10 (1964).

Intensity correlation techniques very similar to those studied in this text have been treated by

10-6. M. L. Goldberger, H. W. Lewis, and K. M. Watson, *Phys. Rev.* **132,** 2764 (1963); *ibid* **142,** 25 (1966).

These authors have also applied such methods to problems of scattering and the information about the scatterer that can be learned thereby.

INDEX

BRIDGET McGURN
40- $30.00